W9-ASA-819

Science and Faith

SCIENCE AND FAITH

Towards a Theological Understanding of Nature

By ERIC C. RUST

NEW YORK *Oxford University Press* 1967

Library of Congress Catalogue Card Number: 67-28130
Printed in the United States of America

TO HELEN

BELOVED WIFE AND COMPANION IN CHRIST

Preface

This book has been shaping across many years since, as a young science student at the Royal College of Science in the early 1930's, I became increasingly concerned with the relation of the Christian message to this scientific age. The concern was a potent factor in sending me into the Baptist ministry in England, and it has been a prime consideration throughout my life as Baptist minister and subsequently as Seminary Professor in Great Britain and in the United States. It has become commonplace now to remind ourselves that we live in a secular society which has largely been shaped by scientific discovery and its technological ramifications. Now, more than ever, it is evident that we must express our faith in terms appropriate to our contemporary situation.

I am convinced that the historical faith which the Church has treasured down the centuries is still relevant to our time. It needs to be re-expressed. The techniques of biblical criticism, the contemporary concern with the nature of religious language, the scientific exploration into the origins of man and of the universe, the increasing understanding of man's psychosomatic nature, the new attempts to understand divine revelation and to justify divine transcendence—all require that the ancient faith be poured into new wineskins. It has been my concern in this book to face such problems. My theme is centered in the Incarnation and the understanding of the Cosmic Christ. I believe that we cannot for long avoid a concern with such central aspects of our faith. I believe also that we may not completely reject the insights of philosophical idealism, however much our approach to metaphysical understanding may have been modified by existentialist thought, scientific positivism and empiricism, and linguistic analysis. I do not share in the idea current in some quarters that "faith" is free to express itself without any metaphysical shackles. I am not persuaded that the latter are shackles. I do, however, believe that we are more free than ever in the Church's history to seek our own metaphysical base since there is no current dominating metaphysics. Pluralism at this level opens the door, yet to speak to thinking man we must develop sooner or later a coherent wholeness in our thought, always subservient to the divine disclosure.

It will be noted how dependent this book is upon the thought of Michael Polanyi and I. T. Ramsey. No one can approach modern science without such indebtedness, and I would refer the reader to their works if my own position needs a more intelligible basis, although I can only claim my own understanding of their thought. Again the works of Teilhard de Chardin and Karl Heim have influenced much of my thinking. I am convinced that the tendency to divorce science from what is for me the deeper and intuitive approach to reality—the area of religious affirmation and ideal value judgments—can lead only down a blind alley from which, sooner or later, mankind will clamor to escape. Man may, in the meantime, work untold destruction for himself and sidetrack the evolutionary creative process, for which God has now made him responsible. These thinkers have helped me to gain a stance from which such convictions can be expressed.

I had intended to include a chapter dealing with the Christian doctrine of creation and current scientific speculations in cosmogony. I felt, however, that little tension is now experienced in this area, especially because we have long since rejected literal interpretations of the biblical creation stories. The material concerned has been included in Chapters II and III. I saw little merit in discussing attempts on the parts of the late Professor E. A. Milne and the late Sir E. T. Whittaker to prove the divine existence on the basis of current scientific cosmogonic myths. In any case, few Christian thinkers believe that the arguments for the divine existence have much validity!

In some respects this book is a sequel to my earlier books on the theology of history, especially *Towards a Theological Understanding of History* (New York: Oxford University Press, 1963). There I contended for a historical realism which placed the Incarnation and the Resurrection in the center of the historical process. Wolfhart Pannenberg has helped to confirm me in such a stand. I do not believe that we can retreat from *Historie* into *Geschichte* alone in the historical revelation without falling into a form of Gnosticism. In the present book I have tried to expand my earlier discussion of revelation and to examine the nature of miracle. The Cosmic Christ theme has been more fully developed. Those interested may consult the above book and also *Nature and Man in Biblical Thought* (London: Lutterworth Press, 1953) for a fuller discusssion of the biblical material relevant to this study.

The book has grown in an annual elective course Science and Religion at Southern Baptist Theological Seminary. I would also express my indebtedness to many colleges and universities which have given me the opportunity to develop its theme in lectures. The Norton Lectures for 1952 at Southern Baptist Theological Seminary, Louisville, Kentucky, first helped me to shape the material. Since then special lectures have been given, among others, at Baylor University, Campbell College, Conrad Grebel College at the University of Waterloo (Ontario), Golden Gate Baptist Theological Seminary, Kentucky Southern College, Stetson University, Union College at Barbourville, University of Louisville, University of South Carolina, and Wake Forest College. In addition many lectures and dialogues at student conferences have helped to clear and challenge my mind, while faculty friends at other schools, my own colleagues at Southern Baptist Theological Seminary, and my graduate students have kept me on the mental rack.

I am especially indebted to my friends Dean Penrose St. Amant, Professors Glenn Hinson and Wayne Oates for perusing and criticizing my manuscript. They are not responsible for its content, but they have helped to remove some of its blemishes and inconsistencies. Mrs. Glenn Hinson and Miss Jean Aiken have helped me skillfully at the secretarial level, bearing patiently with my vagaries. Mr. Manfred Grellert, B.D., my graduate student and teaching fellow, has helped me with the index. Finally, to my wife, to whom this book is dedicated, I express my gratitude for many decades of fellowship and for encouraging me in my intellectual pursuits.

E. C. Rust

Southern Baptist Theological Seminary
Louisville, Kentucky
June 1967

Contents

PART II WHERE THE TWO FORMS OF KNOWLEDGE AND THE TWO LANGUAGES MEET

Part I

Revelation and Science—Two Languages

1

The Roots of the Scientific Approach to Nature and the Religious Issues Involved

The term "nature" has a variety of meanings as is manifest when we consult a modern dictionary or when we examine historical usage since the time of the Greeks. In the thought of Aristotle nature could describe the internal principle that accounted for the structure and development of any individual thing, and it could also stand for the totality of all such things. Mainly in this last sense do we find its contemporary meaning, although we still speak of the "nature of a thing" or of an entity acting in accord with its nature. Modern science has, however, long since eliminated from its consideration the refined animism of Aristotelianism with its substantial forms. For science, nature describes the general cosmic order, the aggregate of all observable or potentially observable entities, including man himself, insofar as man is a subject for scientific inquiry. It is thus the nexus of entities in the universe as they exist at the physical, vital, and psychological levels and as they are interrelated through their somatic and physical behavior. The scientist uses the word "order," for he is concerned with the orderliness of this interrelatedness: the order in its measurable aspects and as a basis for prediction of future behavior. He is concerned with order and regularity.

At the theological level, the world of nature is also the realm of created things. Man as a creature is a part of nature and yet he also stands apart from it. His identity with nature is indicated in the Biblical language which includes man with other creatures in the embracing term "all flesh." His distinctive aspect is brought out in the Biblical description of man created in the image of God. Thus man both is in the natural order and yet transcends it in his characteristics of self-transcendence and personal freedom. Furthermore, not only in the case of man does theology move beyond the scientific description of nature, but also in the consideration of the whole natural order, for faith is aware of a dimension of depth in nature which is not empirically discerned and thus not the concern of most scientific inquiry.

The issue for our time lies in the legitimacy of such a theological description of nature and man and in the validity of any language, like theological language, which cannot be verified at the empirical level. Yet such an issue is not implicit in science itself. It lies rather in the arrogant assumption that the scientific way of knowing is the only way of knowing. In other words, it results from the attempts to elevate the scientific description of the structure of nature at its own specific level of inquiry into an all embracing world-view. It will be our major concern to investigate the legitimacy of such a claim and, at the same time, to show that the scientific evidence is equally consonant with a world-view grounded in the Christian understanding of God.

At the outset we need to remember that much of the so-called conflict between science and religion is false. It is caused in part by a false identification of the Biblical *Weltbild* with the Biblical *Weltanschauung*. The Biblical revelation testifies to a self-disclosure of God in the movement of human history. As such, the revelation is given within the thought atmosphere of a particular period of human history and within the cultural milieu of the Hebrew people. The world structure of such a time would evidently be prescientific, and, as Biblical scholars have frequently reminded us, the people envisaged a three tier universe—a flat earth in the shape of a disk with mountains around its rim; a firmament like an inverted hemispherical bowl resting upon the mountains; a subterranean cavern below the earth for the shades of the departed—the whole surrounded by a watery deep. No knowledge of the expanding universe or of an evolutionary process can be expected in the testimony of the Biblical writers, nor was their human psychology familiar with the categories common to the contemporary psychological knowledge of man. The redemptive disclosure of God which came to them had to be expressed in their prescientific categories, and the failure to allow for this has led churchmen to make often tragic mistakes in meeting the findings of science. Instead of regarding only the divine self-disclosure in Hebrew history and in the Incarnation as authoritative, men of faith have extended the authority to the prescientific framework in which it is expressed. It seems needless to say here that these past decades have seen the Church emancipating itself from such an unnecessary entanglement with an outmoded world structure, and its accompanying psychological understanding of man, and from a groundless conflict with scientific findings.

1. *The roots of modern scientific method*

The truth is that science is in part a child of the Christian faith and in part of the Greco-Roman tradition. Our modern Western culture has its roots in Athens and Jerusalem, and to emphasize either at the expense of the other is to minimize one important aspect of our heritage.

The later Greek was fundamentally a rationalist.[1] For him nature was permeated by mind, and its rational structure was akin to the structure of his own reason. All regularity and

[1] For a discussion of the issues in the next few pages the reader should consult articles by Michael B. Foster in *Mind,* Vol. XLIV, pp. 446 ff.; XLIV, pp. 430 ff.; XLV, pp. 1 ff.; and also his book *Mystery and Philosophy* (London: S.C.M. Press, 1957), pp. 87 ff.; and T. Boman, *Hebrew Thought Compared with Greek,* trans. J. L. Moreau (Philadelphia: The Westminster Press, 1960), *passim;* J. Baillie, *Natural Science and the Spiritual Life* (New York: Charles Scribner's Sons, 1952), pp. 15–32; A. N. Whitehead, *Science and the Modern World* (Cambridge: Cambridge University Press, 1932), pp. 1–24.

orderliness were, for him, indicative of the presence of mind, and hence he regarded nature as both alive and rational. Individual living creatures were focalizations of this all-pervading rationality, and every entity possessed both physical and psychical characteristics. The Heraclitean logos, the Platonic realm of ideas, the Aristotelian thesis of the inherent forms in individual substances, the Stoic principle of an all-pervading logos manifested as a seed logos in human minds—all these remind us that the Greek was concerned primarily with rationality. His model for the universe was to be found in the structure of his own reason. Human self-consciousness at the rational level was the key to unlock the meaning of nature.

Moreover, so akin was the human mind to the rational structure of being for the Greek that he minimized the empirical approach. The rational structures of the human reason were the microcosm in which the intelligible pattern of the whole could be discovered. The human reason itself participated in the logos of the cosmos. Hence it contained in itself the structure which permeates, is participated in, or is imitated by the natural order. Man has only to consider and develop the a priori contents of his reason to discover the structure of the universal reason. This rational structure was basically mathematical. The Pythagorean preoccupation with a mysticism of numbers and geometrical forms expresses a continuing element in Greek thought.

Thus the empirical aspect of knowledge was minimized and the mathematical-rational pattern of nature became central. Observation was not so important as intelligible structure. Plato could reduce astronomy from the observation of actual phenomena to a discussion of the geometry of circles in his *Republic*. Even Aristotle, who was more of an observer, was concerned with the intelligible forms, universal structures which the reason could grasp.

All this meant that for the Greek nature was composite of the divine and the non-divine, of being and not being, of form and matter. Man himself, as a part of the natural order, participated in both being and becoming. In his rational soul he participated in the ultimate reality, the rational structure of being. In his bodily form and psychic appetites, the non-divine was manifested. There was a fundamental dualism here which produced an "over-againstness" of the divine and the non-divine and which saw such "over-againstness" in man himself in the meeting of sensual desire and rational reflection. With all his concern with the transcendence of the divine in Plato and Aristotle, yet the Greek emphasized the immanence. Nature was permeated by the divine, because divine being was reason. Yet within nature and man this divine and rational element was beyond the spatiotemporal. It was not subject to becoming but struggling against not being and matter. We thus have a dualism of being and becoming.

The Greek understanding of personal being is based, therefore, on rationality. The element of rationality in human self-consciousness is its divine and immortal aspect. The ideal is not action but reflection, not will but reason. Morality is to be measured by the control of reason over desire. God is static, unchanging rational being, and not dynamic will and outgoing love. He confronts men as the object of reflection and not the subject of personal disclosure, as rational pattern and not as personal claim.

The Hebrew-Christian approach to nature is quite different. The Hebrew emphasis was on will rather than reason, on personal being as a dynamic whole rather than on static reflective rationality. As far as ultimate reality was concerned, which the Greek described as being, the Hebrew understood God as personal and dynamic. He thought of God in terms of will and personal disclosure. If man was to know God, he would know him not as the end of a ratiocinative process, the finale of a logical argumentation, but only insofar as God chose to make himself known. Furthermore, the world was set in contrast to God as the divine creation. Man and nature were alike regarded as God's creatures. The divine and non-divine were not to be found as twin aspects of nature and man. Neither nature nor man himself participated in the divine substance, for they had been created by the divine fiat. At the behest of the divine will they had been called into being "out of nothing," and, as such, they stood over against the personal God who had called them forth. That man had rational capacities was acknowledged, but there was no suggestion that his reason was divine. He was made in God's image, but the Hebrew meant by this a God-given capacity to live in fellowship with God, to live with God in obedience and trusting commitment. The emphasis fell on the human will and the response of love and commitment. Man must not be arrogant in his rational powers, for he could not by searching find out God. He could only humbly submit himself to the divine self-disclosure. Knowledge of God sprang out of obedience and responsive trust. Man was no divine or semi-divine being, and nature had nothing of the divine about it. They were both creaturely and, as such, stood in contrast to God who sat enthroned in the heavens.

The Greek tended to a transcendence in Plato and Aristotle which envisages the divine or ultimate being placed beyond the spatiotemporal order, and yet also speaks of an immanence that identified certain aspects of nature and man with the divine. The Hebrew spoke of a divine transcendence which was otherness. God was not man. Yet in this tradition God is also immanent as Spirit and creative word, present with the order of nature and the lives of men, creating and sustaining, even suffering within, the spatiotemporal order. God's otherness is not envisaged fundamentally as separation from his creatures for he is also personally present with them, providentially sustaining and guiding them. This understanding is brought to a focus in the understanding of the Incarnation. Jesus Christ is Immanuel, God with us. Transcendence and immanence are alike aspects of the personal creative Being who is other than his creatures and yet in their midst. That the Hebrew used spatial imagery to describe the divine otherness must not lead us to confuse this Hebrew personal transcendence with the Greek idea of the divine reason as beyond the spatiotemporal. Nor may we confuse the Hebrew's plea "whither shall I go from Thy Spirit?" with the Greek's identification of divine omnipresence with human reason and the all-permeating rational structure in nature. Here the Incarnation provides the key to our understanding of "Creation."

Because God is personal being, other than his creatures, he is also mystery. Man may not reflect on the a priori and universal structures of reason to arrive at God or at the structure of his universe. If he would know God, he must await on the divine self-disclosure. If he would know the wisdom of God in creation, he can know it only as that wisdom is disclosed within the natural order and discovered by observation and experiment. Scientific empiricism is almost nascent in the Hebrew-Christian understanding of God. The Hebrew-Christian realism did not seek to fly from the contingency and changefulness of becoming to the universality and rationality of being. Had not God declared his creation to be good and did not the Incarnation imply an identification of God with his creatures? Yet God was sovereign in his otherness, absolutely free in his creating. The created order was his free choice. He was subject to no arbitrary rational standards beyond himself, nor could man in his creaturehood proudly assert that his own rational structures were those which dominated ultimate being. Indeed, modern relativity theory and the plurality of mathematical systems are making us much more humble than the Greeks, for whom Euclid and Pythagoras were sovereign mathematical arbiters. We can never return to Greek science, but we can listen to the Hebrew-Christian tradition. In his mystery of personal being God freely chooses his created order and calls it into being by his sovereign fiat. All man can do is to wait on the divine disclosure and seek patiently to fit together the fragmentary observations of his world, striving to understand the divine mind.

Let us note the concomitance of divine disclosure and human discovery. There are certain aspects of reality which man can discover by the exercise of his rational powers. He can rethink the thoughts of God in creation as he seeks to piece together his empirical observations of his world. Did not God endow him in creation with the power to subdue nature and have dominion over the lower creation? Yet even here an intuitive insight that is strangely akin to disclosure seems almost a necessity. Moreover, such discovery does but touch the outskirts of the divine ways. Human and creaturely wisdom cannot penetrate to the heart of reality without that divine self-disclosure in which God bares to his creature something of the heart of his personal mystery.

In the first centuries of the Christian era little attempt was made to emphasize this Hebrew-Christian tradition. In the Greco-Roman world, Greek categories of thought tended to dominate. We should add, at this point, that Greek science was not in this period very active and thus presented no challenge to the Christian point of view. Greek thought was mainly assimilated at the theological level. Irenaeus more mediately and Tertullian more extremely tried to deal with the issue of Athens and Jerusalem. But it waited on Augustine to attempt the first great synthesis of the two traditions. This towering and creative thinker gave a profound analysis of the Christian doctrine of creation, of the meaning of Incarnation, and of the relation of faith to reason. Though inhibited in part by the dominant Neoplatonic philosophy of his time, he recaptured for his contemporaries many major insights of the Christian revelation. The understanding of the created order as issuing from the sovereign freedom of God by creative decree and as gathered up in the Incarnation of the Son of God recovered an emphasis which later Augustinians were to employ in the development of an empirical concern with their world. The understanding of human reason, *scientia*, as operating always within the prior knowledge born of disclosure and faith, *sapientia*, reminded men that reason was always subject to absolute presuppositions from which it could not escape, which were arrived at pre-logically, and which were present, consciously or unconsciously, in all thought, directing its logic. The full significance of the Augustinian revolution at these levels was appreciated only with the passage of the years.

It is significant that the first signs of an experimental approach to nature appear within the Franciscan order with its Augustinian tradition.[2] In the medieval period the rediscovery of Aristotle and the acceptance of his theory of motion and of his view of the universe hampered discovery until Franciscan thinkers achieved a breakthrough. Roger Bacon and Roger Grossteste, Bishop of Lincoln, opened up at Oxford University new possibilities in empirical observation, while Jean Buridan and Nicolas Oresme at the University of Paris challenged the Aristotelian ideas of motion with their new theory of impetus.

Hitherto, the medieval approach to nature had offered little of any genuine experimentation. Medieval thinkers were cumbered by the Aristotelian categories and viewed nature always through the spectacles of the great Greek thinker. They did, of course, observe, and they recorded what they observed. They compiled encyclopedias in which actual creatures and fantastic beings were described as equally real. They accepted the highly complicated geocentric universe of Ptolemy with its concentric crystalline spheres on which the celestial bodies from the sun and planets to the fixed stars moved by heavenly induced motion around the earth. As observations of the heavenly bodies became more available, they complicated the celestial machinery by introducing more and more crystalline

[2] See C. E. Raven, *Natural Religion and Christian Theology* (Cambridge: Cambridge University Press, 1953), pp. 74 f.; H. Butterfield, *The Origins of Modern Science* (London: G. Bell & Sons, Ltd., 1949), pp. 1–14.

spheres rolling upon one another. Yet the celestial and ethereal nature of the heavenly bodies forbade any attempt to view them as subject to the changes known in the terrestrial realm. So the geocentric cosmology with is unwieldy machinery was retained. It was accepted that bodies moved unnaturally only when other moving bodies were in contact with them. There was no idea of the inherent inertia of a physical body whereby it persists in rest or uniform rectilinear motion when no other force is there to alter its motion. Theories, fantastic from our modern standpoint, had to be developed to explain the continued motion of a cannon ball once the expulsive force of the gunpowder had ceased to operate upon it. The absence of any idea of the force of gravity led to the suggestion that earthly bodies fell more quickly to earth the nearer they got because they were hurrying to their own place.

We can be grateful to the pioneers who in the fourteenth and fifteenth centuries began the breakthrough which made modern science possible. Their inspiration lay in that same Christian tradition which had so long harbored the older approach to nature. Let us add, however, that Aristotelian physics did have a basis in common sense. Its theories did seem to agree with normal observation. It would seem, for example, that the sun and heavenly bodies were moving around the earth. The new science required an imaginative readjustment at all levels that common sense found difficult to attain.

Alongside of this growing empirical concern and closely bound up with it we must note the rebellion against and modification of scholastic rationalism from Duns Scotus through William of Occam. This marks a retreat from rationalism with its concern with the realism of universal ideas to an emphasis on the particular objects of sense experience. For the Occamists, the particulars mattered and universals became a posteriori class names rather than a priori rational principles. The stage was being set for modern science.

When modern science did finally emerge, it showed itself to

be the child of both the Greek and the Hebrew-Christian traditions. Copernicus with his heliocentric cosmology was not emancipated from his Aristotelian past.[3] He still gloried in the divine perfection of circular motion and spoke about the celestial nature of the sun's substance in its central position. Tycho Brahe was the observer, but even he still accepted a modified Ptolemaic geocentric universe. It was Kepler, building on Brahe's observations and Copernicus's cosmology, who manifested the principles of the new science that was emerging—even though Greek elements were still present in his thinking. His theory of elliptic paths for the planetary orbits round the sun was carefully demonstrated on an empirical basis and his laws of planetary motion were empirically derived. Still more must we turn to Galileo in whom the new method of understanding nature came to fruition. This protagonist of the new science for the first time arrived at an understanding of inertia and of the nature of gravity. He showed that bodies fell with an accelerated motion and that this acceleration could be expressed in mathematical form. He turned the problem of motion "into the problem of geometrical bodies moving in geometrical space." [4] Thereby he was able to explain the parabolic path of a missile fired from a gun. He carefully measured his observations and related them in a mathematical formula. He constructed a telescope and demonstrated that the heavenly bodies had the same properties as terrestrial matter and were subject to change. The old conservative framework was shattered, and a new way of understanding nature was on its way.

In Galilean science two presuppositions are evident: the first is that the realm of nature has a causative rational structure which is at basis mathematical; and the second is that this structure can best be determined by empirical observation and experiment. The first has its roots in Greek rationalism and

[3] H. Butterfield offers an excellent account of the breakdown of Aristotelian science: op. cit. chs. 2, 4, and 5.

[4] H. Butterfield, op. cit. p. 92.

the second in the Hebrew-Christian tradition. Let us, at once, note that Aristotle did not ignore observation but he took refuge in common-sense interpretation and developed a rational structure on this basis. It seemed evident from experience of falling rocks and falling leaves that heavier bodies fell more quickly. But Galileo undertook a refined experimental investigation which confounded Aristotle's rationalism of common sense. In doing so he moved beyond the entities which were immediately evident to sense perception and took the great step of "daring to describe the world as we do not experience it." [5] As von Weizsäcker reminds us, "he stated laws which in the form in which he stated them never hold in actual experience and which therefore cannot be verified by any single observation but which are mathematically simple." He postulated a vacuum which Aristotelians regarded as a natural impossibility. His model for inertia was an ideal resistanceless space without any forces operative within it. He banished Aristotle's common-sense world filled with unobservable forms by a world of such mathematical entities as acceleration and force, not immediately evident to sense perception. Science was launched upon a path of hypothetico- and mathematico-rationalism conjoined to experimental observation of entities which the mathematical structure carefully defined.

The new method was not merely observation but experimental observation—putting a question to nature by an experiment and carefully defining by the experiment the limited response that one would observe. This approach was made possible because of the preparation in the Greek and the Hebrew-Christian tradition.

II. *A mechanistic universe and the "God of the Gaps"*

The first scientists of the modern period were religious men. Galileo, though disciplined by the Inquisition, remained within

[5] C. F. von Weizsacker, *The Relevance of Science* (London: Collins, 1964), p. 104.

the Roman Catholic Church. Kepler, who on an empirical basis had established the elliptic paths of the planets round the sun, celebrated their wonderful and law-abiding harmony as a heavenly music. In the music of the spheres he was reading the mind of the Creator. In his mathematics he was adoring God, whom he specially associated with the central position of the sun. Descartes, whom we shall consider immediately, regarded God as at least a minimal necessity in his system. Malebranche, who spread the teaching of Descartes, sought to make Cartesianism a basis for a Christian polemic. He and Descartes alike held that they were concerned to establish the validity of Christian truth. Robert Boyle, the father of chemisty, was also deeply religious and wrote a book in which he endeavored to reconcile science and religion, *The Christian Virtuoso* (1690). Sir Isaac Newton regarded nature as the divine sensorium and was so devout that he increasingly devoted his time to a study of prophecy, especially the book of Daniel and the Apocalypse. Pascal undertook physical experimentation and also was concerned with deep religious contemplation. John Ray, the famous Cambridge biologist, wrote *The Wisdom of God Manifested in the Works of the Creation.* Yet the foundations were being laid on both sides for a rift between scientific knowledge and religious faith.

Descartes established in modern science the basis for a new rationalism. Francis Bacon [6] had in his writings emphasized the new empirical approach. This new approach meant moving forward on the basis of "putting nature to the question" by experimental investigation. The results of such empirical observation would be tabulated in "tables of invention," common relationships between them established, and general laws adumbrated on the basis of which the future behavior of nature might be predicted. He banished from nature all Aristotelian forms and nonobservable entities. Any view of

[6] See H. Butterfield, op. cit. pp. 96 ff.; F. Sherwood Taylor, *Science Past and Present* (London: William Heinemann Ltd., 1949), pp. 96 ff.

nature as vital, alive, immanently intelligent, was to be eliminated. It remained only for Descartes to emphasize the rational aspect of such an approach to nature which is absent from Bacon's reflections.[7]

Galileo had already differentiated between the primary sense qualities of extension and motion and the secondary qualities of color, sound, smell, and touch which he regarded as due solely to the bodily senses. Already nature was being reduced to the status of an extended order of purely physical bodies in motion. One strand of Greek thought, the materialistic atomism of Democritus and Leucippus, had centuries before advocated such an approach to the natural order. In Descartes it was asserted still more.

This thinker contended that true knowledge was bound up only with those ideas that were clear and distinct, and he indulged in a process of radical skepticism in which he finally arrived at one basic conviction: his own existence as a thinking being. He thus radically isolated man and enthroned reason as the arbiter of all things. God and the world must alike be established as existent realities by processes of ratiocination. The universal presence of the distinct idea of the former set over against his own finitude led Descartes to postulate the actuality of a divine being who alone could cause such an idea in his mind. Such a perfect being would guarantee that the clear and distinct ideas of sense observation were not deceptive. So Cartesianism re-established a world of extension and motion, since these primary sense qualities were distinct and unequivocal, but all secondary qualities must be bandished from that world—they could not be measured. Now empiricism faded into the background and the mathematical rationalist took over. Descartes developed a mechanical and

[7] See H. Butterfield, op. cit. pp. 96 ff.; F. Sherwood Taylor, op. cit. p. 98; R. G. Collingwood, *The Idea of Nature* (Oxford: Oxford University Press, 1945), pp. 103 ff.; W. C. Dampier, *A History of Science* (Cambridge: Cambridge University Press, 1961), pp. 134 ff.

geometrical universe in which the whole spatial plenum was filled with moving matter, for he was sufficiently medieval still to deny a vacuum. The universe consisted of a system of vortices out of which the circular motion of the planets round the sun could be accounted for. There was no idea of physical atoms involved, however, for nature was a continuous whole of moving matter. Descartes was now not concerned so much with empirical observation and experiment as with his own rational schemes.

In this kind of thought God and mind were banished from nature. Descartes's *Cogito, ergo sum* had isolated the human reason in solitary splendor, but it had also introduced into nature a fatal bifurcation between mind and matter. Thinking and unextended substance, mind, was distinguished from an entirely alien unthinking and extended substance, matter, the two meeting only in human personal being and there held together in an incomprehensible way by God. Thus God was dragged in to account for the contrarieties of the Cartesian system; yet both he and the human consciousness were alien to the vast mechanical order of nature. The latter was no longer characterized by an immanent rationality, and the dominant Greek and medieval conception of matter as the unrealizedness of immanent intelligible form had disappeared. What rationality material nature contained was imposed on it from without, and its regularity was due to mechanical and mathematically expressible laws imposed on it externally. It expressed an intelligence which was beyond it and which had designed its machinelike structure for a definite purpose. Within such a structure the human mind found an uncomfortable and indefinable resting place. God had become a transcendent creator and ruler who imposed the laws and, at least, started the process going. Here Descartes felt that at least he required God. He dragged him in to "fill the gaps" for which his rationalism could not account. God set the world in motion, ordained the laws of nature, and, at the appropriate moment, breathed the human mind into a machinelike body; for even living things were reduced by Descartes to machines.

Some Protestant and Catholic theologians alike realized the danger of the Cartesian system. Descartes's works were put on the Index in 1663. He himself died in exile. Yet within a matter of decades his approach to nature was accepted by the intellectual world, and even the Church used the Cartesian method as a basis for Christian apologetic. From Malebranche, the Catholic Cartesian, to Paley, the Protestant apologist, the Cartesian approach took over. Men found themselves in a world of moving and extended matter, a vast machinelike nature whose behavior was ruled by laws which "never could be broken."

The Cartesian continuous matter was replaced by a model which better fitted empirical observations. Atoms, like smooth billiard balls, moving in empty space, replaced the filled plenum of Descartes, but the whole system was mechanistically determined and mathematically expressible. Immanent teleology and dynamic purposiveness gave place to a machine directed by laws imposed from without. Butterfield describes the position as follows:

> God, the human soul and the whole realm of spiritual things . . . escaped imprisonment in the process of mechanization, and were superadded presences, flitting vaporously amongst the cog wheels, the pulleys, the steel castings of a relentless world-machine. It was very difficult to show how these two planes of existence could ever have come to intersect, or at what point mind or soul could ever join up with matter.[8]

It was Newton who finally formulated the accumulating views of his contemporaries and gave them a systematized mathematical expression in his *Principia Mathematica.* Others had already grasped various aspects of the laws of motion

[8] H. Butterfield, op. cit. p. 110.

which he formulated,[9] but Newton both made possible an all-embracing view of the universe and devised the mathematical instrument—his calculus—that made such a systemization possible. The result was a universe which was one vast machine, explicable solely in terms of mechanical forces and expressible in laws which could be formulated mathematically. Such a universe, bound together by mechanistic causation, was thoroughly deterministic. There was no room for relativity. Causation held absolute sway over material bodies whose matter was absolutely indestructible. They moved in a framework of absolute space and absolute time, about the measurements of which all observers would agree. We must hasten to note that Newton did not himself hold such an all-embracing mechanistic view of the universe, but he did lay the foundations for it.

Newton repudiated Cartesian metaphysics. He clung closely to empirical data and abolished hypotheses, like those of Descartes, which were based on causes not deducible from observation. Thus he could find no explanation for gravitational action at a distance, and wrote that, since he was unable to discover the cause of the properties of gravity, he would "frame no hypothesis." [10] And yet he established a new form of rationalism which embodied the dualism of Descartes and made the principles of Cartesianism the dominant world view. He wrote to Bentley that he "had an eye upon such principles as might work with considering men, for the belief in Deity." [11] He regarded nature as the divine sensorium.[12] And he could still retain his religious faith because he deliberately re-

[9] Christian Huyghens had formulated the third law, that action and reaction are equal and opposite. Hooke claimed to have established mathematically the motions of the planets in elliptic paths.

[10] Sir Isaac Newton, *Mathematical Principles of Natural Philosophy* in *Great Books of the Western World* (Chicago: Encyclopedia Britannica, Inc., 1952), Vol. XXXIV, p. 371.

[11] Sir Isaac Newton, *Four Letters to Dr. Bentley in Proof of a Deity* (London, 1756).

[12] Sir Isaac Newton, *Mathematical Principles,* loc. cit. p. 258.

fused to accept an interpretation of his scientific method which made possible the mechanistic world-view of the French *philosophes*. It is probably true to say in the balance that his work might be more easily interpreted in the latter way, for it did imply a deterministic system at the physical level.

Descartes thought of God as setting the world in motion. Newton, rejecting metaphysical speculation, was more ready to fit God into the gaps which his system left open.[13] Unable to explain the specific paths of the planets, he suggested that these paths were directly determined by the Creator. Because his system was not sufficiently developed to account for the irregularities in the orbital motions of the planetary system, he thought of God as repairing and renewing the system of the universe. When the planets went off their paths, God personally intervened and regulated them. Further, it was God who sustained the fixed stars in their places. Thus Newton endeavored to maintain the medieval idea of a divine *concursus* and sought to express his faith in the divine omnipresence. He rejected a pantheistic idea, however, and his whole system implied a deism which he was seeking to avoid. Yet he was calling on religious categories to account for phenomena which were scientifically explicable, as his successors demonstrated.

It was only a century before Laplace declared that if he were given the exact position and motion of every particle in the universe at any time, he could predict with accuracy any particle's every future state. Asked by Napoleon where God fitted into his calculations, he replied: "Sire, I have no need for that hypothesis." Already by his nebular hypothesis, he had explained scientifically the origin of the planetary bodies, their paths, and their motions. The gap in Newton's system had been filled at the level of scientific explanation. Furthermore, it had now been demonstrated that the gravitational solar system

[13] Cf. H. Butterfield, op. cit. pp. 141 f.; J. Dillenberger, *Protestant Thought and Natural Science* (Garden City, New York: Doubleday & Co., Inc., 1960), p. 122 f.

was self-regulating, and again religious categories of explanation were not needed. Scientific rationalism, grounded in measurable observations and expressed in a mechanical and deterministic model, reigned supreme.

Nor, in the beginning, did this daunt men of faith. In this new age of reason they sought to reconcile reason and religion. Their deity was a transcendent lawgiver who had given to the machinelike universe its unbreakable laws and thus determined its motions. This motion was a directed one. The machine existed for a purpose and so did all its parts. Teleology took over—not the immanent teleology of Aristotelianism, or an organismic teleology, but the teleology of a design imposed on nature from without, a mechanical teleology. From John Locke to Paley, across two centuries, men sought to demonstrate the reasonableness of faith and especially employed the argument from design to support their case. Fundamentally their emphasis fell on transcendence, for divine immanence could have little significance for a deterministic and mechanistic view of nature. Miracles were divine interventions in a process that had been divinely created to run in accord with fixed laws ordained from creation. For Paley, the universe was a watch and God was the watchmaker. The more extreme deists, like Matthew Tindal in *Christianity as Old as Creation,* sought to reduce Christianity to reason and eliminate what did not conform to reason. Most men sought, in the miracles and prophecies accompanying the Biblical revelation, evidences of its validity. And everywhere, beyond all else, men sought for purpose. Since God had created the world, it must be the best possible, and there could be nothing in it which did not serve a purpose. This theme of Leibnitz is echoed repeatedly.

There were occasional rebellions against this mechanistic world-view, notably by the Cambridge Platonists who included Ralph Cudworth, Henry More, and John Ray, the biologist. Cudworth could write that "the root of all atheism consists in making senseless matter the only existent thing, and the original of all things . . . and mind as nothing but local motion in the organic parts of a man's body." [14] Very sensitive to the evil in the universe, he could argue that this was not the best of all possible worlds and that the facts argued against the mechanistic scheme with its all-powerful creative engineer. He found his refuge in a more organic view of nature and taught the presence of a "plastic nature," a "vegetative soul," in the natural order and living things.[15] This could account for the deviations, as John Ray, the biologist, argued. He took up the thought of Cudworth and argued that the divine purpose overrides the effects of such "plastic nature," so that design is evident throughout nature.

Thus the argument from design found support in those who tried to retain a more organic view of nature. Ray, in *The Wisdom of God Manifested in the Works of Creation,* could point to the adaptations of living things—the organs of the human body especially intrigued him [16]—as indications of the divine wisdom in the plan of creation. He cites the camouflage of the tiger and the way in which medicine is derived from the most vile insects. He sees plagues of insects as instances of divine judgment and, as did Paley later,[17] glories in the perfection of the human eye.

Furthermore, even among biologists who sought to retain a

[14] R. Cudworth, *The True Intellectual System of the Universe,* Vol. I, Teggedn (London, 1845), p. 321. There is an excellent discussion of Cudworth in Basil Willey, *The Seventeenth Century Background* (Garden City, New York: Doubleday Anchor Books, 1953), pp. 157 ff. Also in C. E. Raven, op. cit. pp. 111 ff.

[15] See C. E. Raven, op. cit. pp. 114 ff.

[16] John Ray, *The Wisdom of God Manifested in the Work of Creation,* 11th ed. (London, 1743), pp. 287 f. For John Ray, see C. E. Raven, op. cit. pp. 117 ff.

[17] W. Paley, *Natural Theology,* Vol. I (London, 1836), p. 81. He believed that the structure of the eye was alone sufficient, without any other contrivances of nature, "to support the conclusion that we draw from it, as to the necessity of an intelligent Creator." See J. Dillenberger, op. cit. p. 152.

more organic point of view, the fixity of the species from creation was accepted. There was no thought of creation as a process. John Ray defined the "works of creation" as those "created by God at first, and by him conserved to this day in the same state and condition in which they were first made." [18] This view was also taught by Linnaeus and was accepted by all subsequent systematizers of living things. Here the mechanists and the organicists were agreed.

Generally we may say that physics and astronomy were the sciences in the ascendant. Their success conditioned the way in which living organisms and human bodies were to be understood. The work of John Harvey on the circulation of the blood and Vesalius's description of the fabric of the human body set the pattern for the acceptance of the Cartesian viewpoint. As the machinelike structure was more adequately perfected in the mind of the scientist, there were less gaps to fill with God. Yet, at least, the design of the whole and the striking adaptations of the individual entities within it pointed to a creative designer, a cosmic engineer who had designed it and started it going. This was the best of all possible worlds, however much Voltaire might scoff against it.

Yet such a deterministic universe could hardly be consonant with divine self-disclosure or human freedom. Also a transcendent cosmic engineer was hardly the God of Jesus Christ. The ultimate outcome of such a world-view would tend, sooner or later, as Hobbes had seen, to be a materialistic one. This materialistic tradition, stemming from the Greek atomists, and re-established by Hobbes, found fuller expression in the eighteenth century. The physiologists of the French Encyclopedia became its fervent advocates. D'Holbach and de la Mettrie could describe man as a machine and could speak of mind as a secretion of the brain.[19] The age of reason had provided an

[18] John Ray, op. cit.

[19] For an illuminating discussion of *Les Philosophes,* including D'Holbach and de la Mettrie, see G. Boas *Dominant Themes of Modern Philosphy* (New York: The Ronald Press Co., 1957), pp. 302–50.

uncertain truce between the new world view of science, obtained by extrapolating certain scientific attitudes into descriptions of ultimate reality, and the Christian faith, even though the former had its roots partly in the latter. Skepticism was in the air, and it found adequate expression in the reflections of David Hume.

Descartes had isolated the human self-consciousness and turned attention to the human mind and the nature of the knowing processes. Thus idealism could be an alternative to materialism in the situation created by the new science. It was Hume who contributed signally towards this possibility, although himself a skeptic. Since on the Cartesian and Lockean basis all that man actually knew were ideas, Hume sought to investigate the nature of our sensations. In consequence, he demonstrated that neither causation nor substance were involved in the sensations themselves. All the knowing mind had at this level were recurrent successions in time or frequent associations in space of like sensations. But the mind possessed certain natural beliefs which could not be rationally demonstrated, and it was in this way that causation and substance were associated with the sensations. In the same way, the mind was itself a bundle of sensations and the attribution of "soul" or "self" was again a natural belief. Finally, in his two discussions of religion, Hume carried his skepticism into the religious realm and demonstrated the inadequacy of any attempt to demonstrate rationally the existence of God. Although he speaks favorably at times of the argument from design, his skepticism wins the day. It would seem that for him "God" too is associated with natural belief—certainly not with reason.

Awakened by Hume from his dogmatic slumber and taking refuge in his "transcendental ego," Kant sought to overcome the impasse of a mechanistic determinism and establish a place for human freedom and religious belief in God. Like Descartes and his predecessors, he retreated to his self-consciousness and sought for a solution in its moral aspect. For him the mind is fitted with certain a priori structures into which sense experience fits the actual world, the thing in itself. Thus the realm of causation and matter in its spatiotemporal framework is a phenomenal world, the construct of the knowing mind, offering no knowledge of ultimate reality. Arguments based upon it or upon the ideas associated with it in the mind can have no validity. They never take us beyond the phenomenal. Thus the realm of mechanistic causation and scientific determinism has not the last word. This lies in the affirmations of the moral consciousness, the experience of oughtness with its accompanying recognition of rightness. Here we move beyond desire and the phenomenal self to true self-hood, the noumenal ego. If the pure reason, operating upon the phenomenal world, fails, the practical reason, dealing with the experience of the moral judgment, can take us to the heart of reality. Oughtness at the moral level carries with it the postulates of human freedom, personal immortality, and the existence of God. So the noumenal world is a realm of moral beings under God, and for Kant scientific theories are bypassed and religion reestablished rationally.

Kant in his *Critique of Judgment* even sought to find a place for the purpose and design that his biological studies tended to emphasize. In *Critique of Pure Reason* he dealt with Newtonian physics; in *Critique of Judgment* he turned to the area which was still awaiting Darwin. He felt that animate nature had its purposive aspect, but, as with the physical level of nature, he ascribed this teleological element to the human understanding; even though he seems to have put a little more emphasis on its possible relation to the "thing in itself" than that of the efficient causation of the Newtonian order. Teleological categories help us to understand nature where the a priori category of efficient causation fails. They help us to systematize our experience and enable us to bring appearances under rules. Thus, for Kant, teleological categories belonged more to the reflective judgment than they were basic conditions for having any experience at all, as were the a priori categories of causation and substance. Biological phenomena were sufficiently distinctive to require unique categories for interpretation, but they were still phenomena and no mystic "purposiveness" must be ascribed by reason to the noumenal reality on such a basis. We could, however, treat them as if they were related to purposive divine reason. All nature was phenomenal finally, and reason beginning with sense experience could not arrive at ultimate reality.

Kant's skepticism at this level, following on Hume's total skepticism, tended in the course of the next century to introduce an antimetaphysical and antitheological bias into science. If scientific principles were not in nature but read into nature by the human mind, it was a short step to the positivism of August Comte which regarded science as descriptive and rejected all metaphysics. It was also an easy step to the allied naturalism and secularism of this century and to the agnosticism of T. H. Huxley. The scientist was not looking for ultimate causes, and he must not speculate beyond his scientific evidence into any invisible and unobservable supranatural realm. Positivism increasingly lifted its head and the way was prepared for modern secularism.

Thoroughgoing monistic idealism, such as the Hegelian system, provided a reconciliation of science and religion by reducing the universe to a totally rational basis as the manifestation of one Absolute Mind in its dialectical movement; by making man but an adjectival reason within this universal reason; and by regarding religion as a way of dressing up the rational ground of the universe in mythical forms and symbols. Generally, however, it is true to say that religious men sought other ways of expressing their faith and their personal freedom within a deterministic order of nature. They took the way of Kant, identifying religion with morality. Or they took the way of Ritschl and identified religion with value judgments. Or they took the way of pantheism and identified religion with pure feeling as did Schleiermacher. Or they endeavored to fit science and religion together in uneasy alliance by filling gaps, such as the origination of life, the origin of man, the relation of body to mind, with religious categories, instead of recognizing that here too science might offer descriptions at its own level.

III. *The Darwinian revolution and Christian faith*

In the nineteenth century, when such efforts at fitting faith and science together were being made, the Darwinian challenge asserted itself. By the end of the eighteenth century a concern with history as a distinctive area of knowledge had made itself evident. The work of Vico,[20] the interests of Voltaire, and the new attempts to write intelligible histories had directed attention upon an area where general laws and universal principles were not so discernible. At the scientific level the growing volume of geological and paleontological evidence turned men's eyes back to the origination of living things, and the doctrine of the fixity of the species was being challenged by biologists such as Buffon, Lamarck, and Erasmus Darwin. Evolution was in the ideological atmosphere, and men were beginning to look at nature from the historical standpoint.

It waited, however, for a man of genius to grasp some integrating principle by which the evidence for change could be correlated. Charles Darwin,[21] himself a field biologist, accumulated material from his travels which challenged the

[20] G. Vico, *The New Science,* trans. T. G. Bergin and M. H. Fisch (Ithaca, New York: Cornell University Press, 1948), see E. C. Rust, *Towards a Theological Understanding of History* (New York: Oxford University Press, 1963), pp. 26–30.

[21] For excellent discussions of the historical development of Darwinism, the reader should consult C. E. Raven, op. cit. Ch. IX; J. Dillenberger, op. cit. Ch. VIII; William Irvine, *Apes, Angels, and Victorians* (New York: Meridian Books), *passim.*

accepted position. Then, by an intuitive leap, he applied the thesis of Malthus about human population equilibrium to the development of nature. As a result, he suggested that the species changed by small, chance variations which were spread across a species because they enabled the members to survive in the struggle for existence. Environmental conditions and the competition with other living things brought about a selective process in which favorable changes were given more chance of propagation. At the same time, William Wallace had been working along parallel lines. Although Darwin himself interpreted "by chance" in his theory to mean that he did not know the cause, his advocates, and in particular T. H. Huxley, emphasized chance and natural selection to such a degree that once more religious faith seemed in jeopardy. As McNeile Dixon reminds us, "Darwinism was a God-send to disbelievers in God." Once more teleology was threatened and a purposive aspect in nature seemed to be called in question.

The theory fitted in well with the dominant utilitarian outlook of Victorian England, and Herbert Spencer made it the universal key to a philosophy of the universe. Enlightened churchmen, however, recognized that the mechanism of evolution was only one aspect of the process, and that the mechanism itself might still be a directed one. Yet sentimental Victorians shuddered at Huxley's celebration of a ruthless warfare in nature. Tennyson, the poet laureate, was disturbed at the wastage of the process and wrote:

> That I, considering everywhere
> Her secret nature in her deeds,
> And finding that of fifty seeds
> She brings but one to bear,
> I falter where I firmly trod . . .

For him, nature was "red in tooth and claw with ravine." [22] The theory seemed to destroy the last remnants of the teleological argument of which rationalistic theology had made so

[22] Alfred Lord Tennyson, "In Memoriam" in *Poetical Works* (London: Oxford University Press, Standard Authors Edition, 1953), p. 243.

much. Chance and internecine warfare between the species seemed to have replaced design.

Furthermore, the dignity of the human species seemed to be undermined by the doctrine of descent from the lower animal order. Copernicus had dethroned man's habitat, and now Darwin seemed to dethrone man himself from any unique place in the universe. Viewed naturalistically, man had become a species of higher mammal. Even his religion, already dealt with skeptically by Hume, could be reviewed in evolutionary categories and described as a projection of his basic needs upon the backscreen of the universe. It was man calling in the universe on his side. Hence Feuerbach could describe man's ideas of God as projections of his own wishes, while Marx could find the roots of religion in man's economic hungers.

It was clear that the older mechanistic view of living organisms was being challenged by a view which emphasized chance rather than determinism and which looked to history rather than nature as the key to understanding the universe. This was not immediately evident in the last century, and there were many scientists who still retained a materialistic and mechanistic view of living things.

Materialism as a live option was countered by a vitalism which postulated a vital element in organisms, Driesch's psychoid, which inhabited the organism, like a ghost in the machine, and which accounted for the difference between animate and inanimate nature.[23] Since such a "psychoid" or vital element was, like the human soul, scientifically unobservable, its presence was a matter of faith. The vitalists found

[23] There is an incisive analysis of the mechanistic-vitalistic issue in C. D. Broad, *The Mind and Its Place in Nature* (London: Kegan Paul, Trench, Trubner & Co., Ltd., 1947), pp. 43–94. The neo-vitalist position is stated clearly by H. Driesch in his Gifford Lectures, *The Science and Philosophy of Vitalism* (London: Macmillan & Co., Ltd., second edition, 1929). There is also a somewhat dated discussion of the issues involved in B. Bavink, *The Anatomy of Modern Science,* trans. H. S. Hatfield (London: G. Bell & Sons, Ltd., 1932), pp. 385–403. W. C. Dampier, op. cit. pp. 262 ff., 357 ff. also outlines the debate.

exceeding difficulty in maintaining their position as more and more of the gaps between the living and the nonliving were filled at the physicochemical level, including the chemical synthesis of organic molecules found in living things. The laboratory synthesis of urea forms but one example of such investigations. Yet the distinction of "wholeness" which marked off the organism from the inanimate substance still remained a mystery, although attempts to fill the gaps by nonscientifically observable entities, even God himself, raised serious questions in scientifically oriented minds. Even for the religious man, scientifically trained, it might well be that the creative process could be uncovered in its physicochemical aspects.

As such questions increasingly come to the fore, the physicochemical basis of heredity was clarified at the beginning of the twentieth century by the discovery of chromosomes and genes. The purely empirical work of the Abbé Mendel in the mid-nineteenth century was now given a theoretical basis, and his laws both accounted for and expanded. At the same time, the true mechanism of evolutionary change became identified with mutations in gene structure under the impact of radiation or chemicals taken as foods. Darwinism received a more carefully defined form as the operation of natural selection upon such small random mutations, whereby the latter which possessed survival value spread across a species and ultimately, by cumulative effect, produced a new species. We shall discuss later the difficulties presented by the theory, but it remains true that biological consensus is still neo-Darwinian, since no other comprehensive and satisfactory theory of change and species origination has presented itself.

Philosophically, various thinkers accepted evolutionary development as a constituent element in the universe.[24] Often

[24] E.g. C. Lloyd Morgan, *Emergent Evolution* (London: Williams and Norgate, 1927); S. A. Alexander, *Space, Time and Deity*, 2 vols. (London: Macmillan & Co., Ltd., 1934); J. C. Smuts, *Holism and Evolution* (New York: The Viking Press, 1961); Henri Bergson, *Creative Evolution*

"evolution" became a key analogy and was applied to all realms of human experience, as well as to the biological order to which it properly applied. It is significant that the emphasis now fell on the wholeness of living things and upon the inexplicable emergence of new qualities in the process. The word "emergence" has become common coinage to explain the appearance of novelty as the evolutionary process has moved forward in increasing complexity of organization.

Yet, when the living processes are identified with the models employed by biochemistry and biophysics, instead of treating them as representative analogies, it is easy for a naturalistic interpretation to be offered of the phenomena associated with living things. Such a metaphysical extrapolation from the experimental models is made easier by recent experimental work.

The contemporary discovery of the DNA molecule, and thus of the nature of the chromosomes and their constituent genes, is a reminder that a reductionist naturalism is very much a live option. Furthermore, the element of chance and contingency is still in the center of evolutionary thinking as the emphasis falls on small *random* mutations. It is certainly true that the old rationalistic theology with its emphasis on design has little to say to the scientist of today, especially if he is naturalistically oriented. Again, we cannot at the level of life summon religious categories to our help in filling gaps in our scientific knowledge. The nature of the virus at the borderline of living and nonliving and the possible synthesis in the next ten years of a DNA molecule, and even a rudimentary living cell, should warn the religious man against mixing his categories and expecting to find God "under his microscope."

(New York: Random House, Modern Library Edition, 1944). Numerous other writings by these and other thinkers could be cited. A. N. Whitehead in his many writings also makes evolution a key idea in his "philosophy of organism," *Science and the Modern World* (Cambridge: Cambridge University Press, 1932), *Process and Reality* (Cambridge: Cambridge University Press, 1929).

IV. *The new world of physics*

The mechanistic model with its ideas of rigid determinism has disappeared also from contemporary physics. This model envisaged the universe as an assembly of atomic and molecular particles obeying strictly the laws of motion and set within an absolute framework of space and time. Mechanistic causation ruled supreme in such a world. All observers would agree in their spatial and temporal measurements. Matter was itself indestructible, an absolute object. Action at a distance (gravitational and electromagnetic force), the nature of radiation, the seeming dependence of the chemical qualities of the different elements upon their atomic weight—all these remained extraneous elements in such a scheme, and at these points the scheme finally foundered.

At the microscopic level the discovery by Planck that radiation possessed an atomic or quantized nature and the demonstration that the atoms of all substances were composed of electrified particles, electrons and protons, led to the postulation, by combination of these two discoveries, of a quantized model for the atom. This brought about a radical transformation in atomic and subatomic realms. No longer could a mechanical model be regarded as best representing atomic phenomena, even one based on the solar system, for stationary orbits, closed shells, spinning electrons became added furniture. Moreover the electrons and protons could manifest wave as well as particle properties, and it became a matter of the *sitz im Leben* which picture should be adopted. Again, atomic phenomena could be pictured solely in mathematical equations which employed symbols for entities often only ideally observable. Such equations could give only probabilities, not certainties, and Heisenberg's indeterminacy principle has come to be accepted in atomic physics. Position and speed, energy and momentum, are not at the same time to be determined with absolute accuracy. There is an element of uncertainty at the basis of atomic phenomena. Furthermore, matter and radiation, both manifesting wave and particle characteristics, are recognized as forms of energy, forms which can be converted into one another under appropriate conditions. The solid material world of the classical physics has dissolved into a realm of probabilities describing the dynamic behavior of various forms of energy. Determinism has disappeared at the atomic level, and contingency has taken its place.

At the macroscopic level a corresponding revolution has taken place. The discovery of the invariance of the speed of light, whatever be the frame of reference in which it was measured, led to Einstein's epoch-making development of his special and general theories of relativity. Absolute space and absolute time disappeared from the physicists' models to be replaced by the relativity of all spatiotemporal measurements to the observer. Along with this, gravitational action at a distance could be explained as due to the geometry of the spatiotemporal continuum. At the macroscopic level also the new model identified radiation and matter as both forms of energy and as alike possessing mass. Once more the model was expressible best in the form of mathematics, and the absolutes of Newtonian physics had disappeared to be replaced by relativities: relativity of space measurements, time measurements, and even mass measurements to the observer.

We are thus left in contemporary physics with a realm of relativity and contingency in which mechanistic causative models have been replaced by mathematical equations. Newtonian physics applies alone to medium scale phenomena, as an approximation of the conditions holding at the microscopic and macroscopic levels. Determinism has been replaced by indeterminacy, and physical laws become descriptions of the expected average behavior of an assembly of particles, that is to say, they are statistical. That such statistical averages would normally be expected is a far cry from the model of a machinelike universe whose laws could never be broken. It is not surprising that religious men such as Eddington and Jeans should make much of this new physics and use it to validate their faith.[25] The situation in the physicochemical sciences is certainly more amenable to providing a natural framework for religious insights.

Yet we are still dealing with models, as we shall soon emphasize, and the Christian faith must not be made dependent on any scientific theory. Least of all should we mix scientific and theological categories as some have been tempted to do. Contingency no more than determinacy provides a base for a natural theology, while the disappearance of the old absolutes is no justification, as Heim believes,[26] for rehabilitating the divine absolute, attractive as his apologetic theology may be. Relativity may describe the whole process and contingency may be its key. The religious man does not begin with science nor try to fit God into its theories. What he must do is show that the scientific world-view is not incompatible with and may be embraced within the Christian understanding of the universe.

v. *Man the enigma*

It is at the level of human personality that the challenge to faith is brought to a focus. The physical bases of human

[25] Lord Eddington, *The Nature of the Physical World* (Cambridge: Cambridge University Press, 1928), *New Pathways in Science* (Cambridge: Cambridge University Press, 1935), *The Philosophy of Physical Science* (Cambridge: Cambridge University Press, 1939), *Science and the Unseen World* (London: Macmillan & Co., Ltd., 1929); Sir James Jeans, *The Mysterious Universe* (Cambridge: Cambridge University Press, 1930), *The New Background of Science* (Cambridge: Cambridge University Press, 1933), *Physics and Philosophy* (Cambridge: Cambridge University Press, 1942). There is an excellent discussion of the approach of these scientists in L. Susan Stebbings, *Philosophy and the Physicists* (London: Methuen & Co., 1937).

[26] See Karl Heim, *The Transformation of the Scientific World-View*, trans. W. A. Whitehouse (London: S.C.M. Press, Ltd., 1953).

personality in the secretions of the endocrine glands, the hereditary structure of genes and chromosomes, and the functioning of the cerebral cortex have driven home the intensely psychosomatic nature of the human organism, and have made it easier for the naturalistic thinker to contend that man is nothing more than a higher organization of physical energy. Mind becomes simply a secretion of energy manifest in its more complex convolutions, and talk about the human personality as essentially spiritual is dismissed along with ideas of survival beyond death and a transcendent spiritual order. The attack upon a religious interpretation of man also arises on the other flank in the speculations of Freud and other depth psychologists on the nature of mind and the unconscious. Here naturalism lifts its head in a new way by postulating religious experience as wish fulfillment, reducing moral imperatives to hidden parental influences, and explaining away God as a projection of our frustrated needs.

It is significant that the nearer we get to human personality, the more science ceases to function in its boasted objectivity. Scientific theories become increasingly colored by the metaphysical bias of the scientist himself, and a subtle philosophical presupposition often permeates the interpretation of the scientific evidence. This is particularly true of psychology, which falls apart into a multitude of theories as the attempt is made to penetrate the inner sanctum of human personality. It is probably true to say that the behavioristic psychologist, who rejects introspection and concerns himself with observable human behavior, is nearer to the scientific ideal, except that he too tends to interpret his observations naturalistically and to dismiss mind as having no reality.

All such thought is challenging the Christian thinker, however, to consider afresh what he means by such terms as "soul" and "mind" and to detach himself to some degree from those idealistic presuppositions which have too often colored theological thought. Since theological thought is concerned with the issue of transcendence, both at the level of persons and in the understanding of the divine, the issue of religious language immediately raises its head. If we accept the presupposition of naturalistic thinkers of the logical-positivist variety that a sentence can only be meaningful when it can be empirically verified or falsified, then religious language is only at best emotive. Even the newer school of linguistic analysis often retains such an empirical reference but at least recognizes the right of the religious man to play his "language game," provided he is prepared to define the function that his language performs. The Christian does, however, believe that his language is cognitive and that religious statements have a factual content which is based upon divine disclosure. Thus when he looks at nature, he believes that "creation," "providence," "miracle" have cognitive content and, at the level of man, he affirms the reality of "spirit" and of personal self-transcendence. Furthermore, language about God, divine love, and the Incarnation, although not empirically testable as the naturalist requires, yet opens up areas of human experience which the naturalist cannot adequately explain.

It is at such a level that the Christian thinker takes over from the scientist, not by rejecting scientific models and scientific data, nor by seeking to put his own categories into scientific statements. Rather he would suggest that there is an element of depth in nature, in human personality, and in the universe as a whole, which science is not adequate to plumb, but which is describable in theological language. Further such language may well illuminate scientific statements and make them more meaningful. This language is grounded in the intuitive awareness of a personal depth in our intercourse with other persons and in our encounter with the universe, an awareness which responds to a personal disclosure at all levels.

It would seem that any discussion of the issues raised by scientific thought and theological thinking will have to deal with the naturalistic interpretation of science by carefully considering the nature of scientific method and the limitations set to scientific knowledge. Yet, at the same time, in order to speak to the scientist, the religious man has to be prepared to validate his own claim to knowledge in his theological statements and to demonstrate the nature of religious language. Furthermore, while endeavoring to elaborate a theological understanding of nature, he must recognize the rightful claims of scientific method to express the observable aspects of nature in its own language. Nor may the religious man attempt to use theological categories to fill gaps which the scientist can hope to fill sooner or later as his own knowledge expands. Rather, the Church must show how its own understanding throws light upon the work and thought of the scientists upon nature and adds a dimension of depth which in no way contradicts or replaces the legitimate results and pursuits of scientific method. The Christian apologist does, however, have a right to intervene when the scientist moves outside his own field of study, the observable aspects of the world, and seeks to interpret his evidence, not just at the scientific level, but with a metaphysical bias, turning scientific knowledge into "scientism."

II

Scientific Knowledge:
Its Limitations and Implication

We have seen how the possibilities of tension between the Christian faith and scientific knowledge have arisen and delineated the general issues involved. In particular we face the naturalistic claim that scientific knowledge is the only genuine knowledge and the equally confident assertion of the man of religion that the statements of faith are also cognitive and convey valid knowledge. The man of faith does not rule out science but rather allows its method a proper sphere of inquiry, holding that faith also is a legitimate way of knowing. No defense of such a position is possible unless the scientific mode of inquiry is investigated, its legitimate sphere of operation delineated, and its limitations indicated.

1. *Scientific knowledge: Its presuppositions and its limitations*

Galilean science, as already noted, held that the universe has a rational structure which the human reason is able to grasp and that this orderliness is of a causal nature such that every event has an efficient cause or causes. Furthermore, it held that such a causal structure was empirically observable. H. K. Schilling has well defined nature from this point of view as "the whole economy or system of observable phenomena and things, including man, existing in time and space, and held together in a field or web of cause-and-effect relationships." [1]

Bacon could define the scientific method as "putting nature

[1] H. K. Schilling, *Science and Religion* (New York: Charles Scribner's Sons, 1962), pp. 22 f.

to the question," yet science is not so grounded in empiricism and inductive logic as Bacon tried to make it, nor is science the kind of rationalism that Descartes would have made it. Empirical and rationalistic ingredients are both present, but no particular balance of the rational and the empirical can be stipulated as typical for every scientific investigation. Scientific method cannot be laid out according to a rule of thumb. Furthermore, it is not a matter of haphazard observation. Experiment is not experience. Sense observation is here directed. If when nature is put to the question in scientific experimentation, it is asked a specific kind of question to which a particular answer is required, that question is determined by the rationalistic structure out of which it has emerged, and the measurements and observations are related to the apparatus and observable qualities which the structure dictates or suggests. As Reinchenbach puts it: "An experiment is a question addressed to nature; by the use of suitable devices the scientist initiates a physical occurrence, the outcome of which supplies the answer 'Yes' or 'No' to the question." [2]

Hence in the early physics, terms such as "force," "mass," "acceleration," are related to the mechanistic rational structure brought to full expression in Newton. They are not commonsense quantities, and their observation requires certain experimental devices in order that the right questions about them may be put to nature. Kant noted this nearly two centuries ago when he stated that "accidental observations, made in obedience to no previously thought out plan, can never be made to yield a necessary law, which alone reason is concerned to discover." [3] Thus the rational and the empirical are closely intermeshed, and their relative roles will depend upon the investigation that is being undertaken.

Certain aspects of the method need at once to be stressed,

[2] Reichenbach, *The Rise of Scientific Philosophy,* pp. 97 f.

[3] I. Kant, *Critique of Pure Reason,* B. xiii, trans. N. Kemp Smith (London: Macmillan & Co., Ltd., 1950), p. 20.

however. One strong presupposition in natural science since its inception has been the assumption that the structure of nature is mathematical and that this structure is empirically measurable. In part, the reason for this has lain in the increasing recognition of a certain subjective and fallible element in all sensible qualities, and thus in an effort to attain a communicable objectivity in what is observable. Color blindness and tone deafness are only extreme reminders that the sensible qualities of taste, smell, color, sound, and touch are variable. But measurements are to a much higher degree less subject to the physiological and psychological variabilities. In the early days of science we find Descartes the rationalist, Locke the empiricist, and Galileo the practical scientist agreeing in their retention of the primary sense qualities of extension and motion and the rejection of the secondary sense qualities just listed. Hence, fundamentally, the physical sciences have a mathematical base; and exact science increasingly seeks such a base, often at the cost of reducing the sciences of life and mind to bases in physics, chemistry, and statistics. It would be true to say that the physical sciences offer the norm for all natural science. Science is a symbolizing activity, seeking to abstract from reality what is relevant to its purpose of controlling nature; and its way of symbolizing reality tends to be mathematico-logical.

We need to remember that one object of science is to control nature. Hence it seeks to understand nature in order to predict its future movements and to guide, as far as possible, its activities. It looks, therefore, for generalizations of increasing breadth of coverage and tends to ignore individual entities except insofar as they have characteristics which they hold in common with other entities. When to such generalizations we add the factor of abstraction by concentration upon the measurable and the mathematically expressible, it becomes evident that the language of science is removed from the language of common-sense perception. We are dealing with forces and relationships which are not immediately perceptible; and science is offering us an intelligible model of the intuited rich and complex natural realm which divests it of much that belongs to our ordinary experience. For its own purposes, since Francis Bacon first attempted to formulate the scientific approach to nature, scientists, generally speaking, have ignored qualities and values, concentrating on quantities and measurable relations. The teleological and dramatic aspects of ordinary language are thus eliminated, and a scientific language results which is increasingly mathematical. Intelligibility at this level clearly does not mean what it does in ordinary language. It is bound up with a causative framework and mathematico-logical consistency.

The scientist is therefore looking for an intelligible model which will enable him to understand his world and which is subject to mathematical formulation. As noted earlier, in the classical period of modern science such models were sought at the geometrical level and mechanical causation was regarded as the key. The natural universe was pictured as a mechanical structure in which solid billiard-ball-like atoms, in motion and in ever more complex structural patterns, behaved in a purely mechanical fashion in an absolute framework of space and time. It was presupposed that the model was mechanical and that it was an exact copy of the universe. To understand any phenomenon the scientist made a model, and the model represented the universe and was usually accepted literally. Such understanding associated with a model was denominated a theory. Thus we have the kinetic theory of gases. The relations between the observable quantities of the pressure, volume, and temperature of a gas were expressed experimentally by the gas laws of Boyle and Gay Lussac and understood scientifically by means of a dynamical model consisting of a swarm of molecular particles. Again the laws of conduction of heat arrived at empirically were understood by a theory employing the model of a flowing fluid; while the laws governing light were given intelligibility by the wave theory of light, using models derived from hydrodynamics.

Already this mechanistic type of model had been challenged in the seventeenth and eighteenth centuries by Cudworth and Ray. In the eighteenth and nineteenth centuries, as the historical perspective began to take shape, a nonmathematical and non-mechanistic model appeared. Evolutionary models began to break up the mechanistic model, however mechanically T. H. Huxley and others sought to interpret specifically the evolutionary model of Darwin.

At the turn of the nineteenth century, the mechanistic picture really began to break up. We have already discussed, and shall consider later in some detail, how the absolute framework of space and time was replaced by the relativity of such measurements to the observer; how absolute causation gave place to indeterminacy and statistical probabilities; how absolute matter faded into a realm of energy in which matter and radiation were merged. The solid atom disappeared to be replaced by a mysterious realm of subatomic particles, possessing both corpuscular and undulatory characteristics. Radiation was likewise picturable in both forms, while it and matter were mutually transformable. When models for the atom were retained, elements were introduced which broke with the old classical mechanical picture. Thus the solar-system model of atomic structure was furnished with stationary electronic orbits in which radiation did not take place, with closed shells of circulating particles, and with spinning electrons. Furthermore, radiation was quantized and itself became atomic. Already the way had been prepared for such a breakup of the classical picture in the sphere of electrodynamics, where light was pictured as an undulating electrodynamic field and any perceptible model had disappeared.

The idea of the model as a literal copy was being replaced by the idea of the model as a symbol in the physical sciences.

The model was no longer picturable, and the mechanical presupposition was being replaced by a concern with more abstract mathematical equations. No longer could Euclid's geometry or mechanistic causation hold the key. Rather the model was now best expressed in mathematical form. Riemannian geometry, differential wave equations, matrices and the theory of groups provided the theoretical structures by which observable phenomena were made intelligible. The theory of relativity, in its special and general forms, is understood only in the complicated mathematics of four-dimensional and thus unpicturable geometry. We need to remember, however, that this highly symbolic view of model is confined to certain aspects of the physical science. Particularly in the area of biology, picturable models such as those associated with evolution are still retained. Furthermore, at the levels of macrophysics and astronomy, classical mechanical models are still employed.

The behavior of the atom and also of radiation are best expressed in mathematical equations. From the differential equations of Schrödinger's wave mechanics we move to the noncommuting matrices of Heisenberg's quantum mechanics, and thence to the relativistic wave equation postulated by Dirac and generalized by Eddington. Dirac's theory shows how abstract and ultimately unpicturable atomic structure has become. It is true that he retains the language of observable phenomena in speaking of quantities such as the position and momentum of a particle. Yet he describes these as "operators" and means by this that the presence of such symbols in his equations is a signal that a certain type of mathematical operation is to be undertaken. Theoretically such entities may be observable, but actually their meaning is much more restrictive than any observable equivalent since our instruments are much too crude to make observation possible. What matters is the result of such operations in which we find a pattern of relations identical with experimental observations. An observable pattern in nature is thus transferred to or derived from mathematical symbolism.

It is increasingly difficult to picture the subatomic world in any visual model. Rather, we must concentrate upon what is observable and forms a part of measurable experience. We must not fall into the trap of illegitimate literal interpretation of Bohr's stationary orbits or spinning electrons or Dirac's operators. All that we can say of many scientific concepts is that the measure of their truth must lie in their utility for predicting accurately and for communicating knowledge comprehensively. By their very nature, we cannot observe them. All that we can observe are the numerical relationships which are predictable when we manipulate groups of mathematical symbols, possessing a certain type of structure and themselves wholly abstract. Concreteness and reality in this realm have a minor place in the physicist's thought. Mechanical models have disappeared, and we have turned to a mathematical formulation in which observables, measurable quantities, can be embodied so that their transformations constitute a definite structure. Accurate numerical prediction, which can be experimentally confirmed, results from the logical manipulation of this mathematical setup.

It is evident that imagination plays a significant part in scientific investigation alongside of experimental observation and mathematico-rational theorizing. Indeed, it forms the cement which binds the two together. Phillip Frank has reminded us that one important activity of science is "the invention of symbols from which our experience can be logically derived. This system is the work of the creative imagination which acts on the basis of our experience. The work of the scientist is probably not fundamentally different from the work of the poet." [4] Morgenau [5] likewise reminds us that models (or

[4] Philipp Frank, "Contemporary Science and the Contemporary World-View," *Daedalus*, Winter, 1958, p. 65.

constructs as he prefers to call them) are not found ready made but are inventions. This factor of creative imagination moves beyond the rational structure and often shatters it. It has the qualities associated with an intuitive insight into the natural process. In other words, the imagination is at this point molded to a reality existing beyond the human mind of the scientist. The great advances of science have come not just by a pedestrian combination in differing proportions of these two elements, but rather by an intuitive hunch in which much of the preceding structure of theory and models has been swept away.

In our own century we have seen this happen with the theory of relativity, the quantum theory, and the application of the mathematical theory of groups to physical analysis. The experimental observation of the invariable nature of the speed of light by Michelson and Morley called forth many attempts, such as those of Lorentz and Fitzgerald, to explain this invariance within the accepted structure. Einstein, with intuitive insight introduced his revolutionary ideas and, borrowing from the pure mathematical theories of analysis and Riemannian geometry, suggested a radical new approach which swept away much of the old structure. Men such as de Broglie, Schrödinger, Sommerfeld, Bohr, Born, and Heisenberg—following up the experimental investigations of Planck on radiation and Rutherford on the atom with a revolutionary approach to atomic structure—have given intuitive insights which have transformed our view of the universe. It was the intuitive insights of Dirac and Eddington which combined the relativistic point of view with the quantum theory by using the abstract mathematical theory of groups investigated originally in relation to Kümmer's quartic surface. Incidentally, in biology it was the intuitive hunch of Darwin which applied the sociological investigations of Malthus to nature and exposed

[5] Cf. H. Morgeneau, *The Nature of Physical Reality* (New York: McGraw-Hill Book Co., 1950), p. 70.

some of the mechanism of evolution. The interesting point is that the mathematical structures were already available at the rational level, and that the empirical observations challenging the older scientific theories were at hand, yet it waited for the intuitive insight to bring the two together. Because such mathematical structures had already been independently established, their inner logic was known to the pure mathematician and ready at hand for scientific application.

Undoubtedly, various factors may be discerned in the creative imagination of the scientific innovator. One is the recognition of the utility of Occam's razor, that it is impracticable to multiply unobservable entities in order to retain a challenged theoretical structure. Another is an aesthetic element, very evident in attempts to delineate the structure of complex carbon compounds, like the ring-compounds, but also evident in the recognition of simplicity and harmonious order in certain mathematical formulations. Morgenau [6] notes the significance of "elegance of formulation" alongside of "simplicity of conception" in controlling scientific progress.

Again, contemporary social conditions and categories of thought often point the way to new models. Mary Hesse cites the way in which the scientific understanding of human beings has been influenced by the most typical machine of any particular age, so that the model of a heat engine was employed in the last century because of the dominance of thermodynamics, while in our own time the tremendous success of mechanical brains and the emphasis on electronics provide a new model.[7]

Finally, however, there is the intuitive aspect, a feeling for a new wholeness, a new kind of patterning in nature. This suggests that there is in science a synthetic as well as an analytic approach to reality, and that the intuitive grasping of a whole is often more significant than the mere analysis of the parts. In

[6] Ibid. p. 76.

[7] M. Hesse, *Science and the Human Imagination* (New York: The Philosophical Library, 1955), p. 140.

this intuitive insight, disparate and widely distributed data are integrated into a new and revolutionary pattern. The intuition and the experimentation are often mutually stimulating, and what we find is of one piece with the emphasis of Gestalt psychology in our normal processes of perception. Often this grasping of a whole may precede the discovery of much experimental data and may lead to new forms of experimentation in which such holistic insight is confirmed. Indeed, one important aspect of scientific advance is that often such intuitive insights bring about completely new and unanticipated disclosures of the structure of the natural order. The search of science for regularities and invariants of the natural order is thus often enriched by entirely new and unexpected aspects of behavior, which are predicted by new theories and confirmed by subsequent experimentation. An instance is afforded, for example, by Dirac's quantum theory with its postulation of positively charged electrons and negatively charged protons, subsequently verified by experimental observation, so that the existence of "anti-matter" is now an accepted scientific fact.

It would appear that the models which form the basic elements of scientific theories are molded to natural reality. The fallacy arises, however, when the natural order is so completely identified with the model that the analogical nature of the latter is ignored. At the best, the model is an analogy, and all aspects of it are not necessarily applicable to the structure of nature. Thus abstraction is involved to greater or lesser degree, and we are liable to fall into one aspect of what has been called by Whitehead "the Fallacy of Misplaced Concreteness," the mistaking of the abstract for the concrete.[8] The more embracing the analogy and the more prolific the new avenues of natural knowledge that it opens, the closer it may be to the structure of the nature which we are seeking to understand.

[8] A. N. Whitehead, *Science and the Modern World* (Cambridge: Cambridge University Press, 1932), p. 72 f.

In this sense, every new model may bring us nearer to understanding and controlling nature. The model thereby certainly serves a heuristic purpose. It aids in discovery and is often discarded when later discoveries enable the scientist to construct better and more useful models. Thus Hooke used the model of a particle attached to a fixed point by a string to describe the motion of the earth round the sun, a more refined and mechanistically intelligible model than Kepler's magnetic model; but Newton's discovery of the nature of gravitation made a new and more satisfying model possible. A satisfactory model is evidently one which makes obvious the self-consistency of a theory and which furnishes a base for prediction.

L. Susan Stebbing reminds us that "intelligibility in science consists exclusively in necessary connections. The fact is no longer isolated and is therefore intelligible."[9] We would question her use of the qualification "exclusively," for this might suggest that science is purely positivistic and that its models have no ontological significance. In that case, our description of them as analogues would be superfluous. We must return to this later. It is certainly true, however, that the model establishes a pattern of rational relationships between the data. The fact that in quantum physics both the corpuscular and the wave models are necessary, each dealing with certain aspects of the empirical evidence, is a reminder that a literal interpretation of these models in increasingly impossible. The movement toward the much more abstract mathematical model or analogue is an indication that science is increasingly concerned with the pattern of relationships. Thus the physical sciences tend to move from substantial models, objects and things, to an emphasis on order and relations.

We need to remember that often the element of necessity in nature is more a property of the model than of nature itself, at

[9] L. S. Stebbing, *A Modern Introduction to Logic,* (New York: T. Y. Crowell), p. 391 f.

least in the form in which it is expressed. This is true of the mechanistic determinism which until the modern period of science dominated man's interpretation of nature. Too close an identification of the model with the structure of nature produced an objective dogmatism with which religious faith was peculiarly at odds. It is, of course, equally true that men of religion ought not to build an apologetic too closely on the contemporary emphasis on chance and probability. Indeed, religious faith stands to lose as much in a universe dominated by pure chance as in one dominated by mechanistic determinism. That there is a logos, a rational structure in the deeps of nature, is a basic conviction to which certainly the religious man and also a concerned scientist must hold.

As we have already emphasized, a model provides a logical or mathematical structure by which various experimental data may be brought together in a self-consistent whole. It is the pattern or structure that is most important, and an analogical understanding of a model can alone account for the fact that, in some of its aspects, the model bears no resemblance to the phenomena of nature under consideration. There are, indeed, aspects of the model which become redundant in the understanding of nature as scientific inquiry progresses. One example of this is the association of an imponderable and perfectly elastic medium, the ether, with the electromagnetic theory of light in which the wave theory is retained without this crude accompaniment. Furthermore, the analogical nature of a model makes it possible for future development. A scientific "fundamentalism" which takes models literally would freeze up theories and ignore their heuristic purpose.

The limitations of a model belong to the particular sphere of discourse from which it is borrowed and significantly remind us that similar limitations do not necessarily apply to the natural environment of the scientific data which we are endeavoring to understand. Mary Hesse cogently reminds us that

> there is an analogy between the human brain and an electronic calculating machine, but this does not mean that their structures are identical. The mathematical structure has one sort of relation to the calculating machine, its use being hedged about by qualifications proper to electronics, and a quite different relation to the human brain, being even more drastically hedged about by qualifications about the behavior and nature of human persons. The mathematical pattern is not predicated univocally of machine and brain because they are in obvious ways different sorts of things, and the similarities cannot be simply abstracted from the differences, but only used analogically.[10]

There is often more than one possible form of mathematical construct in which empirical observations can be expressed. The scientist has no fixed rules by which he may choose one more than another. His intuitive insight into the *Gestalten* of the natural order and his grasping of the right model are often much more akin to art, as Michael Polanyi and others point out. Polanyi suggests that *"scientific knowing consists in discerning* Gestalten *that are aspects of reality,"* [11] and argues that scientific discovery should be likened to the creative acts in the arts. Indeed, all our scientific "facts" carry with them the theoretical perspectives from which we start, and, insofar as the assembling of them enables us to predict and control, we may believe that we have grasped some aspect of reality. In distinguishing between the relevant and the irrelevant data in a scientific inquiry and between possible mathematical models, in deciding upon the next move in his investigation, the scientist has to be guided by intuitive insight, to exercise creative imagination and to manifest a scientific conscience. Rules of thumb which nicely balance the inductive and deductive fall by the wayside.

[10] M. Hesse, op. cit. p. 146.

[11] M. Polanyi, *Science, Faith and Society* (Chicago: The University Press, 1964), p. 10.

All this suggests that scientific knowledge is far more personal than many would admit and that our empirical observations are loaded with theory. H. K. Schilling argues that "*factual statements are interpretations as well as summaries of observed findings.*"[12] We may illustrate from the biological realm where the cellular structure of living tissue is an accepted fact but where statements about the structure of the cell have varied as new theories have replaced old. Schilling cites Boyle's law, which remains invariant as a fact about the relation of pressure and volume in a gas but which is currently interpreted in terms of the kinetic theory of gases—statements about it involve this theory or model. Even the observations that we seek are conditioned by our models and sometimes lose their relevance when our theories are altered. After all, a scientific fact so called is the result of correlating a mass of empirical data in the light of some interpretative model, which itself may guide the operational methods by which much of the data is determined. There is "an interplay of observation and experimentation with theory" in the gathering of the data upon which the structure of science is based. Often when our theories change our facts change too, since they are facts only as interpreted by and significant for some model.

Furthermore, this personal aspect of scientific knowledge becomes very evident in the fact that science is a community effort, and that the scientific community is, at its own level, a believing and committed community. Many contemporary thinkers point out that there is a scientific orthodoxy and that scientists do not easily move from a generally accepted position. Scientists will, indeed, ignore certain "facts" which seem to falsify a current theory until the scientific conscience is sufficiently awakened and a model is offered which is sufficiently convincing and coherent to awaken conviction as to its

[12] H. K. Schilling, *Science and Religion* (New York: Charles Scribner's Sons, 1962), p. 103.

truth. In the process of the centuries the scientific community has built up a body of traditions, in the light of which it adjudicates what is and is not scientific.

Every propounder of a new theory has to defend his new insight against an accumulated body of theory. Polanyi cites van 't Hoff's thesis that compounds containing an asymmetric carbon atom are optically active. The thesis waited not only upon experimental confirmation, for it was a theoretical insight, but also upon a growing consensus. Contemporary instances are afforded by the struggle of Rhine for the scientific status of extrasensory perception; by the current debates between geneticists of the neo-Darwinian school, with their emphasis on chance mutations, and such scientists as Dalcq, Vandel, and others, who contend that there is a harmonious adaptive power directing the origin and emergence of higher forms of life; by the contentions of the neurologists Eccles and Penfield and theoretical thinkers such as Mays and Kapp that will and decision are realities to be reckoned with in cerebral structure against the accepted position of neurologists which regards mental processes as epiphenomena cast around physical cerebral events. Such "pretenders," as Polanyi puts its, "do not deny the authority of scientific opinion in general, but merely appeal against its authority in a particular detail and seek to modify its teachings in respect of that detail." [13]

Science is indeed embedded in commitment. Its basis is a system of belief, experimentally and theoretically derived, growing in a body of tradition, to which the scientist, if he is to be a scientist, must be committed. The scientist's passions as well as his logic are thus involved, and discussion of the objectivity of science must not forget this personal element. What objectivity science possesses rests in part upon scientific consensus and the community of commitment in which it is pursued. This issue becomes very clear when we remember the

[13] M. Polanyi, *Personal Knowledge* (Chicago: The University of Chicago Press, 1958), p. 164.

ease with which the mechanistic model was identified with the structure of nature, only later to be discarded.

This might suggest a complete subjectivism and relativism in science and thus undermine our contention that the scientific theory offers a model which is an analogue of reality. There are indeed many who would take this position, especially in the physical sciences, the more so since the models have become increasingly abstract and mathematical. As we have seen the scientific analogues have moved from mechanical models which have a sensuous correspondence to nature through pseudo-sensible entities, like electrons, protons, and atoms, to abstract mathematical formulations and symbols, like the Hamiltonian momentum operator of quantum mechanics which are totally nonsensible. The middle group of entities is not directly sensible, and the dual wave/particle picture indicates the difficulty of determining their particular mode of existence. Propositions involving them can, however, be translated into statements involving actual observables and thus can be indirectly verified. Yet there are those who would point out that such verification in no way confirms the actual existence of molecules, atoms, and subatomic particles. They may be useful fictions. This positivistic attitude is still more a live option when we move to the abstract analogues of relativity and quantum mechanics. It is easy to affirm that the scientist is imposing order upon a chaotic substratum of experience and that his analogues are heuristic devices bearing no ontological significance.

Positivism can lead to naturalism but must not be identified with it. Naturalism presupposes a complete identification of the models with nature, and thus is inherently ontological. The only valid knowledge is scientific knowledge, and the only knowable realm is the natural one with which science deals. The phenomenal, to use Kant's language, is to all intents and purposes the sole reality. All ideal values are rejected in the sense of being ultimate and are to be explained in terms of the natural processes that science studies. Whereas the positivist refuses to speculate on the ontological nature of scientific analogues or models, the naturalist identifies reality with the scientific models.

We might, of course, argue against the positivist position that the communal aspect of science and its intersubjective communication would support the objectivity of its knowledge. After all, the findings of any scientist must be communicable and must make sense to the scientific community, especially to experts in his area. This element of measurable objectivity and communicability is retained in the theory of relativity. This theory keeps communication at the center of the scientist's world by relating the various variable frames of measurement through the invariant nature of the speed of light, the radiation by which communications can take place. Yet the positivists of various types can still argue that the presuppositions of the scientific community, its agreed theoretical structures and its experimental operations which are shaped by these, would lead to unanimity in selecting the appropriate pattern from the raw material of experience, which may of itself be quite formless.

It would seem that, at one point at least, this kind of position is challenged, namely, scientific observations that cannot be fitted into the accepted scientific structure. Examples of these from our own time are afforded by the invariance of the speed of light and the quantization of radiation. The scientific conscience would seem here to be determined from beyond itself, for it is sufficiently sharpened to cut across and transform tradition once a new position demonstrates a more acceptable coherence among observables and an increased fruitfulness in unveiling new and unexpected data.

This positivistic attitude can be traced back to post-Renaissance philosophical thought. Descartes introduced a fatal dichotomy between the knowing mind and matter in which nature was stripped of all secondary qualities and became a realm of extended stuff in motion. The way was set to Hume's skepticism and ultimately to Kant's preoccupation with the knowing mind. From Kant's conclusion that the world of science is phenomenal, offering no clue to ultimate reality, it was an easy step to Comte's positivism and to modern naturalism.

Yet was this Cartesian *faux pas* necessary? Whitehead describes it as an example of the "fallacy of misplaced concreteness." It ignores the wholeness of the universe by leaving the thinker with two substances bearing unreconcilable differentiating characteristics, separated by an apparently unbridgeable gulf, and yet incomprehensibly affecting one another. Knowledge, however, lies in the relationship of knower to known, and the Cartesian dualism is a false abstraction. There is a quality of wholeness which is found throughout experience and which constitutes the background of knowledge. William Temple points out that mind emerges late within the evolutionary process and yet is able to conduct a progressive apprehension of and control over the process. Mind has a kinship with nature. Hence he comments: *"That the world should give rise to minds which know the world involves a good deal concerning the nature of the world."* [14] Deep in modern science there is the conviction that the scientist is grappling with a "given"—something beyond himself challenging his investigation. The presence of intuitive hunches in the great advances of scientific understanding gives the impression that the scientist is responding to a "given" which is meeting him.

Not only did post-Renaissance philosophy introduce a dichotomy between mind and matter, but it also emphasized the analytical role of reason and ignored its intuitive or synthetic aspect. This is illustrated in science where, at the physicochemical level, an analytical approach to nature has predominated. Whitehead has argued that the idea of "simple

[14] W. Temple, *Nature, Man and God* (London: Macmillan & Co., Ltd., 1956), p. 130.

location" has dominated scientific inquiry and regards this as yet another illustration of the "fallacy of misplaced concreteness." The original wholeness of nature has been broken up so that it is viewed as an assemblage of configurations of matter separated from one another in a spatiotemporal continuum. Each thing is set at a particular place at a particular time. Thereby a particular configuration of matter can be isolated so that to understand it we need not refer to other regions of space and time. This idea lies behind the mechanistic model. Throughout the modern period the physical sciences, by their very mathematical presupposition, have dealt with models consisting of assemblies of detached units bound together externally by causal relations. Qualitative differences and particular characteristics are ignored. Analysis took over with the conviction that the natural order could be completely understood by an analysis of its parts and that there is nothing transempirical.

The tremendous success of this analytical approach at the physical level has led to a reductionism in which all other natural sciences tend to seek expression solely at this level and to employ its categories exclusively. This is seen in the large developments of biophysics and biochemistry and in the preoccupation of psychology with behavioristic psychology and the statistical method. In consequence, life and mind have come to be regarded naturalistically as behavioristic descriptions of more complex patterns of physical energy. What J. C. Smuts [15] has called the "holistic" factor in nature has been ignored, and it has seldom been recognized that a whole is often more than the sum of its parts. A mere analysis of observable particulars and then their assemblage as simply located units within a structure of external relations is not sufficient to account for the aspect of wholeness in nature. The physical sciences have failed to grasp by their techniques the

[15] See J. C. Smuts, *Holism and Evolution* (New York: The Viking Press, 1961).

living, psychic, and spiritual wholes which unify, are manifested through, and yet transcend the observable particulars with which the sciences are concerned. Yet in the great intuitive hunches that mark scientific progress, it is just this holistic aspect of reality which is operative.

II. *Intuitive insight and our awareness of wholes*

It needs to be stressed, as against naturalistic positivism, that there are two aspects of knowing—one in which there is an intuitive grasping of wholes and one in which we concentrate on the various parts which are embraced in that whole. By intuition is meant a direct apprehension which is not the result of logical mediation. Often the word is used of sensible experience, but it applies to far more, for it opens the door to the transempirical aspect of reality. As we shall see later, our knowledge of life and mind, of ideal values and personal being, of the holy, owes much to man's capacity for intuitive awareness. Intuition always carries us beyond the parts and grasps some whole, some holistic pattern, within which they are embodied. As we move more and more up this scale of knowing, the feeling is engaged and the imagination is called into play. Such an intuitive insight will often defy an adequate expression in a propositional form embodying only the parts—it will be concerned with a unitary whole which is more than simply the aggregation of the parts.

Polanyi has reminded us that as we concentrate on the one aspect of knowing, the other fades into the background. Thus what we may call the synthetic type of awareness, in which we concentrate on coherent wholes, tends to push into the background our awareness of the particular elements which constitute that whole. On the other hand, the analytic type of awareness concentrates on the particular elements and loses sight of the whole of which they are constituents and to which they point. The rationalistic method and thus that of science tends to be analytic, to explain the whole by building it up out of its constituents. Yet we have suggested that its greatest advances occur when there is an intuitive hunch, a grasping of some patterned whole, in which the scientist moves beyond the formal arguments so far offered and radically rearranges the scientific data so that a new pattern of relationships is established. This new pattern cannot be regarded as the result of logical mediation from past formulations. It has a psychological, not a logical base. It involves a new apprehension and gives the impression of a direct insight into reality. Furthermore, it gives passion and direction to the ratio-empirical processes which then result. The intellectual quest of science without such passionate concern is difficult to understand. To a certain extent it calls forth a commitment akin to religious faith.

If such insight and commitment are to be found within the course of scientific investigation, they also lie in the background of the whole scientific enterprise. There are an intuitive awareness of the reality of the natural order, without which science would never have been possible, and also an insight into its rational and mathematical structure which set modern science upon its way. What Collingwood has called absolute presuppositions underlie all our reasoning. They are pre-logical and the result of direct or intuitive sight. As such they determine the movement of the logical argument and involve a prior commitment on the part of the thinker. Such presuppositions underlie not only metaphysical thought but also the discipline of science, and they are evoked by insight into that aspect of reality with which the thinker is concerned. In this way, intuition is the starting point of all knowledge, and science is as much involved here as any other discipline. Consciously, and often unconsciously, the scientist is building on intuitive apprehensions. Nature evokes in him a commitment and a lure to investigate its mysteries. He is aware that he is grappling with a "given."

This suggests that the starting point of all analytical and discursive reasoning, in which science participates, is an intuitive awareness of a whole which cannot be totally embraced in the analytical approach and comprehended by dissection into parts. William James [16] has suggested that the infant's *first* sensation is for him the universe. It is within this whole that the awakening consciousness differentiates individual things and moves from percepts to concepts. Now the success of the physical sciences has lain in their analytical approach, in the building up of individual atomic entities into ever more complex aggregates. In the same way, philosophy in the modern period has tended to work on this basis, and falls into the same error of misplaced concreteness. Atomic items of knowledge have been built together by logical procedures into complex systems. We find this illustrated in the rationalism of Descartes as well as in the empiricism of Locke. It still persists in the naturalistic and positivistic traditions.

Now we would agree that often the initial intuition of a whole is vague and indistinct, yet its presence implicitly guides our investigation of the parts. The significance of rational and empirical procedures is to clarify the original intuition and make it more intelligible, and in such procedures we ought never to lose sight of the original unitary wholeness nor deny it by emphasizing, or confining ourselves to, the analytic. In this sense the positivistic interpretation of science ignores the intuitive apprehension of a "given" order of nature without which science itself would never have begun to function.

Plato's insight was thus correct to the degree that we apprehend reality before we comprehend it. We have intimations of a hidden structure in our universe before we seek to comprehend that structure by the methods of induction and deduction. We are responding to a "given" which is meeting us. This is why the reductionist and analytic emphasis of

[16] W. James, *Principles of Psychology,* Vol. II (New York: Henry Holt & Co., 1896), p. 8.

science gives us such a limited and one-sided picture of reality. Dilthey differentiates between "knowledge" and "understanding" (in the German *das Erklaren* and *das Verstehen*). "Knowledge" is what science offers. It explains an atomized world in terms of causality and general laws. "Understanding," on the other hand, comprehends the part within the whole. It belongs to the level of intuitive insight and imaginative empathy. Dilthey writes: "In understanding we start from the system of the whole which is given to us as a living reality, to make the particular intelligible to ourselves in terms of it. It is the fact that we live in the consciousness of the system of the whole which enables us to understand a particular statement, a particular gesture, or a particular action." [17] Although Dilthey was concerned with history and sociology, his differentiation holds also of the natural order. Science knows, and yet the knowledge of science attains its true meaning only as such knowledge is embraced within the understanding of the whole. And, as Dilthey again points out: "we always understand more than we know." [18] Intuitive insight moves beyond the perceptual and conceptual structures with which science is preoccupied. Yet this approach of science is possible only because the "given" has awakened within us intuitive insights which guide our pursuit.

It may be recalled that Kant in his *Critique of Judgment* hints at such intuitive insight only hurriedly before he withdraws. It is true that he concerned himself with the aesthetic feeling, with what is beautiful, harmonious, and fitting. Yet he suggests that we are immediately apprehending the universal through the particular in the experience of beauty. He concludes that our feeling for what is fit and sublime in nature arises from the presence of organic life and that this is the product of some teleological principle. Thus, although the

[17] W. Dilthey, *Gesammelte Schriften,* V, p. 172, translated by and quoted in H. A. Hodges, *Wilhelm Dilthey* (London: Kegan Paul, 1944), p. 29.

[18] Ibid. p. 19.

"pure reason" at the scientific level never gets beyond the phenomenal, aesthetic judgment as related to living nature may offer a dim discernment of ontological reality. We would go beyond such a limited view, yet it is significant that, dominated though he was by the scientific and analytic approach, Kant sought a place for intuitive feeling.

It is on such grounds that A. N. Whitehead can describe science as "an enterprise in which reason is based on faith." [19] He can even contend that its faith "cannot be justified by an inductive generalization." He argues that "it springs from a direct inspection of the nature of things so disclosed in our own immediate present experience." [20] The scientist is a committed man, and his approach to nature is guided by the presuppositions that underlie his thought. He believes in a rational structure in the universe, a "hidden" which is there for him to discover, a "hidden" which is also given to him and open to his investigation.

Against such a background, a more realistic interpretation of scientific models and analogues is possible. We do not start with states of our own consciousness and endeavor to justify the existence of a world beyond the knowing mind, as Kant sought to do. We begin with the mutual relationship of knower and known, with an awareness of the otherness of our world. It is within this basic awareness that the structures of relationships in the scientific consciousness are formulated. Only on such an intuitive basis can we describe such structures as analogues. There is a primary knowing relation to that which is "beyond" the knowing mind. It is true that the scientist is selective in the formulation of his analogues, but such selection takes place within what he experiences, and his analogues help to correlate and make sense of his experience at the level where they apply. Furthermore, their predictions are confirmed in the epistemological oneness with his world.

This would seem to suggest that the analogues at the molec-

[19] A. N. Whitehead, *Science and the Modern World,* p. 83.
[20] Ibid. p. 6.

ular, atomic, and subatomic level are molded to reality. Although we cannot form visual pictures of these structures and although the principle of complementarity with its dual wave/corpuscle description is as near as we can get, yet we may affirm that they represent actual structures in nature. Indeed, since Einstein's study of Brownian movements, and the experiments associated with the Wilson cloud chamber, it would be difficult on any realistic base to deny their presence. Furthermore, since the new techniques of X ray and other forms of microscopic investigation have made possible our observation of viruses and chromosomes with their gene structure, we should have no reason to deny that structures of a lower order exist, although we may not, by a method of extrapolation, apply to them the forms perceptible at the level of normal observation. Mary Hesse comments that "it is difficult to see how a rigid ontological distinction can be made anywhere in this hierarchy . . ."[21] We can, at least believe of the realm of nature that it has measurable aspects and that science is offering us increasing and discerning knowledge of such aspects.

What we have said about the intuitive aspect of knowing has special relevance at the biological and psychological levels of the natural order. At these levels, higher than those dealt with by the physicochemical sciences, there are intuitive apprehensions of living and mental wholes which cannot be filled in with increasing comprehension if we resolve organic and personal beings into the mere aggregation of their parts at the physicochemical level. Such apprehension of wholeness occurs through the empirical particulars and is thus sensibly mediated. But it involves an empathy in which the knowing subject grasps the entity holistically through such sensible manifestations. In this approach, the knowing mind is so concerned with the whole that it pays little direct attention to the sensible particulars themselves. We do not concur in Bergson's downgrading of the intellect, but we do agree with his contention that

[21] M. Hesse, op. cit. p. 151.

life is intuitively apprehended. Whatever can be an object of sympathetic intelligence may be perceived intuitively, and this covers all living things from the lower organisms through the animal orders to persons, and including our own self-awareness.

Biological organisms disclose a distinctive wholeness. Except at a very elementary level, they do not grow by adding bricks externally, like a crystal, but by internal differentiation. They do not move only because they are set in motion by some force from beyond themselves, as do the objects of inanimate nature. They are self-moving. They are also self-regulating. As they grow they disclose a specialization of their parts to serve particular functions. Living things manifest an increasing individuation, a movement to selfhood, and such individual selves are self-regulating. Indeed, however much chemistry and physics may help to describe the mechanism of a living thing, the living thing would seem to manifest a wholeness, a degree of organization, at a higher level than the physicochemical.

From the beginning the physical sciences have sought to describe everything in terms of efficient causation, especially of that associated with mechanics. They have also ignored any suggestion of teleological causation or purposive activity. Yet attempts to eliminate teleological concepts from the biological and psychological sciences have not been successful. We are continually using terms that savor of human experience—adaptation, regulation, aim, urge, drive, co-ordination, selection, struggle for existence, survival of the fittest. They all belong to what has been called "dramatic language" and all suggest purpose. Certainly living things, as wholes and in their particular parts, seem to manifest something akin to teleology. It is true that we are in danger of reading in anthropomorphic concepts at this point. Yet it is also true that we know life in ourselves from within and so can intuit its presence in other living things.

Braithwaite, who has offered us one of the most searching

contemporary investigations of scientific method,[22] acknowledges that teleological concepts still have a place in biology, although he seems to believe that *in principle* all teleological explanations should be reducible to physicochemical explanations of the causal sort. He rejects anthropomorphic coloring of teleological concepts and would seek an interpretation of them which would not contravene "the usual determination principle of science." [23] At the same time, he holds that not all biological laws can be reduced to those of the physicochemical level and that teleological ideas suitably modified can have a place in such laws. In biology we have a plasticity of response which is not evident at the inanimate level. An organism has more than one sequence of steps by which a certain goal may be attained. This variety of causal chains makes possible persistence towards that goal in different ways according to the prevailing circumstances. Thus, an organism manifests plasticity in its goal-directed behavior. It is here that teleological explanation becomes especially valuable. As Braithwaite says: "It seems ridiculous to deny the title of explanation to a statement which performs both of the functions characteristic of scientific explanations—of enabling us to appreciate connexions and to predict the future." [24]

Yet it is doubtful whether Braithwaite's treatment goes far enough. When biochemistry, biophysics, physiology, and neurology have all made their contributions at the level of physiochemical causal explanation, we are still dealing with a whole which transcends all the mechanism thus described. In its totality its behavior calls for teleological forms of explanation, and such forms of explanation are not makeshift until the behavior can be embraced within the laws of physics and chemistry. They hold because by no stretch of imagination can we

[22] Braithwaite, *Scientific Explanation* (Cambridge: Cambridge University Press, 1955).

[23] Ibid. p. 328.

[24] Ibid. p. 334 f.

feel for the inanimate the same kinship as we have with living things. This is true of machines. As we shall see in detail later, however much the mechanical brain may simulate consciousness, it cannot produce the dramatic genius of Shakespeare or the poetry of a Goethe. Nor, at the human level, does a computer manifest the capacity for intuitive insight and self-awareness that characterizes man. Polanyi contends that: ". . . whenever we are confronted by a work of genius and submit to the leadership of its author, we emphatically acknowledge originality as a performance, the procedure of which we cannot specify." [25] He points out that while living things do have "machine-like contrivances" yet they are also characterized by inventiveness. Once more we come to Braithwaite's plasticity of response.

Such inventive powers are manifested in Lashley's experiments.[26] Rats that have learned their way in a maze are mutilated by the cutting of the neural channels through which learning took place. Yet they still find other motor patterns by which to attain their objective. Memory, purpose, and inventiveness are retained, and other operational principles are called into play to effect the original aim. Restitutive and regenerative powers in the lower organisms may also be cited.[27] Thus, the physicochemical basis with its mechanical procedures would appear to be directed by an inner drive of the organism associated with its wholeness, a capacity to adjust itself in pursuit of its goal. Teleology becomes more than a mere heuristic device. It would seem to be almost an unconscious or very primitive conscious (depending on the level of life) pursuit of an end. The mechanism becomes instrumental to *"the resourceful achievement of a comprehensive right-*

[25] M. Polanyi, *Personal Knowledge* (Chicago: The University Press, 1958), p. 336.

[26] K. S. Lashley, *Brain Mechanisms and Intelligence* (Chicago: The University Press, 1929), pp. 136 ff., cited in M. Polanyi, op. cit. p. 337.

[27] Cf. the work of Hans Dreisch on the embryo of the sea urchin.

ness."[28] But such an understanding of a living thing is associated with our awareness of its wholeness, and it finds no place in the analytical procedures to which reductionism leads. Polanyi suggests that there is "an active center operating unspecifiably in all animals."[29]

We might suggest that biology can be understood only as we view its various scientific disciplines from biochemistry upwards as a hierarchial structure at the apex of which there is a type of understanding or explanation which is quite distinct from what holds at the physicochemical level. There are parts of biological science where physicochemical language applies, and only by such language is the living process manipulatable at this level. But there are also parts where a different symbolism is required, and so often biology ignores this level of irreducible vital aspects. Equally, however, what we say at the physicochemical level cannot be gainsaid by what we say at the higher level. Furthermore, we must not attempt to answer questions that belong finally to a higher level in terms of structures investigated at a lower level. The whole gamut of biological investigation is thereby necessary for the comprehensive understanding of living things. In this way, we should ensure against excessive use of teleological language in biology and restrict it to its proper level. At the same time, it would show the inadequacy of purely physicochemical explanations.[30]

This awareness of wholes suggests that there are depths in nature beneath the empirically evident. Hume demonstrated convincingly that discursive and analytic reason operating upon empirical data is unable to demonstrate or attain the transempirical, in particular, the existence of the principle of causality, the human soul, and of God. Yet, he could still de-

[28] Polanyi, op. cit. p. 340.

[29] Ibid. p. 336.

[30] H. P. Habgood, "The Uneasy Truce Between Science and Theology," *Soundings*, ed. A. Vidler (Cambridge: Cambridge University Press, 1962), p. 37. (A most stimulating essay.)

scribe the concept of causation and the existence of the human soul as "natural beliefs." Indeed, it would seem that in such beliefs he also included the existence of God, although this is not so clearly stated.[31] Even in his skepticism he was here acknowledging tacitly the intuitive aspect of human knowledge in which man is immediately aware of the personal and the divine in and through the empirical order. He was also indicating that such direct apprehension precedes his interpretation and pursuit of the empirical. The analytic procedures of the physical sciences have blinded man to this, but at the biological level he is finally unable to close his eyes to it. The primary intuitive awareness of wholes that are more than the aggregation of the parts, even though they are known through the parts, points to nonobjectifiable depths in nature which can be described as life and mind but which are never completely susceptible to conceptual objectification. In the end we finish with mystery which is intuitively grasped, however much our sciences may have enabled us to comprehend it more fully.

Still more is this true of the personal. However much scientific methods may seek to embrace the personal within the generalized forms and universal laws of behavioristic analysis, the "I" eludes comprehension at this level. Always in my knowing there is present that which cannot be objectified—the "I" which knows and knows that it knows. I may even reflect upon my own knowing activities, but as I objectify them, they move from the present into the past, and the mysterious subjective still eludes the objective way of knowing. However much of myself at physiological and psychological levels I may seek to investigate, there is always an aspect of "I" which transcends the part of the self which I have objectified—that aspect which knows, the subject. It is this nonobjectifiable and nonobservable "I" of which I am intuitively and immediately aware, and, at this level, I am also sure that I am free.

[31] Cf. W. T. Blackstone, *The Problem of Religious Knowledge* (Englewood Cliffs, N.J.: Prentice Hall Inc., 1963), pp. 78–81.

However much we may criticize Descartes's *faux pas,* at least he grasped this ineradicable insight of self-consciousness in *Cogito, ergo sum.*

Behavioristic psychology has adopted the mathematical-physical language and uses its analogues, but the mental and personal level of reality, like the biological, also has its introspective and internal approach and with its emphasis on mental categories must also be listened to. Once more, we find ourselves concerned with a hierarchy of scientific disciplines, each of which makes its own distinctive contribution to the understanding of personal being. There are aspects of personal self-hood which, because it is embodied, require the analyses fixed by the physicochemical sciences including biochemistry, physiology, and neurology. Equally, however, there are aspects of personal being which raise issues that this level is unable to answer. Ultimately, as with life, we have to turn to the inner recesses of the consciousness. Even at the biological level there are aspects of instinctive behavior which require more than explanation in terms of reflex mechanism but rather demand some understanding of mental activity at an unconscious level or at the level of lapsed consciousness. Words such as "will," "intention," "freedom," "oughtness," "duty" also say something about man, and we do ourselves and humanity a disservice when we try to account for what such words describe in terms of the lower analytical level of the physicochemical sciences. They belong to man's intuitive insight into the basic nature of personal wholes, most of all in his own self-awareness and his own intuition of freedom.

Let us consider, in brief, this matter of freedom and determinism. The naturalistic type of scientist, who is satisfied to reduce man to the physicochemical level may convince himself that freedom is an illusion. But actually his scientific approach does not find man determined. By the very analogues he has chosen he has concerned himself only with those aspects of human behavior which can be embraced within his causal scheme. Yet other analogues may be necessary and other aspects of human behavior may have to be examined if a full understanding of personal being and also of life at the biological level has to be undertaken.[32] The understanding of man needs the concepts derived from all levels, including introspection. Such aspects of understanding should complement one another. To exclude any is to ignore the fullness of personal being of which we are aware in other ways than the analytical. It is to betray our human birthright. Any scientific analysis of the parts, by biological and psychological investigation as well as at the physicochemical level, is then seen to point to a whole which transcends these parts and yet unifies them into a personal and subjective unity.

Ever since Bacon applied Occam's razor to final causes, science has not concerned itself with underlying reasons but with empirically discernible structure. But with man who is the observer, the subject as well as the object, the inner side is known in self-consciousness. Outwardly a man may be where he is because of forces in his natural environment and because of physiological and neural mechanisms in his bodily structure. But inwardly he is aware of motives and intentions which have brought him where he is. It is true that he cannot know the inner motivation of his natural environment, although nature too may well have such an ontic side. He can begin to enter into such an inner side at the level of life by intuitive empathy. But he does know the "reasons" which have guided his own conduct from within, and he can, by empathy and through the disclosures of communication, understand the inner "reasons" which have guided his fellows in their relationship to him. Once more we find ourselves with Dilthey's distinction between "knowledge" and "understanding." Mysteriously my

[32] Cf. W. M. Urban, *Humanity and Deity* (London: George Allen and Unwin, Ltd., 1951), p. 364.

conduct outwardly is expressed in a dynamic pattern of secondary causes, but inwardly I am aware of "reasons" which guide the structure and movement of that pattern.[33] I know myself to possess a measure of freedom. I am more than this physicochemical mechanism. Later we must look more deeply at man's psychosomatic personal wholeness. Here it is enough to note that we do not "understand" human behavior by a "knowledge" of efficient causes. As John Baillie reminds us: "If there is a natural science of psychology, there is also a knowledge of the *psyche* which is not a natural science at all." [34]

There is a "given" to which the scientist is responding, and yet the true scientist is aware also of the hiddenness and mystery which too are present. The more he discovers and the deeper he penetrates into nature, the more fresh problems arise. Nature has an ontic side to comprehend, and the analytical approach does not suffice. This becomes very evident as we move upwards in the hierarchical structure of the sciences through biology to psychology. If the depth of the ontic side of nature be ultimately personal, as the Christian faith affirms, this should not surprise us. Nor should we be puzzled if our psychologies multiply and become attached to metaphysical attitudes as we approach the nature of the knowing subject.[35] A. N. Whitehead has pointed out [36] that the scientific choice of analogues has been bound up with sense perception while ignoring other and richer aspects of experience such as emotion and purpose. Organism, personal being, and values may also provide analogues. Mary Hesse comments: "It is now being slowly recognized that the attempt to explain everything in terms of analogies drawn from one particular aspect of experience, and that the least highly organized [she refers to

[33] Cf. J. Baillie, *Natural Science and the Spiritual Life* (New York: Charles Scribner's Sons, 1952), p. 42.

[34] Ibid. p. 41.

[35] This will be discussed fully in Chapter V.

[36] A. N. Whitehead, *Nature and Life* (Cambridge: Cambridge University Press, 1934).

the statistical model of a swarm of particles] is not profitable in the present state of science." [37]

III. *Time becomes significant and historical thinking enters science*

In the last century and a half our world has become very much more historically conscious, and even science has had to take time seriously. The historical consciousness dates from the end of the eighteenth century when the tremendous success of the physical sciences had engendered a belief in progress and a vision of a heavenly city being realized on earth. It was this century too which saw Vico's postulation of history as the "new science" and his attempt to examine the nature of historical thinking. But from the scientific point of view, the most significant factor was the development in geology and paleontology. The discovery of fossils in the layers of geological strata led ultimately to a recognition that life had a long history of development. Evolutionary ideas became ingredients in the atmosphere of thought and attained full expression in the theory of Charles Darwin. Historical thinking had entered science at the biological level.

With the advent of Einstein's theories of relativity, time became a dimensional aspect of scientific thinking at the physical level in a new and revolutionary manner. Its measurement and those of space became relative to the location and speed of the observer, and the whole Newtonian framework with its absolute space, absolute time, and Euclidian geometry was upset at the level of large-scale and cosmic phenomena. Indeed, the geometry of the space-time continuum became intimately linked to the concepts of matter and gravitation. Matter has thus become bound up with motion and activity. Harnessed to our astronomical and cosmological investigations,

[37] M. Hesse, op. cit. p. 158.

this led to an increasing concern with cosmogony, the science of the origin of the universe.

What happened at the macroscopic level had its counterpart in the microcosm at the level of atomic phenomena. It was discovered that the quantum mechanical models and analogues involved time as a potent factor. If a spatio-mechanical analogue be employed for the model it has spatial characteristics which contradict our normal understanding of space. When an electron jumps from one stationary orbit to another in the atom and radiation is emitted or absorbed, the transitional jump cannot be described in terms of the continuous motion of the electron in space. The idea of continuous space does not apply. The electron disappears at one level and reappears at the other without traversing the space between. Space appears to be quantized. This is only one of many reasons why attempts to picture the atom in a visual mechanical model have given place to mathematical analogues which simply offer patterns of relations. But it appears that time is quantized too. This involves a little more discussion of what science means by its concept "energy."

We have already seen how energy has become a fundamental entity in the physical sciences, manifesting itself in the forms of matter and radiation. In popular speech the word is associated with vigor of personality, force of action, active operation. In the scientific terminology, however, it is a measurable quantity and describes a capacity for doing work. The energy of a body is the measure of its capacity to perform work. Relativity theory has shown that the mass of a material body varies with its speed relative to an observer. If it is at rest relative to the observer, its mass is described as its rest mass, and it possesses an energy measured by the product of its mass or matter content and the square of the speed of light. Since the latter is 186,000 miles per second or 3×10^{10} centimeters by second, its square becomes a tremendous number: 9×10^{20}. This enables us to understand the enormous availability of energy in a small entity, like the atom, the kind of energy displayed in the destructive result of the atom or the hydrogen bomb. At the measurable level, whatever else it is, energy is a capacity to do work.

Now ordinary classical physics had also introduced the quantity "action," which it defined as the product of energy and time, again a measurable observable. Like "energy," this term too, has a specialized meaning and must not be taken in the ordinary sense of, for example, Newton's law, which states that action and reaction are equal and opposite. Classical physics gave it special significance in its principle of least action, according to which, in any actual motion, the "action" as just defined must be a minimum.

Relativity theory introduced this conception of action into its cosmic structures and identified it with the curvature of the universe. It had further demonstrated that it is an absolute, quite independent of the way in which space-time is divided up by any particular observer. But action had also appeared at the atomic level. As we have already noted, Planck had discovered the quantized nature of radiation and arrived at his constant "h." This is termed the "constant of action," since the energy of radiation may be measured by dividing Planck's constant by the time of oscillation of the radiation. Since action is measured by the product of energy and time, this would mean that the action of any radiation is always Planck's constant. Hence action is atomistic and occurs in multiples of "h." Now action fits better into the spatiotemporal framework of our modern relativistic model since it involves the product of the spatial quantity energy and time. Thus, it is four dimensional, and relativity can affirm its absolute nature. The quantity "h" becomes a cosmic constant, like the speed of light, independent of any observer.

One possible interpretation of the quantity "action" is important for us, namely, that energy has duration. It only fits into the four-dimensional framework of modern science as it is multiplied by duration and given temporal thickness. Since matter is a crystallization of energy, of a capacity for work, at the measurable level, this new description means that it takes time for any entity of the material world to disclose itself. Action measures the operation of energy for a duration of time. Because action is atomized and indivisible below the measurable level "h," energy takes time to manifest itself. The idea of continuous growth in time disappears in the subatomic realm. To quote E. W. Barnes: "We cannot say that action grows during the very small time when we wait for its appearance: 'it was not and it is' seem to be all that we can say." [38] Once more we find ourselves dealing with structures which are unpicturable in models taken from the realm of normal sense experience.

Heisenberg's principle of indeterminacy is bound up with this time dependence. The observation of the energy of a matter wave requires a minimum time, the time of vibration of the matter wave. Because this time is so small, the accurate measurement of energy at the macroscopic level appears to be simultaneous, but actually it is not independent of the time factor. The Uncertainty Principle states that the energy of a particle and duration of observation of a particle are bound together within certain limits of accurate measurement. Increased accuracy in the measurement of the one means decreased accuracy in that of the other. The measurement of energy requires time.

We are left facing mysterious depths in what we call matter. There would appear to be a substratum of something which in its measurably aspect we have called energy, a capacity for work, activity. It may take the forms of matter or radiation, but we must not fall into the trap of identifying such forms *in toto* with energy in this specific definition. These physical entities may well possess qualities or attributes which are not

[38] E. W. Barnes, *Scientific Theory and Religion* (Cambridge: Cambridge University Press, 1933), p. 267.

measurable and do not belong to energy as scientifically defined. We might use the word "energy" generally to describe this substratum, but if we do so we must acknowledge that, like Aristotle's "primal matter," it is nonobjectifiable, nonconceivable. Further, we are moving beyond science to metaphysics and speculation. Energy is known in what it does. It may assume transformable forms—matter and radiation—which are ordered energy at the measurable level. We may observe their capacity for work. They may possess other characteristic qualities, however, which defy ultimate scientific analysis and which are the results of some kind of creative activity immanent in energy itself and even transcending it.[39] The higher organizations of matter at which life and mind emerge would seem to indicate such creative activity, in the light of our contention that living and personal wholes are not reducible to the physicochemical level. We might even say that something akin may hold in the emergence of matter and radiation from the substratum, and that, when they are transformed into one another, one form of wholeness gives place to another. If so, Aristotle may in some ways have been near to the truth!

Now energy takes time to disclose itself. The action distributes and redistributes itself in a rhythmic dynamic pattern to describe which wave and particle models have to be strangely intermixed. We are left at the atomic level with a realm of infinitely small entities which have neither definite speed nor definite location and which defy our sensible experience of the continuity of space and time—neutrons, protons, electrons, positrons, mesons, mesotrons, neutrinos, antiprotons. We can picture this microcosm only in mathematical structures

[39] This is the view of Lloyd Morgan in *Emergent Evolution* (London: Williams and Norgate, 1927). S. Alexander, *Space, Time and Deity* (London: The Macmillan Co., Ltd., 1934) defines the primary as space-time and argues for the progressive emergence of new qualities as this primary stuff becomes organized into increasingly complex patterns.

of relationships. We have rhythmic concentrations of "energy" in which classical ideas of causal determinism break down and statistical laws offering probabilities take their place. It is a process such that nature as we know it takes time to exist. Each natural entity has its own appropriate time, and in a lesser duration it could not exist. The specific rhythmic process which is this entity can only occur in a specific time. Whitehead reminds us "that there is no nature at an instant." [40]

In the last two paragraphs we have made overt the metaphysical bias with which we have approached the scientific method. Of such bias no scientist is free, but he should, however, be conscious of what he is doing. Our generalizations about the nature of "energy" receive no support from science which is concerned solely with energy as a measurable quantity. An unconscious movement to the metaphysical level is continually plaguing science and makes a distinction necessary between what science really says and what the scientist seems to say when his statements are translated into ordinary language. This is particularly true at the physicochemical level where mathematical analogues and a technical symbolical language have taken over. Yet it also holds, as we have already seen, at the biological and psychological levels where the technical scientific language is mixed in with dramatic and anthropomorphic forms borrowed from ordinary speech. If the dramatic elements be dismissed as anthropomorphic, science speaks to us only at the mathematical level and must not be taken literally.

If the scientific approach be accepted as the only way of knowing, it does imply a certain type of metaphysic. Its rejection of all qualities and values, the mechanistic connotation of its models or, even when they are mathematically formulated, its ignoring of purpose and teleology—all suggest a covert naturalism. Indeed, if its statements are the sole source of

[40] A. N. Whitehead, *Nature and Life* (Cambridge: Cambridge University Press, 1934), p. 48.

knowledge and if we ignore as complementary the insights of the poet, the artist, and the religious man, or if we explain away the latter, the inevitable outcome is a depersonalization of man and a mechanization of nature. Once we delete from nature descriptions in the dramatic language molded on human experience, even though these would seem to be needed at the biological level, science leads to a metaphysics and becomes "scientism." But this is not necessary, for, if we regard science as a hierarchical structure of sciences which supplement one another and if we take its insights as complementary to those of history, religion, and the arts, we may build an understanding of life and the universe which will give full value to science and yet find a place for ethical, aesthetic, and religious values, for personal life and purpose.

Now this naturalistic interpretation of scientific statements comes exactly at those points where science becomes cosmological and moves to the consideration of origins. In our modern period not only has time become involved in scientific analogues, but so also has history. For history is time acquiring meaning, and time has been acquiring meaning at the level of nature. Hence, at the physicochemical level we have cosmological and cosmogonic investigations which, though couched in mathematical symbolism, say much more when translated into dramatic speech. When we move to the level of evolution, concepts and figures borrowed from dramatic speech become much more in evidence, however much such concepts may be denuded of anthropomorphic reference. Here, too, a translation into the normal language of human experience may say much more than the actual scientific speech is saying. A covert metaphysics may be unveiled, unless we recognize, at the same time, the contributions of other and equally valid aspects of experience which science has excluded by its method.

The astrophysicist, since the advent of relativity theory, has extended the concept of evolution beyond the realm to which it initially applies, the area of biology, and applied it to the origins of the universe. We have moved with Einstein to an understanding of the vastness of our universe. If it is hyperbolic, space is infinite and unbounded. If it is spherical, space is finite and unbounded. The choice between the two is not yet decisively possible on the basis of available astronomical and astrophysical data. But speculation about the past of the universe *as we know it* has been helped by the identification of vast island universes much like our galactic universe. These galaxies, at great distances from us, are receding at speeds proportional to their distance. This determination is made possible by the "red shift" evidenced in their spectra, that is to say, the measured wave length of their light emissions shows a displacement to the red end of the spectrum. This "red shift" indicates an increased wave length due to the recession of the galaxies, on the principle of the Döppler effect.

On this basis a multitude of models have been extrapolated from the available evidence. They generally fall into two types.[41] There are those based on the idea that the present state of our universe began in a highly concentrated and unstable compression of energy which, on bursting, gave rise to an expanding universe. This model postulates that space itself is being stretched like a plastic ballon. The other type postulates a steady state universe in which there is a continually renewed background of hydrogen, very rarified but sufficient to give rise to new galaxies. The first model accounts for the recession of galaxies in terms of the expansion of its model. The second type rejects the idea of expansion, assumes that the universe remains always in the same state, and accounts for the receding galaxies in its model by postulating that they are newly formed. The second type of model has

[41] Typical of the first type are the views of A. S. Eddington, *The Expanding Universe* (Cambridge: Cambridge University Press, 1933), and George Gamow, *The Creation of the Universe* (New York: The Viking Press, 1956). Typical of the second type is the view of F. Hoyle expressed in *The Nature of the Universe* (Oxford: Basil Blackwell, 1950).

been seriously challenged by the evidence of the "quasars" or "quasi-stellar sources" now observed by our radio telescopes. These transmitters are billions of light years from the earth and would seem to support the first model. The evidence that they offer may take us much nearer the origination of our universe in its present state, if the expanding model be adopted.

Let us note at this point, that scientific cosmogony involves us in meta-empirical speculation. In a sense we are creating scientific myths, although we have an empirical basis in the recession of the other nebulae from our own galactic system. In the many forms of the expanding universe model we have extrapolated back in time from our current observation of our physical universe. The geological structure of our own earth, the composition and estimated ages of the various types of star, the recession of the nebulae, the evidence of the quasars, all suggest possibilities about the primordial past, when interpreted in terms of contemporary relativity theory. Since extrapolation from the macroscopic enables us to penetrate the subatomic order, we have no reason to reject such extrapolation into the historical past.

We are using the method of history which by sympathetic imagination and intuitive insight seeks to relive past ages in the light of historical documents, artifacts, archeological remains, and other pieces of evidence.

But let us recognize that we have nothing so concrete as the material with which the human historian deals. In addition, the historian is dealing with man and he knows man from within. Historians have increasingly recognized this as a differentia of history from physical science, since the time of Vico.

The historian of nature basically assumes the uniformity of nature, that the same natural forces and relationships have always operated in the physical universe, and this is an act of faith. This principle has the support of our own experience and of the fact just noted that observation of natural events is bound up with duration. Scientific tradition seems to confirm such conviction about the continuity of the physical. Again the finite speed of light enables us to study cosmic phenomena as they were millions of years ago, and here our knowledge is increasing. Yet, finally, our extrapolation is metempirical, and the models or analogues it creates are scientific myths. In the expansion theory, we retreat to the time of cosmic explosion, but here we face the alternatives of Gamow's "big squeeze" with a contraction which preceded the current expansion, or of a pulsating universe, or of a mysterious quiescent unstable state of infinite duration which suddenly manifested its instability, or of an absolute beginning as postulated by E. A. Milne. Furthermore, we cannot determine at present, by our measurements, whether cosmic space is hyperbolic or spherical. Translated into ordinary speech, many assume that the scientist is speaking about creation. Yet his is a peculiarly secular myth. It is based upon the abstract mathematical models or analogues which are current in scientific thinking, and one can be no more dogmatic about the myths than one can about the current theories.

This holds also of scientific speculations about the end of the universe. Here extrapolation into the future is undertaken, and it suffers from the same metempirical limitation. In our own scientific experience of limited areas of nature we have formulated the Second Law of Thermodynamics. According to this, in a closed system the amount of energy available for work tends to decrease. The total energy of the system remains unchanged, but energy is only available for work as different parts of the system are at different energy levels. Like water flowing from the higher level to the lower level until the two levels have become identical, energy flows from the level of higher availability to that of lower until a distinction ceases to be possible. Then all the energy of the system becomes bound energy, and no useful work is possible. All activity ceases. This bound energy is tied up with the term "entropy," which measures the decrease in availability for work. In a closed system, the Second Law states that the entropy tends to increase. This is another way of saying that, for instance, in a heat engine the available heat energy, which is measured by temperature, will decrease until the system concerned has reached the lowest temperature of the system. The movement is always towards thermodynamic equilibrium and maximum entropy.

But the scientist extrapolates this law from a limited closed finite system to the universe as a whole. He affirms that the total entropy of the universe is tending to a maximum and that the energy available for dynamic motion of all kinds is tending to a minimum. Finally the universe will lapse into the quiescence of complete mixed-up-ness, a kind of heat death. Now at the level of moderate spatiotemporal dimensions the law may be empirically verified, but at the level of the universe such verification is impossible. We are postulating a scientific myth. This does not mean that it is not true, but it does mean that it is an imaginative interpretation of what is happening to the universe as a whole, based on what we know in one limited area of it—the way all transempirical and metaphysical thought has to move. In addition, our own experience yields experience of open systems in which available energy is being built up and entropy is decreasing, systems which sustain themselves against the increasing entropy of surroundings and are sustained by negative entropy. Such systems are normal at the level of living and personal wholes. We have no justification for dogmatism at the level of the universe, for we are dealing with the whole, the total spatiotemporal continuum. We may not talk of it as either a closed or open system for this is and must remain metempirical speculation. If the subatomic world requires an increasing degree of symbolism, which may at least yield empirically verifiable predictions, we need to remember how much more symbolic and mythical are pronouncements about the origin and end of what is illimitable, metempirical, and not subject to empirical observation or verification in its totality. Extrapolation here may lead us to scientific mythology, and if we are not careful, to a metaphysical interpretation which carries us beyond scientific warrantry.

When we move to the issue of biological evolution, once more history enters the area of science. It is not our intention to discuss Darwinism or neo-Darwinism at this point, but simply to point out the way in which this theory of evolution, which remains scientific orthodoxy, can be understood scientifically. We have already indicated that many of its terms have anthropomorphic overtones and are derived from human experience. Dramatic language such as "survival of the fittest" and "natural selection" is a reminder of this. It is true that these concepts are denuded of human values and ideas associated with purpose, yet they are reminders that the analogues here used are taken from the level of human experience. The observable data which such analogues interpret are limited to our contemporary scene to a large extent: natural observation such as Darwin's finches and the evidence afforded on the Galopagos Islands; laboratory data such as that afforded by experiments with the effect of radiation and chemicals upon the *Drosophila;* the findings of genetics and the structure of the DNA molecule; and the study of embryology. Here the theory of evolution is an extrapolation from the somewhat limited evidence available. To this we may add the often limited historical evidence offered by fossils in geology and paleontology, although anthropological investigation here is increasingly offering new material.

The very fact that we are dealing with history, and that history is an area of novelty and the unpredictable, should warn us against too dogmatic an affirmation about the mechanism of evolution. Forces may have been operative in the past and structures of relationship may have been present which served their purpose and disappeared with the passage of historical time. The slender evidence available makes it difficult to dogmatize. At the moment, the Darwinian analogue provides the best method of unifying the data, but it has many critical points where its explanation becomes thin and fails to satisfy, although the faithful neo-Darwinian is often blind to these. Once again, what we are doing at this level is partly metempirical, it is not truly historical in failing to allow for novelties and unique operations in the past. It is abstract in the sense that it ignores any functioning of mind or consciousness, any teleological elements, any ultimate reality for moral and religious values. We should expect the last element of abstraction, but this makes it very evident that we are dealing here with a scientific cosmological myth which has naturalistic implications if interpreted literally and if the contributions of other areas of experience be ignored or explained away by it.

At the level of these cosmological myths concerned with origins and ends, science and religion meet crucially. Purely at the scientific level these myths offer us scientific speculations about the way in which the natural order developed and how it may end. But all historical analogies are speculative, even at the level of human history—how much the more so when they have less evidence from the past on which to work and are chosen from a much more limited field of human experience! The danger is that they should be accepted literally instead of as analogues, should be fastened to a naturalistic metaphysic, and should be made to imply that all our human values and religious insights are the result of accidental collocations of atoms and will one day vanish in the dissolution of the universe. This dogmatism goes beyond science, and here the man of faith stands firm. As W. M. Urban has contended, true science has never told the great lie that "the cosmos, including life and mind, has come from nothing and will end in nothing." [42] Science can say nothing about ultimate origination or

[42] W. M. Urban, op. cit. p. 361.

ultimate destiny. Urban reminds us that the scientist may talk about the dissolution of the physical universe, but the religious philosopher is concerned with the dissolution of being, and there is "no entropy of being." Equally, of course, we must not build our theologies on these myths. Stephen Toulmin reminds us that "if we force astrophysics to serve us with a revised version of Genesis and Revelation we dig a pit for ourselves." [43]

[43] "Contemporary Scientific Mythology," *Metaphysical Beliefs,* a symposium (London: S.C.M. Press, Ltd., 1957), p. 46.

III

Religious Knowledge: Its Nature and Its Language

Although we have rejected attempts to fill gaps in scientific knowledge with religious explanations, we have also indicated the limitations of the scientific method. In particular we have noted its concern with the analytical approach to nature and its ignoring of the synthetic awareness. This concentration on parts and the pushing to the periphery of the intuitive awareness of wholeness has led to great success at the physicochemical level where mechanistic models and mathematical analogues have become the typical ways of representing the natural order. Yet at the higher levels of living things and personal being the intuitive awareness needs to be called into service if a real "understanding" of organismic and personal life is to be attained rather than a "knowledge" of the parts embraced in such living wholes.

Furthermore we have noted that it is a tacit awareness of wholeness in nature which not only lies behind the scientific investigation of the parts but also, again and again, is called into play as with intuitive insight the scientist grasps a new pattern or Gestalt in the aspect of nature which he is studying. It is significant that when we reach the level of the biological and psychological sciences concepts associated with living and personal wholes are needed to supplement the reductive techniques by which we seek to analyze life and mind at the physicochemical level. Although from its inception modern science cut out any concern with reasons and concentrated on cause, we find teleological concepts lifting their heads. Purpose and intention, aim and drive, descriptive of personal experience, find their way into scientific terminology. However much the scientist may seek to denude such concepts of conscious and anthropomorphic associations, they serve to remind us that at the level of life as well as mind personal involvement is a necessary element in true understanding.

The commitment of the scientist to his task is a reminder that his knowledge is personal knowledge at all levels. Even when he is concerned with the mechanism of the organism and uses analogies drawn from human artifacts, he needs to be reminded that analysis of the parts is not sufficient, even for a machine. Such a human artifact may be examined analytically and the relations between its parts determined, but, in any machine, the causative structure of relationship does not give final understanding. We have to see it as a whole and understand the purpose which it is called to serve. We have to become involved with it and understand its total meaning, its value. Polanyi points out that physics and chemistry may account for the malfunctioning of the parts, but they cannot provide us with the operational principle which underlies the whole. Without knowledge of such an operational principle, the machine is not "understood." It is a chaotic ensemble. He suggests that "the understanding of a whole appreciates the coherence of its subject matter and thus acknowledges the existence of a value that is absent from the constituent particulars." [1] Every whole is more than the sum of its parts.

In the end, final causes cannot be eliminated, however successful (and it is remarkably successful) scientific analysis may be. Now at the physical and inanimate level this issue of meaning does not lift its head, and the analytic method of dismemberment succeeds. But once the realm of living things is reached, the machinery we investigate serves specific functions and is directed to certain ends. It is here that living wholes in their internal differentiation and self-regulation show themselves to be selves, wholes which are more than the mere

[1] M. Polanyi, *Personal Knowledge* (Chicago: Chicago University Press, 1958), p. 327.

aggregation of their parts. Whereas physical entities can be understood by the building up of the parts, organic entities increasingly manifest a directiveness. They are self-moving, active, surviving by the orderly functioning of their organs. They seem to have a meaning which they are striving to realize, and to have a center of direction, to show inventiveness in attaining ends. Intuitively, we recognize the presence here of something akin to ourselves, and to understand we have to become more personally involved than at the analytic level of the physicochemical or in the consideration of a machine. The parts have to be comprehended within the whole to which they belong.

The intuitive apprehension of a living whole from which we begin has to be filled in with the analytic procedures of scientific method but ultimately these will only suffice when we finish with a comprehension of the whole. Such intuitive awareness is a vague and tacit background to scientific investigation which glories in clear ideas that can be concisely expressed. Yet the clear-cut mathematical analysis or mechanistic development will not suffice unless it is gathered up to give us a clearer comprehension of the living whole with which we are concerned. Here our personal involvement leads us to find in living things meanings and reasons akin at a lower level to the urges and purposes we find in ourselves. And it is only in this way that we really begin to "understand" the natural order of which, in our psychosomatic aspects, we are so much a part. Imagination and sympathy become primary at this point, and our personal involvement is deeper.

1. *The knowledge of the personal*

What we have said applies still more to personal wholes. We shall discuss later the psychosomatic nature of personal being. Man is a part of the natural order, however much he may transcend it. He has emerged within the evolutionary process and his personal wholeness involves the processes studied at the physicochemical level and at the biological level with its hierarchy of sciences, including animal neurology and psychology. Indeed the naturalist would believe that such sciences are sufficient to account for the human organism. Our purpose, at this juncture, is to investigate our knowledge of other persons and so to prepare a way for the knowledge to which religious faith lays claim. Our criticism of the naturalist position and justification of the position here adopted must wait development in a subsequent chapter.

We have already suggested that we have a primary intuitive self-awareness which is directly linked to a similar direct feeling for the presence of other persons. We must now develop what has already been said about our knowledge of ourselves from within. Augustine [2] reminds us that in my doubting I am aware of my existence; or positively, Descartes states "I think, so I am," *Cogito, ergo sum.* This is not a matter of inference but of direct apprehension. I know that I act, think, and speak. My existence is indeed the presupposition of my discovering anything or doing anything. I know myself as knowing and doing. I know myself as loving and willing. There is in me a transcendent depth, an I of which I am intuitively aware.

When, within this primary awareness, I turn to introspection, the primary unity of the "I" is split up into knower and known. As I turn myself into an object I still also remain the knowing subject, and the latter recedes in its transcendent depth. I do not know objectively the inner depths of I but only my empirical ego. In such introspection I may examine my motives and intentions, criticize my processes of discursive reasoning, call my ideas in question, but I never grasp the I. As we have noted earlier, all introspection is retrospection. Directly I turn myself into an object, I introduce a temporal transcendence into the relation of I to myself.[3] Such knowing

[2] Augustine, *De Trinitate,* IX, 3.

[3] This point is made by Martin Buber, *I and Thou,* trans. R. Gregor Smith (Edinburgh: T & T Clark, 1937), pp. 29 ff.

is not of the same order as the primal direct apprehension. It is knowing in the sense of rational objectification and analysis. It is knowing about—Dilthey's "knowledge" and not his "understanding."

Here Jaspers reminds us that "the self is more than all that is knowable." [4] Empirical self-knowledge comes by observation. It is self-reflection. But in self-awareness I am aware of a self-transcendence, a mystery of being which remains a mystery for both Marcel and Heidegger. There is an ontic depth in "I" which distinguishes it from the objective "he" and sets it apart even logically. "I" am never an object, and in this sense we cannot talk about a substantive self. The sentence "I exist" does not have the same logical form as "he exists." This becomes evident when we remember that I can say meaningfully "he is asleep" or "he is dead," but I cannot say meaningfully "I am asleep" or "I am dead." [5] My psychosomatic wholeness has a mysterious nonobjectifiable depth which I can never fully comprehend, however much I may try to fill in my initial self-awareness with introspective knowledge. A statement about human behavior in the third person is public and objective, whereas a statement in the first person is private and involves the unique inner life of the "I." I act and think from a central depth.

In this inner self-awareness, I know myself to have worth and meaning. I know myself to be a responsible being. I am aware of claim and obligation. As Kant saw, the human experience of "oughtness" is unique and belongs to the noumenal self. It comes to me with my self-consciousness and brings with it an awareness of freedom. This understanding of man becomes central in the contemporary movements which are embraced within the label of "existentialism." In revolt

[4] Karl Jaspers, *The Perennial Scope of Philosophy* (New York: Philosophical Library, 1949), p. 60.

[5] There is an illuminating discussion of this by Professor Ian Ramsey in "On the Possibility and Purpose of a Metaphysical Theology," *Prospect for Metaphysics* (London: George Allen and Unwin, 1961), pp. 163 ff.

against the superficial description of reality which analytical scientific procedures and objective empiricism have made so dominant, existentialism emphasizes man's inner freedom and the importance of decision. Ever since Kierkegaard declared that the essential truth lies in subjectivity and emphasized that truth is what is held with passionate inwardness, there has been a continuing and growing rebellion against the tyranny of the objective. I may choose the meaning I will give to my life. Atheistic and Christian thinkers alike put their emphasis on the centrality of such existential decision.

There is also another aspect of self-awareness. It is the intuitive awareness of others. As the baby emerges out of the primitive consciousness which envelops it with its mother and becomes self-conscious, it also becomes aware of her. The differentiation of consciousness involves a differentiation of personal wholes.[6] Increasingly, it has been recognized in our own time that the origin of self-consciousness is thus bound up with the awareness of other selves rather than with the awareness of objects. Naturalism with its question as to the reality of other minds assumes that we know the objective world of the senses directly but other minds by inference. Buber, Ebner, Marcel, Scheler would hold that knowledge of other selves is primary in the awakening of self-consciousness. We become persons through meeting, and for this we have an inborn capacity. As Buber puts it:

> In the beginning is relation—as category of being, readiness, grasping form, mould for the soul; it is the *a priori* of relation, the *inborn Thou.* The inborn Thou is realized in the lived relations with that which it meets. The fact that this *Thou* can be known as what is over against the child, can be taken up in exclusiveness, and finally can be addressed with the primary word, is based on the *a priori* of relation.[7]

[6] Cf. Buber, op. cit. pp. 25 ff.
[7] Ibid. p. 27.

We might suggest indeed that our awareness of the reality of the external world, which G. E. Moore stoutly defends,[8] is actually in some way derivative from our awareness of persons. Certainly W. E. Hocking adopts this view. He writes: "I do not first know my physical world as a world of *objects* and then as a world of *shared* objects: it is through a prior recognition of the presence of Other Mind that my physical experience acquires objectivity at all. The objectivity of Nature is its community." [9] And again: "The only way in which I can know an object to be common is by catching it in the act of being common, by knowing it as known by other mind." [10]

Yet let us hasten to add that such awareness is mediated to us through sense experience. As with the case of the living whole, the intuitive awareness is a Gestalt-like concern with the whole of the other in which the consciousness does not focus upon individual aspects and characteristics. The latter are present in the consciousness, however, and contribute to the personal patterning of which the subject is aware. Within this consciousness, as Buber and others have pointed out, and contributing to the general awareness of the other, there is a feeling of resistance, of another which encroaches on my sovereignty. As Heim puts it: "I am aware of you as a will with which I must settle accounts, and you are aware of me in the same fashion." [11] It is at this level that Sartre says in his play *No Exit*, "Hell is other people!" [12]

Yet this vague apprehension gives neither "knowledge" nor "understanding." Rather, it stimulates investigation. Indeed,

[8] See "A Defence of Common Sense," *Contemporary British Philosophy*, Vol. II, ed. J. H. Muirhead (London: George Allen and Unwin, 1925).

[9] W. E. Hocking, *The Meaning of God in Human Experience* (New Haven: Yale University Press, 1912), p. 288 f.

[10] Ibid. p. 288, *n.* 1.

[11] Karl Heim, *God Transcendent*, trans. E. P. Dickie (London: Nisbet and Co., Ltd., 1935), p. 166.

[12] J. P. Sartre, *No Exit* (New York: Vintage Books, 1946), p. 47.

like all intuition, it is a response and involves something akin to disclosure. Analytical procedures will not at this point carry me to great comprehension, to penetration to the inner side of the other. Science may disclose the mechanisms of the other person, but its knowledge gives me no understanding of his inner side. Two factors have to come into play. On the part of the other person, there has to be communication in act and in word. Through the behavior and speech of the other, I become aware of a depth akin to the depth in myself. The communicating "word" involving utterance and activity becomes a disclosure, a revelation of the other. But here the other factor becomes evident. The disclosure evokes in me a responsive trust and commitment in which imaginative sympathy becomes active, and I move from my own inner awareness into the personal depth of the other. In other words, understanding comes through love and imagination.

Furthermore, as in love I understand the other as person, so also I become more really personal. Love and the imaginative insight that accompanies it mean that I become personally involved in the other. My knowledge becomes personal knowledge, as, in commitment, I understand the other from within my understanding of myself, and my understanding of myself thereby becomes enriched. Only in this way can an initial apprehension move to some measure of comprehension. As this response is awakened we have what is now often called a "disclosure situation."

Let us note, however, that just as in my own self-consciousness "I" remain a mystery even to myself, so it is with the other. If I am unable to plumb the deeps of my own self-transcendence, I am also unable to plumb the deeps of the other. The other transcends me in quite another dimension, and without his self-disclosure I should never be able to enter into the mystery of his being. The analyzing consciousness of the scientist deals with personal being as a problem to be solved by the analysis of causal relationships between the parts at the physical and psychical level. But mystery cannot, as Marcel points out, be solved like a problem. It does not issue in knowledge that can be logically developed and clearly stated. It can be understood only insofar as it discloses itself and as I become involved in it. It can never stand objectively over against myself. My involvement in such a disclosure situation will bring deeper insight, but a penumbra of mystery will always remain. For mystery describes the transcendent, and personal being always bears a dimension of transcendence. Yet such mystery must not be taken to mean unintelligibility. Being and truth are ultimately one, but this cannot be grasped by the analyzing intellect. As Marcel puts it:

> A problem is something which I meet, which I find complete before me, but which I can therefore lay siege to and reduce. But a mystery is something in which I myself am involved, and it can therefore only be thought of as "a sphere where the distinction between what is in me and what is before me loses its meaning and its initial validity" . . . a mystery, by definition, transcends every conceivable technique.

He adds, however, that "it is the essence of mystery to be recognized or capable of recognition" and suggests that it is grasped by intuition.[13]

This mysterious element in personality is evident when I seek to objectify my knowledge of someone and express my understanding in language. For language is tied to the universal and every person is a unique center of mystery, a fact which is indicated by his given name. George and Henry, Susan and Jane are more than particular illustrations of the genus "man." In their quiddity they are unique. They are individuals, but they are also persons, and "George-ness" is not "Henry-ness." My general concepts and universal categories are broken upon this uniqueness. As I move up the evolu-

[13] Gabriel Marcel, "Being and Having," Gifford Lectures, *The Mystery of Being,* Vol. I (London: The Harvill Press, Ltd., 1950), pp. 211 f.

tionary scale, the generalizing technique of science and of the objectivity of language fails to deal adequately with the singularity of personal being. This begins to be evident at the level of the higher organic beings. I can use my language which is molded to the universal and the objective only in paradoxical form.

The unique and distinctive is communicated to some degree by the unexpected coming together of disjunctive expressions. Lord Granville once described a Russian princess whom he knew in Moscow as "so easy, so *grande dame,* so clever, so insolent, so civil." [14] As Casserley points out, often the paradox is expressed in a more closely knit combination of nouns and adjectives, such as the description of James I as "the wisest fool in Christendom." He continues: "To evade the paradox is to lose the truth. To interpret the paradox as an accommodation to the simplicity of the ordinary mind, with which the more mature can afford to dispense, is not the way of wisdom but the way of intellectual snobbery and conceit." [15] Thus, paradox enables us to express and communicate the elusive, and without it we should be unable to grasp the inner depths of personality. Objectively expressed, the unique simplicity of the personal requires paradox. This paradoxical mode of expression does not arise from complexity but from the uniqueness and mystery of personality. The personal is essentially simple with a simplicity that is consonant with the uniqueness of every "I."

II. *The divine self-disclosure and the Hebrew-Christian understanding of God*

Within man's self-awareness is his awareness of the Other. As I differentiate myself from others I become aware also of

[14] David Mathew, *Action, the Formative Years* (London: Eyre and Spotteswood), p. 82, cited in L. Casserley, *The Christian in Philosophy* (New York: Charles Scribner's Sons, 1951), p. 180.

[15] Ibid. p. 181.

the all-encompassing mystery of being. I am never aware of myself without being aware of my thrown-ness, my *Dasein.* I am a finite being, limited in space and bound to a bodily form, limited in time and having a birth and a death which are not of my determination. Always, I am aware of what Jaspers calls the Encompassing and Tillich the Unconditioned. There is that which transcends my own self-consciousness and meets me both within and without. Through the media of my social and natural environment I apprehend in moments of primary awareness a transcendent mystery and presence. Yet also in the deeps of my own being I am conscious of a deep which calls to my own deep. The divine presence is both within and without.

Furthermore, I am aware of that presence as claim. I know myself as a responsible being. Even atheistic thinkers such as Sartre and Camus have to find a place for this. At least I am responsible to existence. Being presses into my *Dasein* at every point, and I cannot live without a felt awareness of the all-embracing "whole," which at the depths manifests itself as personal claim. Indeed, the fact that I can commit myself in trust and love to others and acknowledge their worth and the rightness of their claims implies a prior awareness of a claim which comes to me in and through their claim, of a rightness enthroned in the universe. As John Baillie has written:

> . . . if "others are the real world," it is because they embody for me, in my encounter with them, something greater than themselves, an intrinsic right and a universal good. My relations with my fellows have the significance of reality for me only because and in so far as they mediate to me this greater reality . . .[16]

We can trust others only because we sense in and through them the presence of a greater than they. If my self-awareness

[16] J. Baillie, *The Sense of the Presence of God* (New York: Charles Scribner's Sons, 1962), p. 36.

originates in and with my awareness of others, it is also grounded in my awareness of the Other.

This primary awareness is but the threshold of religious faith, yet it reminds us that knowledge of God comes by intuitive insight and direct felt awareness. Despite Bonhoeffer's vigorous denial of a religious a priori, most men do seem capable of a religious response to the deeps of the universe, carrying with it an intuitive awareness of a mysterious order which embraces the world of nature and men and underlies it.

In reaction against the rationalism of his time, which had been stimulated by the success of science and which had reduced revelation to the level of natural theology, Schleiermacher sought to isolate religion in feeling and defined it as a pure feeling of absolute dependence. Thereby, he sought to protect it from science and philosophy on the one hand and from morality and conduct on the other and to make a unique place for it. His position has been justly criticized, but let us note that in the first edition of his famous *Addresses on Religion,* he associated intuition with feeling. Although in later editions and other writings he dropped the former term, we must not accuse him of complete subjectivism, for he seems to have retained the intuitive element within his understanding of feeling. Religious feeling can sometimes be described by him as if it were man's own immediate self-consciousness—and let us note that Schleiermacher was essentially pantheistic. But in other passages an element of genuine apprehension of reality is implied, and "feeling" seems to mean a kind of emotional awareness of spiritual things. Feeling, in this religious sense, does lay hold upon transsubjective reality. The general impression in both *Addresses on Religion* and *The Christian Faith* is that, in religious feeling, we are immediately aware of the Infinite Ground of things. Hence Schleiermacher can define God as "the *Whence* of our receptive and active existence" and can write of religious feeling: ". . . in the first instance God signifies for us simply that which is the co-determinant in this feeling and to which we trace our being in such a state; and any further content of the idea must be evolved out of this fundamental import assigned to it." [17]

We have emphasized Schleiermacher's thought at this point because, in his own time, he was endeavoring to meet the successful "scientism" of that day with its rationalism. His weakness lay in his rejection of divine self-disclosure or revelation in the full Christian sense of the term and his preoccupation with man's immediate self-consciousness as the key to religious understanding. He soft pedaled the transcendent and overemphasized the subjective. His pantheism led him to put all religions together as the natural expression of man's God-consciousness, so that really the content of all religion is the original God-consciousness for which all men have potentiality and which needs to be stimulated in them and to be interpreted in the light of some principle intuited by them and their group. Furthermore, his pious feeling is defined as "dependence," and this is not a peculiarly distinctive feeling, although he admits that it has its source in God. His fallacious logic would seem to be that because religion is not merely knowledge, therefore knowledge is not constituent in religion. Yet he was continually bringing it in at the backdoor. When religion is thus reduced to almost complete subjectivity, this is no way to protect it. When the special significance of divine self-disclosure and revelation is ignored and man falls back upon a primary feeling of the self-consciousness, religion cannot finally speak to a scientific age.

We can still be grateful for Schleiermacher's very inadequate attempt to safeguard the intuitive and affective aspect of religion. It did at least point to man's religious awareness of the mysterious depth in the universe. Schleiermacher's fallacious logic, however, made religion abdicate any claim to

[17] F. Schleiermacher, *The Christian Faith,* trans. Mackintosh and Stewart (Edinburgh: T & T Clark, 1948), pp. 16–17.

knowledge, to the area with which science was concerned. What he did was to posit a drastic dichotomy between science and religion. It is true that religion and its insights are quite distinct from science and its knowledge. It is quite another thing to free religion from any claim to what is also within the purview of science, and to argue that the data of science and the subject matter of religion have no relation.

Otto's [18] famous discussion of religious consciousness is more helpful. For him religious experience has its key in the idea of the holy. Whereas the holy carries the connotation of moral goodness, Otto undertakes a phenomenological investigation in which he denudes "the holy" of all rational and moral aspects and isolates what he believes to be the distinctive religious value, the "numinous." The appraisal of the "numinous" is accompanied by the numinous feeling. In itself inconceivable and nonrational, man yet apprehends it as a *mysterium tremendum et fascinans* and intuits it in the distinctive religious feeling of awe, a compound of dread and overwhelmedness, on the one hand, and of captivating attraction and rapture, on the other. This feeling has constituent within it a kind of intuitive awareness of the numinous Being as "wholly other," a "mystery" which defies rational expression and transcends conceptualization.

This numinous feeling has a unique quality and must be differentiated from all natural feelings. Here Otto would seem to part company with Schleiermacher. Otto talks of it as "a hidden 'predisposition' of the human spirit." [19] He bears out our own contention of the primacy of the awareness of God by holding that the sense of the numinous "issues from the deepest foundation of cognitive apprehension that the soul possesses." [20] He agrees that it "comes into being in and amid

[18] R. Otto, *The Idea of the Holy,* trans. J. W. Harvey (London: Oxford University Press, 1931).

[19] Ibid. p. 119.

[20] Ibid. p. 117.

the sensory data and empirical material of the natural world . . . yet it does not arise *out of* them, but only by their *means*." He is thus indicating that man has a primary intuitive awareness of God in and through his experience of his world. As he apprehends others, so with such apprehension there comes an awareness of the all-embracing and transcendent Other, God. However much we may disagree with the cumbersome mental and Kant-like machinery by which Otto seeks to unite this nonrational apprehension of the *numinous* with rational and moral accompaniments, we can be grateful for the emphasis which he has placed upon the uniqueness and primacy of man's apprehension.

This intuitive awareness of the presence of God is but the threshold of faith. It is that in us which provides the basis for true understanding commitment, and such can come only through special divine self-disclosure. At the personal level, the intuitive apprehension of the other person becomes an increasing comprehension as personal disclosure in bodily act and communicated word awakens empathy, trust, and love; so at the religious level the intuitive apprehension of the "wholly other," the depth of the universe, is brought to growing comprehension while the mystery behind all things unveils himself personally to us.

Yet we need to remember that our primary awareness has the quality of revelation. Ninian Smart has reminded us that "intuitions of God only become plausible if they chime in with what is yielded in revelations and disclosures of God (for otherwise why talk of them as 'of God'?); but this already suggests at least some resemblance between revelations and intuitions."[21] We may not dogmatically affirm that all men have such intuitions in some form, but we can feel with Smart "that there may be some intimation of divinity which every

[21] N. Smart, "Revelation, Reason and Religion," *Prospect for Metaphysics*, ed. Ian Ramsey (London: George Allen and Unwin, 1961), p. 82.

man may have." [22] They form the basis of what is often called a general revelation. Through the natural and social orders man can become aware of the divine presence as claim and succor often in a very rudimentary way. At the levels of natural and moral law man can apprehend the mysterious depth which they manifest. The regularities of nature and the moral claims of society become media through which he may be awakened to an awareness of the directing creativity behind them. As Kant saw, both aspects can evoke the response of awe. As man feels the claim of others, he can feel also the claim of God. Along with such apprehension we may place mystical experience with its ineffable visions of the infinite ground of being, visions which are imageless and thus incommunicable and yet which evidence an awareness of deity.

This is revelation, and it does not arise from knowledge of the natural and social orders themselves. The revelation is through them, not in them. As Tillich reminds us: "if it is natural knowledge it is not revelation, and if it is revelation it makes nature ecstatic and miraculous." [23] Hence, we can understand his attack upon such a term as "natural revelation" on the ground that it implies natural knowledge and natural theology. Indeed, the religious consciousness must not in any way be confused with natural theology. Its insights do not result from inference and rational processes. They are direct apprehensions. Tillich points out that

> natural knowledge about self and world cannot lead to the revelation of the ground of being. It can lead to the question of the ground of being, and that is what so-called natural theology can do and must do . . . It is the question of reason about its own ground and abyss.

[22] Ibid. p. 83.

[23] P. Tillich, *Systematic Theology,* Vol. I (Chicago: Chicago University Press, 1951), p. 119.

> It is asked by reason, but reason cannot answer it. Revelation can answer it.[24]

It would appear, in the light of the mounting criticism of all so-called proofs of divine existence ever since the time of Hume and Kant, that such rational theology can have little standing ground. All such speculative thought leaves us with questions which reason alone cannot answer.

Because his apprehension of the mysterious otherness that pervades the universe, its transcendent depth, is mediated to man through the creaturely order, he tends to identify his deity with the media of revelation. Hence, fixing his eyes upon the visible and ignoring the transcendent claim, he takes the ways of idolatry or pantheism, creating his own forms of religion. From such perversions of the original intuition, it is an easy step for modern man to pour scorn upon the perversions themselves and to deny that he has any such intimations as the latter have often effectively covered up.

It is within this setting of general intuitive awareness that the revelation testified to in the Hebrew-Christian tradition must be set. Here we have the final personal self-disclosure of God, the revelation which provides the norm by which all others must be measured and the distortions of man-made religions removed. Lest we here be accused of dogmatism, let us hasten to add that we shall indicate our reason for such an affirmation later. It will be noted that we have described this revelation as a *personal* self-disclosure. Indeed, we have suggested so far that even at the level of primal awareness the intuitive awareness is a response to a personal coming. Furthermore, there are those persons in all expressions of the religious consciousness who have made a personal response of trust and commitment to such a "personal disclosure."

We must emphasize what we mean by the latter term. It implies that the best analogy for understanding our growing apprehension of the divine presence is very much akin to our

[24] Ibid. pp. 119 f.

knowledge of persons. In my encounter with another person, I may treat him impersonally as an "It," evaluating him as an object in my immediate environment, analyzing his external behavior and his somatic structure scientifically, and ignoring his "I-ness." Such an impersonal approach characterizes much of our treatment of our fellows in business and professional circles. But suppose that, into a situation where such impersonal procedures have become normal, there comes one with whom at some time I have had a real personal understanding and friendship, but with whom I have lost contact. As I begin my customary impersonal approach, suddenly a disclosure occurs. I recognize the other and become aware of a personal depth in him or her which shatters the whole framework of my technique. A personal disclosure has taken place. A new dimension has opened up. Indeed, the situation is such that the utterance of a personal name becomes the most adequate response. An impersonal situation has become personal. Through the bodily behavior and appearance of the other, a disclosure has been mediated.

John Wisdom has suggested that the difference between the religious and the nonreligious man lies in their differing discernment of patterns in events. Empirically, both observe the same happening and yet the one sees in it a pattern which is not evident to the other, a providential ordering which the other rejects. Wisdom points out that "it is possible to have before one's eyes all the items of a pattern and still to miss the pattern."[25] Now part of the distinction, he argues, may be attributed to feeling and attitude, but he believes that there is a cognitive aspect. Theological discourse is concerned to fix our attention upon certain patterns in the facts and thus to disclose new facts.[26] To use a figure which he himself uses, we may

[25] J. Wisdom, "Gods," *Logic and Language*, First Series, ed. A. Flew (Oxford: Basil Blackwell, 1963), p. 191.

[26] Ibid. p. 197. He likens the religious pattern to the scientist's model, which presumably does add to our factual knowledge of nature.

suggest that whereas scientific and impersonal analysis is concerned with what is horizontally extensive, religion and revelatory disclosure are concerned with what is vertically extensive. Our concern here is not with Wisdom's further discussion of the nature of theological discourse but with his contribution to our own consideration of personal disclosure. All men have a dimension of depth insofar as there is an implicit metaphysic in all thought, including that of the naturalist. What happens for the religious man is that a new aspect of this dimension is opened up, a new pattern is discerned which gives a different vertical perspective to the horizontal.

The Gestalt psychologists have made us familiar with the way in which certain geometrical shapes may suddenly jell into an unexpected patterned wholeness. Further, such a pattern may be seen by some and not by others. We would agree with Polanyi's contention that such an approach must not be confined to the psychological and subjective but that the experience it describes may also be basic in our cognitive awareness and have objective relevance.[27] Ian Ramsey makes a similar point, and notes that the value of this particular example is that it enables theological apologetic "to make some sort of empirical appeal."[28]

We must hasten to add, at this point, that human personal disclosure is, as we have already suggested, a basic analogy for understanding the approach of the divine to man. As in the scientific realm, so here too, we are finding some model by which such revelatory encounters may be made intelligible. Our previous emphasis on "mystery" is a reminder that to speak of God as "personal" is not to use that word univocally. "Personal" is here an analogous description, and, like all analogies, we must not expect to find a one-to-one correspondence

[27] M. Polanyi, *Personal Knowledge* (Chicago: University of Chicago Press, 1958), pp. 55 ff.

[28] I. T. Ramsey, *Religious Language* (London: S.C.M. Press, 1957), p. 24.

at every aspect of the human personal. The divine perfection and transcendence take us beyond our models to the inner depths of mystery, and the Christian Church has sought to preserve this in its doctrine of the Trinity.

We may see, then, that divine personal self-disclosure involves a different discernment of depth, of a pattern in events. Such events are observed by others also but for us are presented as manifestations of a personal presence. In this way, nature, history, persons, and social groups may become media of revelation, ordered in disclosure situations.

This is evidenced, in particular, in the historical movement of the Old Testament. Here we find revelations through natural happenings and historical events conjoined to the interpretative insight of the prophetic consciousness. The centrality of prophetic personalities is significant at this point, for without them there would be no revelation. They were an integral part of such disclosure situations, whether the latter be the wind driving back the waters of the sea of reeds, the invasive forces of Assyria under Sennacherib, or the conquering might of the Persians under Cyrus. In each of the cases cited, we see a prophetic figure—Moses, Isaiah, Deutero-Isaiah respectively—who is an integral part of the revelation. The word of God through the prophet recreates the historical happening and transforms it into a disclosure situation for those who have ears to hear.

When we turn to the apostles and evangelists of the New Testament, the disclosure situation created by the life, death, and Resurrection of Jesus of Nazareth is one in which they act as inspired interpreters of the revelation. The insight into the true nature of Christ which is given to them has to be shared with others that they too may be brought to see the divine disclosure and respond.

In a very real sense, this is still one function of the Church in its continuing mission, for it too is a medium of revelation. In its testimony, its preaching, and its sacraments a disclosure situation is created in which the original disclosure of Jesus Christ becomes contemporary with every generation. In such a situation the Christian group as well as the preacher becomes constituent of it. What was originally disclosed to the apostles and the evangelists now confronts a new age through a group that is continually being recruited, for its individual initiates have themselves been brought into a similar situation. Kierkegaard [29] has made much of this contemporaneity of Christ, emphasizing that the original revelation in the Incarnation becomes contemporary because Christ is an eternal act as well as an event in time, so that he accompanies all time. Tillich [30] speaks of a dependent revelation in which what was originally revealed to one individual for his group is actually received for all mankind, so that it becomes a dependent revelation as new individuals and groups enter into correlation with it. The original disclosure is the permanent point of reference. We see here a parallel to scientific discovery where the original work is normative. In the case of our Lord, the original disclosure was given to Peter and the apostles, but there is a continuous dependent disclosure down the history of the Church, in which generations are successively brought into correlation with the original disclosure.

We can understand this only if we accept the immanent activity of the Spirit, who takes the things of Christ and makes them plain unto us. As Tillich rightly indicates: "The divine Spirit, illuminating believers individually and as a group, brings their cognitive reason into revelatory correlation with the event on which Christianity is based." [31] Indeed, the work of the Spirit in illuminating the minds of men and making them aware of "the Light which lightens all men" is the subjective aspect of every disclosure situation. Only so is he who

[29] E.g. Kierkegaard, *Training in Christianity,* trans. W. Lowrie (Princeton: Princeton University Press, 1952), p. 67.

[30] P. Tillich, op. cit. pp. 126 ff.

[31] Ibid. p. 127.

receives the disclosure able to penetrate the medium of revelation and grasp the hidden and self-revealing depth. His insight is a part of the revelation. It is disclosure because *he* sees what is hidden from others. This will be found later to be significant for our understanding of science itself.

We note that every such revelation has to be individual, for it involves cognitive spiritual insight and the response of personal commitment. Only as he who receives the disclosure is committed to the God who discloses himself does he too become a medium of disclosure, a part of the revelatory situation, to others. In this way prophets and saints, mystics and preachers, may each become media of a divine disclosure. Furthermore, among such must be included those outside the Hebrew-Christian tradition to whom a divine self-disclosure has been given. We cannot offhand dismiss Zoroaster and Mohammed, Buddha and the Hindu mystics, for they too may have been grasped by a divine disclosure and have gained some insight into the divine nature and plan. In this way men have been enabled to fill out the awareness of the original intuition which primal revelation makes possible.

We need to remember also that man in his sinful blindness tends to identify the media of disclosure with the One who discloses himself through them. The result is idolatry. The media possess no revelatory power in themselves, whether such media be processes of nature or personal beings. Their capacity to be media is given to them. They are creatively directed by God himself. It is he who controls the forces of nature, guides the processes of history, and directs the activity of personal beings so that these are brought into disclosure situations and transformed into media for his revelation. What is significant in any medium of revelation is the measure of its commitment to God. This, of course, applies to personal media. In the case of nature, there is a severe limitation as to the divine qualities which such a medium is capable of disclosing. But because of human freedom, the measure of the disclosure through persons must be seen in the degree of commitment. It is here that the weakness of frail humanity inhibits a full disclosure, a fact very evident in the prophetic consciousness in Old Testament times, as, for example, Jeremiah's revilings and bitterness of spirit and Amos' wilderness puritanism with its almost entire absence of any compassion.

A full disclosure and thus a final one is possible, as Tillich suggests,[32] only when the medium of revelation is totally and unreservedly committed to the living God. Since the personal disclosure of the divine is generally limited by the medium in and through which it appears, Tillich argues that

> the question of the final revelation is the question of a medium of revelation which overcomes its own finite conditions by sacrificing them, and itself with them. He who is the bearer of the final revelation must surrender his finitude—not only his life but also his finite power and knowledge and perfection. In doing so, he affirms that he is the bearer of final revelation . . . He becomes completely transparent to the mystery he reveals.[33]

It is not our concern here to discuss the evidence from the Gospel records which indicates such total commitment and surrender on the part of Jesus of Nazareth. Nor have we space to deal with the mystery of his person, which we have discussed at length elsewhere.[34] It will suffice to indicate our Lord's concern for the Father's will and purpose, a concern brought to a climax in Gethsemane, his utter selflessness and the openness of his love and compassion to all types and conditions of men, his refusal to claim any authority for himself or finality in his humanity in the face of every temptation.[35] He

[32] Ibid. pp. 132 ff.

[33] Ibid. p. 133.

[34] See Rust, *Towards a Theological Understanding of History,* loc. cit. pp. 174–189.

[35] Tillich's able analysis seems to indicate, at this point, an adoptionism, which we have been careful to avoid. Chalcedon must still be heeded!

rejected any attempt to make him King or to interpret his Messiahship in the traditional way. Instead he indicated that he would achieve his disclosure as Messiah through the sacrifice of the Cross. It was only in giving his earthly life in final surrender to the Father's will that he would return to his glory, fully disclose the divine depth in his person. When men had lifted up the Son of Man on the Cross, they would discover that they had lifted him up to his heavenly state, and so see the Godhead behind the humanity. He who, as the humiliated Son of Man, refused to snatch at equality with God and to make his human existence idolatrous was declared to be Son of God with power through the death of the Cross and the accompanying exaltation.[36] Jesus is the center of the Christian's worship and commitment, not as man, but as God. To use Tillich's characterisic phraseology: "Jesus is the religious and theological object as the Christ and only as the Christ. And he is the Christ as the one who sacrifices what is merely 'Jesus' in him." [37]

The mystery of our Lord's person defies all speculative theological metaphysic.[38] He who was the Word Incarnate, embracing in his personal being the finite and the infinite, was truly man. In so partaking of our humanity, we must affirm that his human surrender to the Father's will and his refusal to give in to any demonic pretension were freely chosen. His God-manhood was such that his full humanity was a reality, personally bound to his divine nature from conception and yet freely surrendered unto death. But he could surrender his humanity so fully only because there was a perfect bond of personal union between his manhood and his Godhead. He acts

[36] The New Testament passages here used can easily be identified Mark 8:29–33, 34–5; Luke 24:25–6; John 8:28, 12:32, 34; Phil. 2:5–11.

[37] Tillich, op. cit. p. 134.

[38] Dorner and the Kenotic theologians have probably given the best answer. See Rust, *Towards a Theological Understanding of History,* loc. cit. passage cited in note 34.

as he does because he is God in man. It was such a coming together of free human surrender and inseparable union of God and man in Jesus that makes possible his perfect divine disclosure. The negation of the creatureliness, the flesh, means that his personal disclosure becomes the norm for all divine disclosures. It is in the light of the Incarnation that all such must be judged. In Christ they are both abrogated and fulfilled.

III. *The cognitive aspect of disclosure— the meaning of religious language*

In our discussion so far, we have suggested that the insight of faith is intuitive and thus akin to perception. Its mediated immediacy involves a "seeing," and it is not always associated with the conceptualizing processes of the discursive reason. Indeed, we are not first of all concerned in the experience of faith with natural theology but with divine self-disclosure. Attempts by a rational theology to arrive at a demonstration of the divine existence by the so-called 'theistic proofs,' and at a conceptualized knowledge of the divine nature by analogies drawn from human experience and relationships may have a place within the insight of faith, but they do not bring us that insight.

The nature of the knowledge that faith offers and its relation to the knowledge arrived at by discursive reasoning and in particular to scientific knowledge have been issues since the time of Kant. Prior to his time religious faith had been supported and even replaced by a rationalistic theology which established what it regarded as the basic truths in Christian theology by rational demonstration. Little need was felt for revelation. Hume's radical skepticism, as we have seen, led Kant to dismiss from religious experience all rational demonstrations based on scientific data. The phenomenal world with which science dealt offered no basis for a rational theology. He took refuge in the practical reason, however, and grounded religion rationally in the moral consciousness. Thereby, he preserved human freedom and the belief in God over against the determinism of science. Science and its rationalistic processes provided no key to ultimate reality.

From Kant's time onwards, the closed nature of the universe as most scientists saw it left little room for religion. Men of faith had to retreat elsewhere. Religion could have no standing ground in science, and equally morality seemed to have no necessary connection with religion. The gaps in scientific knowledge could all be filled ultimately by scientific methods without dragging in alien religious concepts. Further, moral behavior could be grounded in sanctions which need no recourse to religious authority. Hence, we find Schleiermacher's retreat to feeling from science and morality. Religion has no relation to scientific reasoning or moral judgments. It is grounded in man's immediate self-consciousness. Thereby, he sought for religion an independent standing ground in what was to be a growing secularism.

So far, we have noted the significance of this approach because it attempts to describe the intuitive nature of faith as a felt insight. We have not, however, criticized the fatal dichotomy which is also involved. This dichotomy is also found in Otto, who likewise would make his *numinous* feeling an intuitive awareness which has no ground in the rational or the moral. We, too, would claim a unique place for man's knowledge of God and would accept its intuitive nature, but we would not want to introduce such a radical divorce from other areas of human experience. It is to be noted that Otto does attempt to rehabilitate the latter in religious experience by an incredible structure of a priori linkages in man's religious consciousness. We cannot accept Ritschl's neo-Kantian subjectivism with its suggestion that we project the figure of God upon the background of the universe to conserve our human values. Christ has the value of God for us, and the value is practical. Yet despite his subjectivism and his antimetaphysical bias, Ritschl did endeavor to make the area of the religious consciousness more embracing.

The problem that these men faced now looms larger than ever. In a world where science and morality can get along comfortably at the rational level without the support of religious faith, where does the latter fit in? The concern has now switched to the nature of religious language. The mystic may claim his insight to be totally subjective, ineffable and incommunicable. But the Church has claimed to share a common experience which is communicable in religious language. After all, if the intuitive insight evoked by the divine disclosure involves cognition, that cognition must be expressed in conceptualized form if it is to be communicated or made the object of reflective theological thinking. If we are to think and speak about God and his relation to men and the world in the light of the disclosure, we must objectify it and express it in the form of assertions. Hence, we have the theological statements and religious affirmations in which men of faith have sought to express the content of their intuitive response to the divine self-disclosure.

In so doing, they appear to be making factual statements about God, about the Christ, about the relation of God to his world, and to men, about the divine activity for the reconciliation of estranged humanity, and so on. But here the issue comes to a head. In an age of naturalism and scientific rationalism, knowledge is confined, as we have seen, for many people, to what can be scientifically demonstrated and validated. Facts—but can one ever talk of bare facts?—are confined to the realm of the empirically observable. At the linguistic level, a statement must be capable of experimental verification or falsification. But the language of religion deals with the inner side of man and his world. It is concerned with the invisible and the intangible. It claims to talk about the transcendent. Hence, for the strict logical positivist with his naturalistic base, it does not convey meaning but is nonsense. Yet let us note, as has often been pointed out, the absolute premise of this positivistic approach is the proposition that meaningful statements must be empirically verifiable or falsifiable and the proposition cannot itself be empirically tested! The "knowledge" of the logical positivist is a form of personal knowledge. The principle by which he proves everything else is itself unproved!

In the current period, however, critical philosophy has switched with the later Wittgenstein to linguistic analysis, and the linguistic philosophers are prepared to admit that language games other than that which is scientifically based may have meanings within their own sphere of discourse. This, however, does not let the man of religion out, for he still has to justify his statements and, in some way offer a scheme of validation acceptable to men who are scientifically oriented.

There are many in the left-wing interpretation of religious language who would cling to a subjectivist position somewhat in the tradition of Schleiermacher. Thus Hare [39] tells us that religious language expresses a certain total attitude towards life and experience which he describes as a "blik." He regards such bliks as prior to all rationality, pre-rational, and somewhat akin to what we have termed "absolute presuppositions." Facts are always relative to the attitude of the person who selects. It is bliks, which make facts possible, and facts cannot prove or disprove the absolute attitudes or bliks within which statements are made about them. Religious facts are important for the man of faith because his life is organized around them, but they mean nothing to the atheist. Now we have emphasized that absolute presuppositions have the quality of faith principles and are associated with some intuitive insight into and intellectual commitment to what is regarded as a key to experience. The difficulty about Hare's position is that there

[39] Hare, "Religion and Morals," *Faith and Logic*, ed. B. Mitchell (London, George Allen and Unwin, 1957).

is no suggestion of a disclosure to which the blik is a response. Still further, how are we to know which blik is the correct attitude, unless such a disclosure is involved? As Ferré [40] has suggested, Hare would seem to reduce religious language to the level of a worshipful attitude about the epistemological importance of bliks. Now the man of faith has his absolute presupposition. No one should dispute that! So has the atheist! The point needs to be made, however, that the blik of the Christian thinker is a response to a disclosure situation made possible by the historical revelation in Jesus of Nazareth. Hare's blik may seem to avoid the verification/falsification test, yet we still have to inquire as to the authority of the Christian's blik, if such authority there be. The Christian's blik is bound up with certain historical events which are seen from the standpoint of the blik and which, as revelatory situations, give rise to the blik.

Braithwaite, himself a professing Christian, has sought to evade the linguistic challenge by taking a way akin to that of Kant and taking refuge in the ethical aspects of the Christian position. Emphasizing moral behavior, he suggests that religious language basically is concerned to express the *agapeistic* way of life. Christianity is characterized by a certain characteristic behavior, describable as the way of love, agape, and illustrated by stories associated with the activity of Jesus Christ. Braithwaite argues that "the primary use of religious assertions is to announce allegiance to a set of moral principles." [41] He states also, however, that one does not have to believe in the historicity of the stories. So long as a man is committed to Christian moral principles, "he need not believe that the empirical propositions presented by the stories correspond to empirical fact." [42] This means that the theological content of

[40] F. Ferré, *Language, Logic and God* (New York, Harper and Bros., 1961), p. 131.

[41] R. B. Braithwaite, *An Empiricist's View of the Nature of Religious Belief* (Cambridge University Press, 1955), p. 17.

[42] Ibid. p. 23.

religious language is largely meaningless, and the reality of any personal disclosure of God is bypassed. Braithwaite would dismiss any Christ-myth theory as unplausible, but evidently the historicity of the Incarnation is of minor importance and at this point any theological assertion is not meaningful. The story of the Christ "may psychologically support the resolution (to act *agapeistically*), but it does not justify it." [43] But this, again, is to denude Christianity of its fundamental conviction that there is involved a divine personal self-disclosure, that the Christian action is associated with a Christian knowing, and that commitment issues in behavior but has its mainspring in an intuitive insight in which a man's emotive response is evoked.

We have already had occasion to cite John Wisdom's suggestion [44] that the religious man sees a certain pattern in events which the nonreligious man does not see. Once more we are at the position of subjective response. This we cannot evade, for all knowledge is "personal knowledge" and involves subjective commitment. Wisdom's position has the virtue of pinning theological assertion to the factual, but it evades the real issue of how such a pattern in events becomes evident. Once more we miss the emphasis on the "given," on revelation as a "coming" of God to which man's "seeing" is a response. Wisdom's famous parable of the invisible gardener illustrates the point. The presence of the invisible gardener who tends the ordered garden in the wilderness may not be empirically demonstrated, but the believing man still believes in that presence despite the failure of all tests. He "sees" what the other does not "see." But how is such "seeing" possible? Is it purely subjective or is it a response? If the latter, what lies beyond the subjective religious consciousness?

It is here that I. T. Ramsey [45] comes to the rescue with his

[43] Ibid. p. 27.

[44] John Wisdom, "God," *Logic and Language*, First Series (Oxford: Basil Blackwell, 1951), p. 191.

[45] I. T. Ramsey, *Religious Knowledge* (London: S.C.M. Press, 1957).

definition of disclosure situations, in which we become aware of a personal depth in the universe. We have already made use of this suggestive approach. We are now concerned with the way in which such a disclosure is expressed and the purpose of such language. Ramsey points to the fact that theological language is logically odd. It adds "qualifiers" to words and thereby gives them an odd and startling sense, going beyond their normal meaning. The words are originally taken from intramundane and especially human experience, and Ramsey gives them the name "model." Thus goodness, wisdom, cause, creation are all in this sense "models." But the qualifying adjectives added to them in religious statements are logically inappropriate to their normal reference. We have already seen that attempts to express our knowledge of persons involve us sometimes in paradoxical statements. We should not therefore be surprised if something of this order arises in any attempt to express an insight into the personal depth of the universe, the utter uniqueness of the ground of being. Ramsey points to expressions such as "infinitely good," "eternal purpose," "creation *ex nihilo*," in which the normal human reference of the words "good," "purpose," "creation" is transformed by logically odd "qualifiers."[46] Again, in the creedal statements, in phrases such as "the eternal Son of God, eternally begotten, begotten not made," "qualifiers" have been added to lift language out of the normal level of meaning of the word "son."[47]

Ramsey suggests that the oddness of the language is an attempt to point people to the same personal depth which the speaker has perceived. The startling and logically odd nature of theological statements should serve to awaken people so that for them too "the penny drops" and they see. The qualifier serves to develop the model in a direction whereby the situation "comes alive" and a religious response is evoked. He has much to teach us at this point, yet we still have to ask whether

[46] Ibid. pp. 49 ff.
[47] Ibid. pp. 156 ff.

theological language expresses something more than pointing and, if so, what the authority of such meaning is. Ramsey is himself very careful to counter any accusation of being totally subjective. The disclosure situations have for him an objective aspect. They come alive because there is an objective "depth." The real issue is how this view is to be defended and validated. The issue of authority is central here, as in thinkers discussed previously.

At this point Ian Crombie[48] carries us a little further. Where Ramsey talks of models and qualifiers, Crombie talks of parables, but he goes beyond Ramsey in seeking for some authority and more basic cognitive content in the parables. Parables retain the ordinary meanings of words but set them within a framework which enables us to understand their theological meaning. They supply us with analogies between ordinary statements and theological statements, and so portray the meaning of the latter. Accordingly, all theological statements are parables, and yet not just parables, since they do refer to our concept of God which is beyond the parable. Crombie can write:

> The point of a parable is that you do not suppose that there is any literal resemblance between the truth which is expressed and the story which expresses it, but you do suppose that if you accept the story, not as a true literal account, but as a faithful parable, you will not be misled as to the underlying reality.[49]

Like Ramsey, Crombie points to the logical oddness of theological assertions, which claim to state fact and yet are both like and unlike normal assertions. Thus, when we say that "God loves us," we seem to be saying something like "Tom loves men," yet it is possible logically to identify Tom. We can

[48] Ian Crombie, "The Possibility of Theological Statements," *Faith and Logic,* ed. Basil Mitchell (Boston: The Beacon Press, 1957), pp. 35 ff.

[49] Ibid. pp. 70 f.

introduce someone to Tom, but we cannot follow the same procedure with regard to God. God is not a proper name in the sense that Tom is. It is an improper proper name.[50] Again, when we state that "God created the world," we seem to assert something similar to "John made a model boat," yet we add "out of nothing" and so introduce an unusual sense. Furthermore, such statements cannot be verified or falsified by any specific empirical observations. The naturalistic empiricist argues that no situations can arise which would seem to be incompatible with such assertions and therefore that they have no meaning. The statement "God loves us" is irrefutable for the theist.[51]

Thus, the statements are not made about any object which falls within normal experience, and Crombie agrees that they are about God as "spirit." Crombie agrees that the "concept of God" is not a concept in the sense of a clearly defined idea. We must accept limitations for its reference range. It does not refer to finite things or empirical events. It is relevant, however, to moral, historical, and cosmological situations. Yet, although it is not an idea in the sense of having an observable reference, Crombie believes that "it is extravagant to say that we have no notion whatsoever of how the word is used." [52] It may be and is a category mistake to speak of God as "spirit," in no abstract sense but concretely, like the noun "man," yet this "mistake" is deliberately committed "to express what we antecedently feel." [53]

The "mystery" is made to some degree intelligible by the parables. When the concept "love" is introduced, it is implied that human love and human making have "some kind of appropriateness," [54] when used theologically. Furthermore,

[50] Ibid. pp. 39 ff.
[51] Ibid. pp. 43 ff.
[52] Ibid. p. 60.
[53] Ibid. p. 61.
[54] Ibid. p. 51.

these parables have behind them the authority of what Ramsey has called a "disclosure situation." The Christian's authority for our assertions is Christ Himself. He feels impelled to accept Christ as divine. He finds in Christ convincing evidence of God's concern for him and "also what sort of love the divine love is."[55] Christ is the image or declaration of God to him and because of this he knows what to say about God. Christ is "the visible, tangible, intelligible image of what stands outside our comprehension."[56] Since he is a declaratory image, the doctrinal statements in which we communicate the image, while inadequate to the "mystery" because in human language, will yet command our trust. In this way, we feel impelled to accept the images of the historic disclosures to Israel and the Church, centering in Christ, as authoritative for us.

As for verification or falsification, Crombie claims that such does arise post-mortem. There is an eschatological hope, so that the empirical test applies in principle if not in practice. Here, we are back to Pascal's definition of God's existence as a wager. John Hick takes the same position. He believes that the variant forms of Christian hope, expressed in the themes of the Beatific Vision and the Kingdom of God respectively, offer a vindication of "the *meaningfulness* of the theistic assertion."[57] Thereby, we are able to envisage an experience which would verify or falsify theological statements so that they are factually meaningful.

The position thus arrived at is partly supported by Austin Farrer. He contends that the cognitive aspect of man's apprehension of God in Christ and in the accompanying historical disclosures to Old Israel takes the form of images. Theological propositions are the effort of the Church to express what is re-

[55] I. Crombie, "Theology and Falsification," *New Essays in Philosophical Theology*, ed. Flew and McIntyre (London: S.C.M. Press, 1955), p. 129.

[56] I. Crombie in *Faith and Logic*, p. 68.

[57] John Hick, *Faith and Knowledge* (Ithaca: Cornell University Press, 1957), pp. 156–63.

vealed in these images. "Theology," he writes, "is the analysis and criticism of the revealed images: but before you turn critic or analyst, you need a matter of images to practice upon." [58] He believes that religious thought belongs to the imaginative level and not the conceptual, so that God gives the images directly to the religious consciousness. In poetry, man's creative imagination moves freely, but in revelation that creative activity is guided by the divine presence. He agrees that not all the images in the Biblical testimony are of equal significance, although the Biblical witnesses thought in vital images, not concepts. Those images are central which are focalized in the life, thought, and activity of the Christ, and it is these images which Christian theology is concerned to explicate in its assertions. By such "images," he means in part what we have already variously referred to as analogies, models, or parables, although Ramsey's use of model would have a wider connotation.

Actually, it is difficult to separate concepts and images so radically. Even our Biblical testimony has propositional statements as well as images. Furthermore, it is difficult to disentangle one from the other. Many of the images show conceptual aspects. Again, if God is giving himself in personal disclosure, such an assertion is not the same as saying that he gives only images. The truth would seem to be that in giving himself to us God gives images in which he and his purpose may be pictured. But he does give himself!

Thus, Farrer holds that "nothing but the image is given to us to act as an indication of the reality. We cannot appeal from the images to the reality, for by hypothesis we have not got the reality, except in the form which the images signify." [59] But surely revelation is not so mechanical. If we do have personal disclosure evoking human response and commitment, we can

[58] A. M. Farrer, *The Glass of Vision* (London: The Dacre Press, 1948), p. 44.

[59] Ibid. p. 58.

envisage the relationship much more in the coming and going of Jacob's ladder. Communion with God means a presence of his Spirit within which we can think of his love guiding the imagination and thought processes of the witnesses within their own human experience, rather than mechanically injecting figures of speech or images into their minds. The authority of the images or parables because of their relationship to the person, acts, and teachings of Christ still remains.

Tillich carries us beyond the realms of linguistic analysis. He raises the question as to whether there can be any apprehension of God which is not symbolic. In so doing, he adds yet another word "symbol" to the array of terms already employed. He is not always careful to differentiate between symbol as an actual existent entity and symbolic language. He distinguishes a symbol from a sign by defining the latter as merely pointing and the former as participating in what it represents. His peculiar contention is that no nonsymbolic statement can be made about God except that God is "being-itself," and he defines as non-symbolic a statement which "means what it says directly and properly." [60] Every other statement about God is symbolic and points beyond itself. Yet the symbol employed in such a statement does participate in God, since all being participate in being itself. Hence, such symbolic statements have appropriateness. The descriptions of God as personal, as loving, as living, are symbolic. They are taken from structures of being at the human level of finite being, and they are appropriate because finite being participates in being-itself. But being-itself is not *a* being. God, as the ground and power of being, transcends all categories and symbols even as he includes them. He is beyond all the differentiations that exist between finite beings. Hence, such symbolic statements must not be interpreted nonsymbolically.

It is evident that when he speaks of a symbolic statement Tillich is close to the idea of analogy. In Thomism, however,

[60] P. Tillich, op. cit. p. 238.

where the *analogia entis* represents a rational movement from some human perfection to God, there is always the structure of revealed theology to provide the coping stone of the natural theology in which the *analogia entis* is employed. Even at the human level we need to have some direct knowledge of what is symbolized, if the appropriateness and meaning of the symbol is to be grasped. But Tillich does not believe in God as a personal, immaterial being who really enters into relationship with human beings. Instead, he thinks of unconditioned being, being-itself, and this is so abstract that any structure of finite being might be an appropriate symbol. As Alston suggests:

> Since we can say nothing non-symbolically about being-itself, a given symbol cannot be judged in terms of the reality or unreality of that aspect of being-itself which it is being used to symbolize. We are unable to specify any such aspect . . . And that means that the affirmations of religious faith are not subject to criticism in terms of the canons applied by science and common sense to statements of fact.[61]

Even the symbols of Scripture associated with the Christ provide no way to direct apprehension. All that Tillich can offer is their self-authentication as making the "new being" possible, as having the power to move lives. There is no way beyond the symbols. All statements about God that involve personal language are symbolic.

Tillich tries to safeguard himself at three points. First, he regards human reason as unable to find its way to God. There is no natural theology or natural religion. Thus, in some sense, the symbols are revelation. Secondly, there is his contention that symbols participate in that which they represent and thus are appropriate to convey something about "being-itself." Yet it remains an open issue how far we may differentiate between

[61] W. P. Alston, "Tillich's Conception of a Religious Symbol," *Religious Experience and Truth*, ed. Sidney Hook (Edinburgh: Oliver and Boyd, 1962), p. 18.

symbols and determine their appropriateness if there is no direct disclosure into which they fit and which they enable us to understand. Here we come to the third point, already mentioned, that the symbols associated with the Biblical testimony to the Christ are self-authenticating in their power to transform personal beings. Yet, finally, we are not left with the Christian understanding of God but with the absolute of rationalism, dressed up more attractively.

If Farrer's conception of God giving us figures of speech is not totally acceptable, Tillich's position is far less so. We have been contending that theological language is concerned with a disclosure of the personal depth in the universe and have suggested that there is in all men some vague intuitive apprehension of a "presence." Otto's analysis of the religious consciousness would find here, basic in all religions, an apprehension of a mystery which both allures and evokes terror. His divorce of the sense of the numinous from moral and rational content has already been criticized. At primitive levels, as H. H. Farmer points out,[62] there is some awareness of the mysterious presence as both claim and succor, as "absolute claim and final succor." In this sense, even at the most rudimentary level, man feels the personal depth. The Christian revelation thus builds upon the general background of the religious consciousness. Here, too, the divine self-disclosure is personal, as any honest examination of Christian devotion makes plain.

The apprehension of God as personal will and love is the way God gives himself to be known. Personal being is the highest form of being which we apprehend in intramundane experience, and he comes to us in this way that is molded to our apprehension. Thus we may say that to understand God as personal involves us in a model or construct drawn from the created order, yet this model is one which is given to us in the

[62] H. H. Farmer, *The World and God* (London: Nisbet and Co., Ltd., 1955), pp. 23 ff.

divine disclosure. We cannot speculate upon what God is in his innermost being, but we can say that he comes to us as personal. He is at least this in his perfection.

Nor may we confuse with the speculation of natural theology this personal model given with the disclosure. We do not arrive at our understanding of God by an approach such as the *analogia entis,* in which we arrive at the idea of divine perfection by arranging human experiences in graded scales of excellence and so extend them indefinitely towards deity. John Baillie reminds us that "such an arrangement could not have been made by us save by the aid of a standard of perfection already present to our minds." [63] Such approaches are possible because of prior divine disclosure. The prior presence in the mind of the idea of the infinite and the perfect makes such thought possible. We have suggested already that some apprehension of God comes with man's own self-awareness. My awareness of my own personal being comes with the awareness of the Other as personal perfection, however rudimentary such apprehension may be. Natural theology is a misnomer, for if we begin with intramundane experience, we cannot move beyond it to the transcendent. We finish where we begin. This is why the so-called "theistic arguments" cannot reach deity even though they may point in that direction. Baillie quotes Kemp Smith as saying, "We cannot reach the Divine merely by way of inference, not even if the inference be analogical in character. By no idealization of the creaturely can we transcend the creaturely." [64] We may, however, use personal models and analogies to describe the divine self-disclosure, and we may do so because this is the way that God comes to us.

When we come to the focal point of Christian disclosure and know what we mean by communion in Christ, it is a denial of

[63] J. Baillie, *The Sense of the Presence of God* (New York: Charles Scribner's Sons, 1962), p. 116.

[64] Ibid. p. 117. Quotation from N. Kemp Smith, *Is Divine Existence Credible?* (1921), p. 14.

the reality of that communion to hold that we represent God to ourselves as personal and thus commune with him as a personal being. We could agree with John Baillie that "our fundamental knowledge of God is such as cannot have been reached by way of analogy from our knowledge of His creatures, but by a mode of apprehension which is no less direct in its own way than that by which His creatures are known." [65] Our criticism of his position arises in his almost Barthian dismissal of any analogical images within the direct fundamental apprehension of God as personal love.

In holding that God discloses himself to us as personal, we are not forgetting that there is a mystery and a transcendent otherness about God. His thoughts are higher than our thoughts and his ways are past finding out, yet he enters into personal relationship with us. He becomes for us the "Thou" who addresses our "I." He manifests himself as will and love. That in his transcendent otherness he passes beyond our comprehension, no truly religious man would deny. We know him only as he relates himself to us. What he is in himself we cannot say, except that he is consistent in himself with his personal disclosure to us as living and active love.

We have affirmed that the divine self-disclosure is brought to a focus in Christ. Here is the final revelation, the one which is ultimately valid and authoritative for the man of faith. And here God meets us as personal demand and grace. We can therefore agree with Gollwitzer that "Christian faith cannot regard as true any talk of God that would seek in the name of God's divinity to forbid the concrete personal relationship." [66] To talk of the suprapersonal is to pass beyond our comprehension or to lapse back into impersonal talk, and in either case we move away from the divine self-disclosure. At least in our

[65] Ibid. p. 122.

[66] H. Gollwitzer, *The Existence of God as Confessed by Faith,* trans. J. W. Leitch (Philadelphia: The Westminster Press, 1965), p. 188.

Christian assertions about God, we cannot pass beyond the personal way of speaking. Again, to quote Gollwitzer:

> The I-Thou relationship between men provides the conceptual structures for Christian talk of God because he in his condescension addresses man as *man*, because he *addresses* him as man, and because in so doing he takes man up into *communion* with himself, and thus makes himself Thou for man and man Thou for him.[67]

Now it is within the divine disclosure and human response that the central images, symbols, analogues of our faith come into being. The disclosure events in which prophets, evangelists, and apostles were made aware of the divine presence as judgment and grace, demand and succor, must be thought of in terms of Jacob's ladder, with the angels ascending and descending upon it. The self-disclosure of God which came to them and their own personal commitment brought to them a personal knowledge of God in which such images moved within their consciousness. We cannot say that the images were fed into their consciousness, as Farrer seems to, or on the other hand, that these men consciously sought for such analogues. Rather their own experience of personal relationships was caught up into their involvement with the divine personal disclosure. The latter irradiated the whole, giving them a deeper understanding of fatherhood and sonship, the marriage relationship and human discipline, as it drew the imagery up into itself. It was in the active involvement of God and man in the Hebrew religious consciousness, drawn to a focus in the Incarnation, that the symbols of Father and Judge, Son and Servant, reconciliation and justification, redemption and estrangement, creation and providential care took their shape.

Such personal involvement brings private knowledge. Even

[67] Ibid. p. 186.

though the knowledge is empirically based in nature and the personal structure of society, there is an apprehension of a personal depth to which the spiritual insight must be awakened. Without such insight, the language of religious faith is meaningless. The naturalistic critic, who is bound to the nonsymbolic meanings of the religious images, will find the statements containing them meaningless. For the society of faith—those who share in common the awareness of the divine self-disclosure—they are, however, meaningful. It is within such a community of faith that our Biblical testimony took shape, and it is within that continuing community that theological language and statements have been molded ever since. Within the worship of the Church, its prayers and its witness, its communion with God and its sharing and its disclosure, Biblical and doctrinal language takes its rise. The truth of such language can be evident only to those who are within this fellowship of believing people and who are personally involved in the divine self-disclosure of which the language speaks.

Religious language expresses personal knowledge, but then, as we have seen, so does the language of science. It is meaningful only within the believing and worshiping community, but then science too has a community of faith, and within that framework many of its concepts alone have meaning. The difference lies in the fact of the private and inward nature of religious experience as contrasted with the empirical and public approach of scientific knowledge. Dependent as it is on a divine disclosure, bound up as it is with what transcends the empirical, it can employ images and concepts molded to the intramundane order only by making them analogical. The result is that the language of religion is logically odd and must not be taken literally. It points beyond the visible to the invisible, beyond the observable to the transcendent. Its authority lies in Christ Himself as the final, the eschatological, self-disclosure of God.

We are left, however, with the issue of verification. There is the post-mortem verification contained in the Christian hope, but we may also ask whether there is not something more direct. At this point we need to note two aspects of religious language itself. In the first place, it serves a testimony function, and here we are indebted to the discussion of I. T. Ramsey. By its very address, its analogical nature, religious language points beyond the intramundane structures from which it is derived to the personal and transcendent depth in the universe. The danger in speaking of it in this way is that we should forget its origination in the disclosure situations that are brought to a focus in the Incarnation. It is true that it points, but that it does this until "the penny drops" is due to the immanent activity of God within and under its human utterance. So the Christian community speaks of the presence of the Holy Spirit.

Once again, we face the situation portrayed in the picture of Jacob's ladder. Our religious and theological thinking is human thinking about God and Christ, but it is within the existential situation created by the divine self-disclosure. Our analogues are "analogues of faith." The very oddness of the language results from the coming together of the divine presence and the human imaginative response. Likewise, its power to evoke insight lies in the presence of God as well as the activity of man. We cannot nicely differentiate the one from the other here more than elsewhere, and the danger is that we should so concentrate on one that the other is forgotten. One has the feeling that Ramsey overemphasizes the human side, whereas Barth overstresses the divine aspect.

IV. *Theological language and the language of science*

The other function of religious language brings it into close relation with metaphysical language. Ian Crombie indicates this when he writes that "the more we try to understand the world in the light of this image, the better our understanding of the world becomes."[68] He is speaking of the image of "creation," but what he says applies to a whole range of significant Christian images centering in the Incarnation. Within science itself, the idea of complementarity has lifted its head. Bohr and Born emphasize the principle of complementarity involved in the Indeterminacy Principle. We can describe the experimental situation of atomic particles "either in terms of accurate positions or in terms of accurate momenta, but not both at the same time. The two descriptions are complementary for a complete intuitive understanding."[69] Bohr has extended the principle more widely and suggested that theologians should also make use of it. He would suggest that religious and scientific languages present complementary views of our world. When we concentrate on the analytical approach expressed in the latter, the holistic approach and concern with transcendence expressed in the former is pushed to the periphery. But both are needed, if we would understand our world.

Hence, we find Crombie suggesting that the conception of the divine "is the notion of a complement which could fill in certain deficiencies in our experience, that could not be filled in by further experience or scientific theory-making; and its positive content is simply the idea of something (we know not what) which might supply these deficiencies."[70] He does, of course, later fill in the conception in the light of the disclosure in Christ and its associated "parables." His statement at least indicates a very significant function of theological language, provided it be not taken as implying a "God of the gaps," an approach we have sedulously condemned. The language of science and the language of theology must not be mixed, and

[68] Ian Crombie, in *Faith and Logic*, p. 81.

[69] M. Born, *Natural Philosophy of Cause and Chance* (Oxford: Clarendon Press, 1949), p. 105.

[70] I. Crombie, in *Faith and Logic*, p. 56.

theological concepts must not be used to offer a substitute for a scientific explanation which is potentially possible.

It is questionable, however, whether "complementary" is a sufficient description of the relation of two languages. By our own discussion, science has been shown to be selective and to follow a process of abstracting from reality what is susceptible to its own peculiar approach. On the other hand, religious language claims to talk about the personal depth beneath the natural order and thereby to speak about nature in a more fundamental way. The two languages, then, are not on the same level. Theological language can embrace scientific language and interpret it. But the reverse is not the case, since science deals only with empirical "observables." Theological language describes a total view of reality, whereas scientific language describes only a partial view. In theology the universe is understood in personal terms, but science abstracts from the personal and concerns itself with the impersonal.

Now it is a property of metaphysical language that it deals with the metempirical and strives to bring logical coherence into the world of experience. Like the language of religion and theology, it has its own special sphere of discourse and its own logical structure. Like theological language, it uses words belonging to the intramundane experience of persons and of nature and applies them analogically. Indeed, Dorothy Emmet [71] reminds us that it chooses a basic analogy from that experience and makes it the key by which it seeks to bring rational coherence to the whole. In this connection it is grounded in faith, in the philosopher's intuitive insight, which brings him a conviction about the meaning of the whole.

For the strict logical positivist metaphysical statements are meaningless, because they are not empirically verifiable and have a metempirical reference. Yet, within their own sphere of discourse, they are verifiable by their inner logical consistency

[71] D. Emmet, *The Nature of Metaphysical Thinking* (London: Macmillan & Co., Ltd., 1945), pp. 5 ff.

and by whether or not they make our experience as a whole intelligible. The basic analogy must throw light on experience as a whole. For philosophical intelligibility, as Urban points out, coherence means "not merely absence of logical contradiction; not merely necessary connections in the sense of science; but that more fundamental coherence which arises out of the demand to round out our experience and to make it meaningful as a whole." [72] This implies an adequacy of the central analogy to deal with more experience than any other live alternative and to do so without distortion. Here, of course, is where every system sooner or later fails.

In a very real sense theological language is evidently closely akin to metaphyscial. It, too, endeavors to illuminate the whole of experience and to make it intelligible in the light of the divine disclosure which it is concerned to describe. It, too, is analogical. And, finally, it would be true to say that its verification would to some degree be afforded by its adequacy to illuminate and make intelligible the whole of experience, including that which is described in the language of science. In doing so adequately, however, it must not distort or "explain away" any aspect of experience.[73] Such a full verification will never be possible, since we finite beings can never see the world *sub specie aeternitatis.*

The linguistic analyst, who demands an empirical test, can argue that Christian theology does not meet all the facts fairly. For instance, there is the contention of Antony Flew that evil in human experience never seems to falsify the Christian assertion that "God is love" and that such theological statements may often be killed by a thousand qualifications.[74] John

[72] W. M. Urban, *Language and Reality* (London: George Allen and Unwin, 1951), p. 674. The reader should consult this book for a more detailed treatment.

[73] Cf. F. Ferré, op. cit. pp. 159 ff. This is a valuable contribution.

[74] A. Flew, "Theology and Falsification," *New Essays in Philosophical Theology*, pp. 96–9.

Baillie, therefore, agrees with Kant's injunction "against employing for the extension of our theoretic or speculative knowledge the conceptions of super-sensible reality which we are led by faith to entertain."[75] Hence, he warns against making the conceptions of faith "the foundations of a metaphysical scheme"—a highly questionable warning! Yet in his own lecture before the British Association for the Advancement of Science,[76] he shows a concern that science and religion should walk together in agreement and that there should be mutual illumination. This, at the best, is what faith can offer. It can show its understanding of the supernatural not to be in conflict with the view of the natural which science offers, but rather to be capable of illuminating it from a depth which science by its methods cannot probe. Insofar as it does this for science and all other ranges of experience more adequately than metaphysical systems, like naturalism, with their rival analogical structures, we may say that it offers some degree of verification.

In this task of illumination there are certain areas where the images or analogues of religious language have to reckon with the concepts and models that science offers. Sometimes the man of faith must submit to the discipline of scientific knowledge, but equally the man of science should bow reverently before the mysterious depths which are disclosed to faith. The images of the creation and consummation of the universe are concerned with the areas where science speaks of the processes of origination and dissolution. The providential concern of God with his creatures and its attendant ideas of his sustaining activity and purposive guidance of the process of nature and of the social structures have something to say in the sphere where the causal structures of the physical sciences and the evolutionary models of the biological sciences are also operative.

[75] J. Baillie, *The Sense of the Presence of God*, p. 161.

[76] J. Baillie, *Natural Science and the Spiritual Life* (New York: Charles Scribner's Sons, 1952).

When the religious man speaks of miracle, the scientific man is concerned with the regularity and continuity of the natural process. When the man of faith talks about purpose, the evolutionary biologist qua scientist speaks of random mutations and natural selection. The issue is joined at the level of man himself. Science qua science with its reductionist methods operates in the same psychosomatic realm as the theologian who speaks of the "image of God" and man's freedom.

The scientist by his method has no place in his approach for the matters with which the theologian is primarily concerned. Often he seems to say things that clash with theology, although, as we stated earlier, this is fortunately generally an illusory clash. Do the assertions of theology illuminate in any way the scientist's structures by setting them without distortion in a larger framework? Are such assertions *in this way* supplementary to the scientist's concerns?

Before facing these issues, we must briefly survey some aspects of the Christian faith which are specifically related to the natural order. As we have suggested, the divine self-disclosure in Jesus Christ brings into a coherent pattern the images and analogues of the Hebrew testimony. Images—the Son of Man, the Suffering Servant, the Messiah, the Son of God, the Word of God, the Spirit of God, the Fatherhood of God, the People of God, the Kingdom of God, the righteousness of God, the love of God, the Covenant, redemption, reconciliation, justification, the image of God, salvation, rebellion (sin), creation, miracle or wonder—take on a new content. The old apologetics based itself on the fulfillment of prophecy in Christ, and in so doing it misunderstood the nature of prophecy. Yet it remains true that our Lord gathers into his Person and his teaching selected images shaped in the prophetic consciousness in the give and take of the historical divine disclosures in which the prophets were involved. Some of the analogues are concerned with the understanding of God and of the Incarnation; others are concerned with the inner nature of man; yet others are concerned with the relationship of God to man and to the world. We can see in the Biblical testimony itself, especially in the witness of the early Church as this is adumbrated in the thought of the apostles and evangelists, attempts to draw out the analogical significance of the images. What Ramsey terms qualifiers are associated with the models, and the otherness or holiness of God is emphasized by various images, notably spatial and personal ones.

Within the life of the Church, as theology has sought to make the analogues of the primary disclosure intelligible to its own day and as it has sought to relate the primary historical event of the Incarnation to the contemporary world, other and new models have been sought. Hence, there are attempts to find analogues by which the coming of God in man, the Incarnation in Jesus Christ, can be made meaningful; or by which the various aspects of the divine disclosure, expressed in the images of Creator/Father, Redeemer/Son, Sanctifier/Spirit, may yet point to one personal depth in the universe; or by which the reconciling love of God operates in the Incarnation and Crucifixion to make atonement possible and remove man's estrangement. At their best such analogues have always been taken from the realm of intrapersonal relationships, for the nature of the divine disclosure as personal is basic to Christian language and central in the original witness.

The issue of the divine transcendence is crucial in our day, especially because the spatial imagery, which has so often been used to make it intelligible, is less meaningful in this age of science. Indeed, Karl Heim has devoted a whole volume to the discussion of intramundane forms of transcendence[77] in which he concludes that none of them offers a basis for an understanding of the divine transcendence. He quotes the bitter jest of Strauss that "The housing-problem has now arisen in the case of God," and reminds us that "the very idea of a

[77] K. Heim, *God Transcendent,* trans. E. P. Dickie (London: Nisbet & Co., Ltd., 1935).

world beyond has become problematical." [78] Hence he discusses the mutual transcendence of spaces in our intramundane experience, using "space" in more than its strictly literal connotation. It is sufficient here to note that he discusses at some length the personal nature of all knowledge, and notes that "my world" and "your world" in which we each objectify our experience are mutually transcendent. Here we have two infinities meeting, and their transcendence cannot be described in terms of the transcendence of one bounded space to another in our experience of three-dimensional space. Their meeting is a boundary of dimension and not one of content. He shows that the same holds for the mutual transcendence of two persons, an "I" and a "thou," and also for the way in which the "I," the knowing subject, transcends "my objective world" in which the "I" also includes himself objectively and yet never really grasps himself. Thus, objectively and subjectively, we can find examples of transcendence within intramundane experience, notably in the mutual transcendence of persons and in personal self-transcendence. Yet Heim argues that the transcendence of God cannot be of such an order but is *sui generis*. It cannot be grasped in any analogues drawn from intramundane experience, but is known only as by the existential decision of faith we enter into God's own space.

The implication is that God has his own unique dimensional relationship to his world and that one analogue available is the somewhat barren one of dimension. It is barren because we cannot understand it even analogically in the light of any of our intramundane dimensions of relationship. The result is akin to the position of Barth. All man has to do is wait for God to speak and disclose himself. Heim rightly attacks the *analogia entis* and all natural theology. But he also shows little sympathy with any suggestion that analogues shaped within the give and take of the divine disclosure and the human response may yet afford some point of intelligible conversation with a

[78] Ibid. p. 31.

scientific and secular world. The dimensional analogue is not without value, however. We have used it in the suggestion of personal depth, and it is a useful figure in describing interpersonal relationships. Heim's monumental work is a masterly attempt to find some analogue within the scientific discipline that may offer a point of contact.

Heim's method dismisses, however, two possible analogues for transcendence which arise at the personal level—interpersonal relationships and personal self-transcendence. We have already suggested that these may offer the key to illuminating the approach of God to man, the more so because God does come to us as a personal "Thou" to our "I." For our day such analogues have more meaning than spatial ones. They have their roots in the images and analogues of the Biblical testimony with its emphasis on word, mystery, marriage and father-son relationships, and the like, and the analogues have always found a place in the Church's theologizing. They are more relevant in our time, because, as John Macmurray reminds us, physical and organic analogues are breaking down in many extratheological realms of thought, and the personal is becoming significant. Hence, they provide a point of contact with an age which, despite its secularism, is also preoccupied with existentialist thinking.

In a valuable survey, Gordon Kaufman[79] stresses two personal models for transcendence—the interpersonal and the teleological. The former we have already stressed with its emphasis on personal mystery and disclosure, living trust and sympathetic imagination. The latter analogue is concerned with the pursuance by the self of formulated goals and ideals which transcend its immediate state of experience. He rightly points out that this latter analogue underlies much theological

[79] Gordon D. Kaufman, "Two Models of Transcendence: An Inquiry into the Problem of Theological Meaning," *The Heritage of Christian Thought,* ed. R. E. Cushman and E. Grisis (New York: Harper & Row, 1965), pp. 182–96. An illuminating discussion.

thinking and supports natural theology and the *analogia entis.* It is indeed the model behind Aristotelianism and Thomism, with their graded hierarchy of beings and their conception of the Unmoved Mover or First Cause. It tends to an abstract thought of God as the transcendent ground of being, and it tends to emphasize man's reflective processes rather than the divine disclosure. "The goal of the self's striving, whether material or ideal," he writes, "is always in some sense *posited* by the self as *his* goal." [80] He finds the interpersonal image more consistent with the central Christian testimony and more theologically illuminating. This we have ourselves sought to show. As Kaufman says: ". . . the analogy of interpersonal transcendence can find no real place for a natural theology in the usual sense; no referent for the word 'God' could possibly be located apart from his revelation." [81]

In understanding transcendence by the interpersonal and self-transcendence analogues, qualifiers with accompanying distortion of the intramundane originals are, of course, inevitable. We must deal with this more fully in the last chapter. The psychosomatic structure of human personhood and the part played by the body as a medium of communication could, without such qualifying distortion, lead to a panentheistic or even a pantheistic interpretation of the world as God's body. The same issue could arise if we overpress some human aspects of self-transcendence with the accompanying immanence of "I" in the psychosomatic wholeness and extrabodily instruments. Kaufman points to these difficulties and inquires whether, in developing the interpersonal analogue, we may "disregard the physical dimensions of interpersonal intercourse—dimensions which appear to be indispensable on the finite level." [82] This issue must be faced later.

In personal transcendence, there is also immanence, for the

[80] Ibid. p. 191.
[81] Ibid. p. 194.
[82] Ibid. p. 195.

personal mystery and beyondness is yet immanent in every aspect of bodily activity and in those modifications of the natural order which also become instruments of that activity. This is brought to a focus in the Incarnation in which the transcendent personal mystery of the universe becomes present in the midst of his world in redemptive activity. In the Incarnation, he gathers nature and humanity into his own life, removing the estrangement and redirecting the whole cosmos.

It is from such redemptive presence that we gain insight into his Creatorhood. He who redeems his world can alone have created that world, he who redeems it can alone sustain it, and he who redeems it will ultimately consummate his work that he may be all in all.

This is the typical testimony of the Biblical writings. The cosmological and creative significance of the Incarnate Word is set within the framework of his redemptive self-disclosure (John 1:1–14; Col. 1:15–17). In the Old Testament the redemptive activity of God in Israel is described in images borrowed from his creative activity. Especially in Deutro-Isaiah, the prophet of the Exile (Isa. 40–55), we find the thought of God the creator linked to that of Yahweh the Redeemer. God's creatorhood was brought to a focus in his re-creation of his people. The Christ who re-creates man is he who created man.

Thus the word "creation" emerges within the give and take of the divine disclosure in "salvation history" and is expressed fully in the "new creation" which comes to actuality in Jesus Christ. Its analogical nature is evident. Its empirical reference is to the work of the artist, the potter, the technician. At the human level, "creation" presupposes a pre-existent material which is shaped and molded. Indeed the Hebrew seems to have thought of a pre-existent chaos which God shaped and molded in the creation sagas of Genesis 1 and 2. Yet in Genesis 1 and in Deutero-Isaiah we find the significant use of the verb *bara'*, to create, which is employed of God alone as subject and which seems to imply absolute creating. However implicit such absolute creating may have been in the Old Testament it becomes explicit in the New Testament, and the phrase "out of nothing" is added to the description of the divine creating. The historic testimony ever since has accepted this qualifying addition and pointed back from the Incarnation and the re-creation of man to the primal act in which God calls the world into being "out of nothing."

This would mean that "creation" is an image bound up with the divine disclosure. It certainly does not belong to the scientific order nor is the act of creation subject to scientific investigation. Some scientists have endeavored to move beyond the scientific significance of the cosmogonic models to theological speculation. The late E. A. Milne [83] believed that his own cosmological model of an expanding universe pointed back to the initial act of creation because of the singularity of the point for zero time in his model. Apart from the fact that he is still playing with his two time scales and not dealing with what transcends time, he also falls into the error of dogmatically accepting his own cosmogonic model literally. In any case, this particular model is seriously open to dispute. Sir E. T. Whittaker [84] began with the more general model of the expanding universe and sought to restate the "five ways" of St. Thomas Aquinas. In the light of the scientific theory, he believed that he could rehabilitate both the cosmological and teleological arguments for the divine existence. Apart from the inherent logical weakness of such arguments, his discussion ignores the facts that he is dealing with a model and not the actual universe and also that zero time in such a model is not necessarily absolute but that other and different states of the universe may have preceded it. Furthermore, he employs

[83] E. A. Milne, *Modern Cosmology and the Christian Idea of God* (Oxford: The Clarendon Press, 1952), *passim.*

[84] E. T. Whittaker, *Space and Spirit* (London: T. Nelson and Sons, Ltd., 1946), *passim.*

another extrapolated model, the application of the Second Law of thermodynamics to the universe as a whole, to justify his arguments for a transcendent "creator." Once more we need to remind ourselves that it is highly risky to use current models as a basis for religious convictions and also that such convictions do not arise by rational demonstration. Our cosmogonic myths remain within the spatiotemporal framework and give no indication of a Creator who transcends it.

The analogical nature of the model "creation" when applied to God needs to be understood, then, within the divine disclosure. When associated with the name "God" and the qualifying "out of nothing" added, the model points to a personal mystery which cannot be contained within our creaturely terms. It is a divinely given model, and in it we move beyond human creative acts to the invisible divine order. Hence, as I. T. Ramsey suggests, the "odd" qualifier is added. Taken literally and at the empirical level, the phrase "out of nothing" makes nonsense, but it points to something of which the man of faith is very sure—the absolute dependence of creation upon God.

In one sense, the theological language about the divine creation is concerned to express both the sense of wonder and the accompanying awareness of total dependence upon the Creator. Just as a human work of art points to the creative vision of its author, so nature can evoke in a man a sense of wonder. Ramsey would leave the meaning of such language at this juncture. He offers no metaphysical discussion. Indeed, he can claim that "whereas *creation ex nihilo* seems on the face of it, and from its grammar, to be talking of a great occasion in the past, it is rather making a present claim about God, and its logical grammar must be understood appropriately." [85] It is true that the phrase indicates the one-sided and absolute dependence of the creation upon the Creator, but surely it

[85] I. T. Ramsey, *Religious Language* (London: S.C.M. Press, 1957), p. 75.

offers and indeed demands an attempt to discern its implications, including the whole issue of the personal relation of the Creator to a created temporal order! D. M. MacKinnon says that such language makes possible "a view of the world that is fertile and illuminating, a posture for men under the sun that vindicates itself." [86]

Let us note briefly that the phrase implies the divine transcendence and otherness, and yet a "beyondness" that is consonant with nearness. The divine word at creation in the saga of Genesis 1 implies that the God who is beyond his creation is also immanently and creatively active within it. But he *is* beyond, bound by nothing except his own creative intention.

Again the phrase reminds us of the creature's condition of dependence. The created order is not even made of the divine substance. It comes "out of nothing." Furthermore, every entity in the created order is contingent and finite in space and time. It cannot order its own time of coming or its duration. It is dependent upon an antecedent chain of secondary courses, and both it and they are radically dependent on God. No natural being, even man, has an inherent logic which accounts for its existence. The "thrown-ness" or "being-there-ness" of the natural order is a sign of its creaturehood. Its existence is marked by insecurity and is overshadowed by the threat of nonexistence. The phrase "out of nothing" points to this. The creature is sustained over an abyss of nothingness from which it is called and to which in its transience it will return.

Finally the phrase has not merely a past reference to some primordial event. It is ontologically significant. Theologically speaking it points to a divine act which transcends time and space. This event stands "behind" the whole created order in both the temporal duration as well as the spatial extension of the latter. Thus we, from the point of view of our time, may

[86] D. M. MacKinnon, Dialogue with A. Flew on "Creation" *New Essays in Philosophical Theology* (London: S.C.M. Press, 1955), p. 183.

speak of God as continually creating and of his sustaining the universe as a continuation of his creativity. The world exists only so long as the creative act continues. The preservation of the created order is an extension of the creative act that grants existence to it. The one eternal act is refracted in our time into a continuing creation and presentation, and the insight of faith sees the depth beneath the succession of secondary causes which science studies.

So behind the observable realm that science studies, faith sees the transcendent presence, immanently active, the personal depth who sustains and redeems his creature, who called them into being out of "not being," and who will ultimately bring them into the perfect actualization of his creative intention. He stands above our spaces and beyond our times, and yet is present in and through all spaces and times, for they are his creative work. Creation and consummation, providential activity and miraculous disclosure, man in nature and yet in his personal transcendence controlling nature—here faith illuminates science as science may illuminate faith. The models of science and the analogues of faith may become complementary.

Part II

Where the Two Forms of Knowledge and the Two Languages Meet

IV

The Creator Spirit, Evolution, and Life

The advent of Darwinism marked the beginning of an historical approach to nature and the advent of a new emphasis on time in the natural sciences. We have already seen how this emphasis on history and directed time has become significant in the physical sciences and have also indicated how the biological sciences became involved early with the concept of evolution. The tension between religious faith and scientific knowledge is not too evident at the level of astrophysics and the scientific cosmogonic myths. Our previous discussion covers this area sufficiently. But at the biological level the tension tends to become more acute, and it is on this level that we must fix our attention.

Darwinism, with its emphasis on random mutations and natural selection, points to a historical development in nature. But it does not offer us any teleological explanation of the natural order. In all its forms it is concerned with the mechanics of biological development. Yet it does more easily fit into a naturalistic approach to the process when lifted to a metaphysical level, and it definitely belongs to that boundary situation where the language of science and the language of theology overlap in what they say about nature. For it is concerned with the temporal beginnings of life and mind, with the historical origins of man, and with the nature of life itself. Let it be remembered that evolution as a fact is not synonymous with Darwinism or with Neo-Darwinism. The latter are theories which attempt to offer scientific explanations or models of the empirical data of development. Neo-Darwinism does, however, at the present time represent biological "orthodoxy," and it is with this theory that Christian thought must deal. Nor may theology dismiss the scientific model presented by Neo-Darwinist theory, since this, up to the present, offers the best available way of correlating the scientific evidence.

1. *The scientific picture of evolution*

Until Darwin's time a few outstanding thinkers had thought of the evolution of the species of living things from one another,[1] but the scientific consensus had been in favor of the fixity of the species. Enough evidence had accumulated, however, by the middle of the last century, for the latter point of view to be called in question, and the genius of Charles Darwin grasped a way through. While it is true that Darwin's original position was nowhere near the whole truth, and while many aspects of the evolutionary process remain unsolved problems, he at least showed the way which future investigation should take. We need to differentiate between scientific facts and scientific theories. The facts point to some form of evolution or transformation of the species. They do not necessarily imply Darwin's theory[2] or require the acceptance of Darwinism.

Let us first look at the evidence that supports some form of transformism or evolution. First of all, we have the evidence supplied by the skeletons of animals preserved in the geological strata of the earth's crust. We can trace, in such remains from the prehistoric past, development within the animal orders, both within families, as in the case of the horse, and across family boundaries, as in the case of some of the shellfish.[3] Secondly, where species have been separated from the

[1] For a fascinating study of this consult *The Forerunners of Darwin*, ed. Glass, Temkin, and Straus (Baltimore: Johns Hopkins Press, 1959).

[2] For Darwin's position consult *The Origin of Species* and *The Descent of Man* in the Modern Library Edition.

[3] Here consult G. G. Simpson, *The Meaning of Evolution* (New Haven: Yale University Press, 1952), A. J. Cain, *Animal Species and Their Evolution* (New York: Harper & Brothers, 1960).

mainstream of animal life by geographical isolation, we find parallel developments and similar species occurring, although with characteristics peculiar to the environment concerned. Thus, the marsupials of Australasia show parallel transformations and types to the development of the normal mammals on the mainland of Asia. Thirdly, we have the unity amid the diversity of animal life, the similarity of structure and function, anatomically, physiologically, and psychologically throughout the animal order. Fourthly, there is the presence of vestigial remains, organs, and tissues, which remain in truncated and obsolescent form, but which once served a useful purpose in the upward surge of life. Fifthly, there is the evidence of embryology, which must not be overemphasized. The human embryo does recapitulate, in its own development, the developmental background of the whole animal order.

We turn, now, to Darwin's theory. Darwin, from his observations during his ocean voyages, became convinced of the transformation of the species. He attacked Linnaeus's doctrine of the fixity of the species and held that new species originated from older ones. He found the key to his understanding of this process in some studies of human population by the English Episcopalian curate Malthus, namely, in the survival of the fittest. Hence he made two assumptions. The first was that all living creatures are capable of an infinite number of minute variations. The second was that such minute variations are weeded out in the struggle for existence, so that only those survive which are fitted to the environment. This combination of small variations with the survival of the fittest by natural selection was sufficient to account for the emergence of any new species. Any variation in structure or function which gives its possessor more opportunity to survive, both in longevity of existence and in fecundity of offspring, will tend by natural selection to spread through the race. Those which do not possess this new and useful variation will be naturally eliminated, and a new species will be produced. In this way a large variety of species could emerge from one or more primary forms.

The virtue of Darwin's thesis was that he proposed a mechanism for the evolutionary process. In assessing it, or any new forms it has taken, we cannot discredit the scientific fact of evolution which his theory sought to explain. Darwin did not go so far as his followers. He believed in the activity of a Creator and could write that "life with its several powers" had "been originally breathed by the Creator into a few forms or into one." Unfortunately he introduced the word "chance" to describe the small variations. By this he meant to imply that the cause of such variations was unknown, but his followers seized upon the adjective as an indication that purpose and design were absent from the whole process. For Darwin, evolution possessed no life-originating impulse, but was a process operating in a situation where life was already present. Even he, however, appears to have had his doubts about an all-embracing and detailed design. T. H. Huxley and his followers developed from Darwin's theory a militant naturalism.[4]

Since Darwin's time we have learned more about the small variations. Darwin's small variations were often incidental changes with no essential significance. The tremendous strides in the study of heredity at the beginning of this century, together with the rediscovery of Mendel's work on inheritance, have brought about a revolution. The variations significant for the transformation of the species are now associated with changes in genetic structure. The latter is concentrated in the molecular chromosomes and their gene patterns which constitute the nucleus of every cell in a living organism. These nuclear protein molecules determine the physiological, anatomical, and probably even the psychological structure of the organism. If the structure of such molecular genes suffers a

[4] For a good discussion of the whole nineteenth-century controversy consult William Irvine, *Apes, Angels and Victorians* (New York: Meridian Books, 1959).

rearrangement of its atoms, commonly termed a mutation, changes in the structure of the organism result. Hence the new form of Darwinism speaks of the operation of natural selection upon the results of genetic mutation.[5]

There are many convinced Neo-Darwinists who are sure that the mechanism of evolution has now been discovered.[6] Thus R. A. Fisher has sought to show, on statistical grounds, that natural selection combined with a slow rate of mutation is sufficient to account for the origin of the species.[7] We know that changes in gene structure can occur through the incidence of natural or artificial radiation, as experiments with the banana fly have demonstrated. Hence the idea of chance mutations operated upon by natural selection is still a regnant hypothesis in many schools of biological thought. On the other hand, others are dissatisfied with the point of view and are looking for a new synthesis of the evidence.

We cannot deny that natural selection plays its part in the process, but many would question whether it is as creative and formative as some biologists hold. It would appear to be more negative than positive. The creative factor is much more the law of force behind the mutations. Natural selection is a specializing process, producing more and more specialization of the organism until no plasticity of response is left. Thus, when natural selection enables an insect to survive because it looks like a stick or twig, it is difficult to see what further plasticity of response is left to this organism. Natural selection tends to

[5] For a discussion of the whole field consult C. D. Darlington, *The Evolution of Genetic Systems* (New York: Basic Books, 1958); E. B. Ford, *The Study of Heredity* (New York: Oxford University Press, 1949); P. M. Sheppard, *Natural Selection and Heredity* (New York: Harper & Bros., 1960).

[6] Cf. Julian Huxley, *Evolution; The Modern Synthesis* (London: Allen and Unwin, 1945); W. H. Dowdeswell, *The Mechanism of Evolution* (New York: Harper & Bros., 1960).

[7] See R. A. Fisher, *The Genetical Theory of Natural Selection* (Oxford: Oxford University Press, 1930).

lead away from the mainstream of evolutionary development. If we liken the latter to the trunk of a tree, and the various families and species to branches from this trunk, natural selection undoubtedly operates along those branches, but it tends ultimately to lead to specialized forms which can adapt themselves no further. It may apply to the upward growth of the central trunk itself, as neo-Darwinists would contend that it does. But others, like J. C. Willis,[8] from his investigation of Brazilian flora, argue that evolution works according to law not chance, and that it proceeds by single definite mutations, which do not necessarily confer any functional advantage upon the organism in which they occur. If this mutation happens to be advantageous, natural selection will probably allow it to survive, but there is, at the same time, no necessary reason why the ancestor should die out. This is an extreme position but it marks one protest among many.

An example that illustrates the same point is afforded by the emergence of the mammals. The Mesozoic Age was a warm and moist period when the cold-blooded giant reptiles flourished, and one therefore in which creatures with fur coats and warm blood would have little survival value. The hot, humid atmosphere enabled the cold-blooded reptiles to survive, and yet, on the fringe of this reptile population, there were, throughout this period, small mammals, who persisted by desperate struggle. They protected their young from their clumsy giant neighbors by carrying their eggs within their bodies and by protective concern for these young when they were born. The mammals' structure had little survival value in this environment, and natural selection could not operate in their favor. Yet they did survive, and when the glacial age supervened, the mammals persisted but the reptiles perished. Natural selection had resulted in the reptiles entering a blind alley, while the mammals had been mysteriously preserved against the operation of natural selection, so that millions of

[8] J. C. Willis, *The Course of Evolution, passim.*

years later they could fulfill an important function in the development of the human race. We must not press our point too far, for ecological factors undoubtedly played a a part in mammal survival. But natural selection is clearly not *the* master key.[9]

Another example is afforded by the mimicry of nature. Darwin held that mimicry arises because it aids survival. But many illustrations can be found in which this is not the case. For example, hover flies in Japan look like wasps, but there are no wasps in the area; therefore this protective significance is nil since enemies would have no response to a wasp carrying a sting.

The overemphasis of Neo-Darwinism on the significance of natural selection is accompanied by an equal overemphasis on the random nature of mutations. Yet it is difficult to believe that all the mutations are random and contingent. Even in Darwin's time, Asa Gray raised the issue in relation to the eye. This is a complex organ, built up of several parts which can function satisfactorily and meaningfully only when they are properly integrated into the whole. Such parts, if they did not appear with the simultaneous emergence of such a whole but appeared individually on their own, would have no survival value. The latter would depend upon their place within and significance for the whole which was not yet formed. The hypothesis that the eye evolved from a light sensitive spot by small fortuitous variations operated upon by natural selection just will not hold water. Mutations of a larger type seem suggested. Furthermore, they would appear to be teleologically directed.

[9] Cf. G. C. Robson and O. W. Richards (*The Variation of Animals in Nature,* pub. p. 316) where they say of natural selection: "We do not believe that it can be disregarded as a possible factor in evolution. Nevertheless there is so little positive evidence in its favor, so much that appears to tell against it, and so much that is as yet inconclusive that we have no right to assign to it the main causative role in evolution."

Again, we have the problems raised by the development of complex modes of behavior, like some of the instincts. The inborn behavior, for instance, of the water spider is difficult to explain on the basis of the accidental correlation of a number of small random mutations. Though an air-breathing creature, this spider builds its nest under water in the shape of a diving bell. The hairs of its body are so constructed that it takes under water, entangled in them, an air bubble. In this way it fills its nest with air, renewing the air also while the young are being reared in it. It is difficult to see how this habit could have been acquired by a land spider through a gradual process of evolution. For one thing, the ordinary spider cannot survive under water, and therefore any modified form of it would have to be completely adapted for submarine operation. Any adaptation would be useless until complete, and yet such adaptations, if gradually evolved, would have no survival values on land. The development of the body hairs, the emergence of the instinct for diving and taking to water, the instinct of making a nest under water instead of on land, are all inexplicable on the ground of small, chance variations weeded out by natural selection, since the small successive variations would, of themselves, have no survival value.

Along side of such issues, we must place the phenomena described under the term orthogenesis. This term describes "the tendency of many species to evolve in a particular direction, as if impelled by some overwhelming force to proceed towards a predetermined goal." [10] Often this tendency leads to blind alleys and to the ultimate extinction of a group of organisms. Too much must not be made of it, but often, as Von Bertalanffy points out, "orthogenetic trends may eventually create prerequisites for other and higher achievements." [11] It is his judgment that orthogenesis indicates that "evolution is not de-

[10] W. H. Dowdeswell, op. cit. p. 97.

[11] L. von Bertalanffy, *Problems of Life* (New York: Harper & Bros., 1960), p. 104.

termined merely by accidental factors of the environment and the resulting struggle for existence, but also by internal factors." [12]

In view of this evidence, it is not surprising to find many eminent biologists advocating an inner drive to adaptiveness which works harmoniously throughout the whole organism in the major evolutionary changes. Dalcq [13] has called the latter "onto-mutations," and connects them up with embryological studies. He believes that the major evolutionary steps affected "the whole chemistry of oögenesis (egg or ovum formation) in such a way as to produce a profound change of morphochoresis (observable development)." [14] He finds it difficult to account for the major changes from one egg type of the animal order to another type in terms of a slow process of trial and error. He describes in detail the different egg types and shows how fundamentally different the organizations of the various eggs are. The gaps between them are such, he contends, that they could not be bridged by a series of fortuitous changes. Rather, in order for one egg type to be transformed into another, there would be required a closely linked chain of transmutations which must have occurred simultaneously as a single onto-mutation.

An intense opponent of the Neo-Darwinism orthodoxy was also the late Richard Goldschmidt.[15] He held that development by the operation of natural selection upon a large number of micromutations might account for small differences within a species, such as the formation of subspecies. But, at the level of large-scale evolutionary changes, macroevolution, he decisively rejected such a mechanism. The subspecies

[12] Ibid. p. 103.

[13] A. Dalcq, *Introduction to General Embryology,* trans. O. Medawar (Oxford: Oxford University Press, 1957).

[14] Ibid. p. 153.

[15] R. Goldschmidt, *The Material Basis of Evolution* (New Haven: Yale University Press, 1960).

formed by the Neo-Darwinist mechanisms were "more or less diversified blind alleys within the species," enabling the organism to adapt itself to specific local conditions. But "the decisive step in evolution, the first step towards macroevolution, the step from one species to another requires another evolutionary method than that of sheer accumulation of micromutations." [16] Goldschmidt points to the absence of any true intermediary forms between species. They can be found only at the subspecific level, as, for example, in the case of the horse where intermediary forms can be traced from Eohippus up to the modern quadruped. He thinks of great hereditary upheavals, far-reaching changes in the genetic material, calling them "systematic mutations." In these, the genetic systems have been radically reshuffled. We should note, at this point, that Dalcq's "onto-mutations" differ in that the Belgian scientist includes cytoplasmic factors as well as the nuclear gene system of the cell. Yet the same point is being made. Goldschmidt talks about the production, at certain evolutionary stages, of "hopeful monsters," rare instances of mutations which are so large that they affect the creature from the fertilization of the egg onward and produce an adult organism entirely different from other offspring of the same parent.

In the area of paleontology, O. H. Schindewolf,[17] a leading German investigator, advocates sudden spurts of macroevolutionary change within the normal durations of microevolution with which Neo-Darwinism is preoccupied. He points out how various biological groups have appeared at specific periods of the earth's history and how no conspicuous additions have been made to such groups since their respective periods of major appearance. Thus the widely differing placental mammals, which nourish the embryo in the uterus, appeared simultaneously in the Paleozoic era, and the cephalopods (such as octo-

[16] Ibid. p. 283.

[17] O. H. Schindewolf, *Paläontologie, Entwicklungslehre und Genetik, Kritik und Synthese* (Berlin: Gebr. Borntraeger, 1936).

puses and cuttle fish) in the Ordovician period. The paleontologist here lends his support to biological investigation on the issue of a sharp division between microevolution and macroevolution.

We thus find a revival of the concept of an inner drive. Lamarck had, years before Darwin, postulated a theory of evolution in which the responsive adaptation of an organism to its environment was inherited by its descendants and so new species were produced. His theory of "the inheritance of acquired characteristics" has never been validated, but never completely discredited. Even Darwin was accused of employing, and actually did employ, some Lamarckian ideas. It could be said that Neo-Darwinism has emphasized the mechanistic and random aspect of evolution, and that, in contemporary criticisms, its opponents are seeking to emphasize an aspect of nature which Lamarck had tried unsuccessfully to formulate. There would appear to be an inner drive in which the mechanics of gene mutation is involved—and possibly even cytoplasmic changes.

The answer of the Neo-Darwinists is to emphasize the time factor and to contend that the long duration of macroevolution is sufficient to account for the large-scale transformations. We have already noted the work of Sir R. A. Fisher on the mathematical theory of population genetics. Dobzhansky, one of the most prominent contemporary biologists, supports such a point of view. He contends that "evolution is, in part, ectogenesis; it is brought about by causes outside the organism, or, more precisely, through interactions between the organism and its environment . . . The environment determines the changes which occur not directly but only by way of natural selection, a process first clearly expounded by Darwin." [18] Elsewhere he notes that "nobody beheld the sight of man's ancestors giving rise to men or of the ancestral horses transforming themselves

[18] Th. Dobzhansky, "Evolution and Environment," *The Evolution of Life,* ed. Sol Tax (Chicago: University of Chicago Press, 1960), p. 405.

into modern horses. We cannot re-enact these transformations in our laboratories. Evolutionary changes of this magnitude (sometimes called macro-evolution) take time intervals of much greater orders than the span of human life; they are accordingly not facts observed but events inferred from observed facts." [19]

Yet even Dobzhansky allows for what he calls, following G. G. Simpson, "quantum mutations." As an example, he cites the evolutionary emergence of man. He suggests that the upright stance, tools, constant sexual receptivity of females, symbolic language, monogamous family, change in food habits, and relaxation of male aggressiveness were changes that "most likely went together, with mutual reinforcement." He continues: "What we are dealing with is the emergence of a whole new evolutionary pattern, a transition to a novel way of life which is human rather than animal." [20] He describes such "quantum mutations" as "infrequent types of evolutionary change," and suggests that they are "unlikely to involve changes of one trait at a time. The whole genotype (gene structure) and the whole phenotype (external form) are reconstructed to reach a new adaptive balance." [21]

It is difficult to see how, in the light of this, Dobzhansky can hold that macroevolution is of the same type as microevolution. He tells us that "quantum evolution, emergence of novel adaptive designs, may involve breaks in the evolutionary continuity when the differences between the ancestors and the descendants increase so rapidly that they are perceived as differences in kind." [22] It would seem that here we are moving near to Dalcq's "onto-mutations," even though Dobzhansky strenuously rejects any idea of an inner adaptiveness or autogensis.

[19] Th. Dobzhansky, *Mankind Evolving* (New Haven: Yale University Press, 1962), p. 5 f.

[20] Ibid. p. 199.

[21] Ibid. p. 199.

[22] Ibid. p. 203.

He admits that the relation of the organism to its environment is one of challenge and response and that the latter is of the nature of adaptive alterations, dependent upon the raw materials of gene structure available.[23] But apparently he still holds to randomness even at the level of the quantum mutations. Such adaptive alterations may or may not survive. Presumably they may have occurred on less favorable occasions and not persisted.

Dobzhansky describes the adaptive responses of the organism in macroevolution as creative. As distinct from microevolution, the changes of macroevolution are unpredictable and nonrepetitive. Microevolution, reproducible in the laboratory, is repetitive and even reversible. Thus, on the large scale, evolution is "a creative response of living matter to environmental opportunity."[24] Such creativity will, however, be characterized by the risk of failure or nonfulfillment. It will equally be characterized by the origination of novelties. In this way, Dobzhansky tries to retain the idea of plasticity of response and freedom by tying up the creativity with the process itself. This kind of immanental creativity will have to be considered subsequently. Yet whether we accept the approach of Dobzhansky or that of Dalcq and other investigators, it is evident that the position of Neo-Darwinian orthodoxy can by no means supply all the answers.[25]

Michael Polanyi[26] criticizes the orthodox position cogently

[23] Ibid. p. 154.

[24] Dobzhansky, in *The Evolution of Life,* p. 425.

[25] Dobzhansky is himself aware of the deficiencies and weaknesses of Neo-Darwinism and holds that he and other advocates should be courageous enough to admit them—art. "Catastrophism versus evolutionism," *Science,* 92:356 (1940), quoted in A. Wolsky, "A Hundred Years of Darwinism in Biology," *Darwin's Vision and Christian Perspectives,* ed. W. J. Ong (New York: The Macmillan Co., 1960). I am much indebted to this excellent essay for some of the material used earlier.

[26] M. Polanyi, *Personal Knowledge* (Chicago: University of Chicago Press, 1958), pp. 384 ff.

when he inquires how entirely accidental advantages can possibly aggregate into the evolution of a completely new set of operational principles. Natural selection emphasizes reproductive advantages and envisages the whole evolutionary process in terms of random mutations with such advantages. But, if we consider a long-range evolutionary progress, such as the development of the human consciousness, the consecutive steps in it would need a special type of adaptive advantage, namely, an advantage that contributed "to a continuous ascending evolutionary achievement." We have already made this point in the cases of the eye and of complex instincts. Apart from the long-range achievement, and entirely on their own, the individual steps would have little or no adaptive advantage. Polanyi contends that everything points to an ordering principle. "The action of the ordering principle underlying such a persistent creative trend is necessarily overlooked or denied by the theory of natural selection, since it cannot be accounted for in terms of accidental mutation plus natural selection." [27] This emphasis on an orderly transforming principle would transform mutations and natural selection into agents which release and sustain the operation of the principle.

Whether we accept the theory of onto-mutations and "hopeful monsters" or the theory of a long-range evolutionary progress, coordination of mutations would seem to be a sheer necessity. In other words, an orderly transforming principle would seem to be at work. No informed biologist would deny that random mutations and natural selection play a part in evolution, especially in the development *within* a species. The real issue is whether other factors come into play at the level of macroevolution. If we accept the theory of long-time orderly progress, it would still remain true that the comprehensive factors making it possible would not be "observable within the short span of contemporary experience, the less so, since any indications of them are likely to be swamped by

[27] Ibid. p. 385.

ephemeral genetic variations which are taking place, as it were, in the interstices of the dominant evolutionary trend."[28] The experimental geneticist will not notice such factors, since he is concerned with microevolution and a short time span. He will explain all hereditary variations without any reference to the action of evolutionary trends. Yet Dobzhansky, a convinced Neo-Darwinist, has almost to hint at the latter even though he endeavors to free his definition of creativeness from any preordained directiveness. As Wolfsky puts it: ". . . the difference between the conflicting views on macroevolution boils down to whether one prefers to believe in a few large-scale 'miracles' or in a large number of small wonders."[29] Directiveness and ordering lift their heads.

Standing at the end of this long process of evolution are self-consciousness and reflective mind. The emergence, at the end of a process, of a mind which is able to understand the process would seem to imply that mind is there all the time. How can a purely fortuitous process throw up a mind which can give it meaning and control it? Mathematical thought and statistical probability shudder at the thought. As G. F. Stout puts it:

> We cannot interpret one essentially dependent part of this continuous process as implying mental agency, and yet refuse to interpret on the same principle the whole which includes it. There is a vast multitude of facts not only analogous to each other, inasmuch as they represent teleological order, but interwoven in one context. By assuming mental agency in nature as well as in human and animal life, we can bring them, in spite of diversity, under one principle, and if this principle is rejected, there is no other which will cover the facts.[30]

[28] M. Polanyi, op. cit. p. 385.

[29] Wolfsky, op. cit. p. 29.

[30] G. F. Stout, *Mind and Matter* (Cambridge: Cambridge University Press, 1931), p. 148. William Temple makes a similar point in *Nature, Man and God* (London: Macmillan & Co., Ltd., 1956), pp. 129 ff. He comments: "That the world should give rise to minds which know the world involves a good deal concerning the nature of the world."

II. *The nature and origin of life*

The Darwinian model of evolution does not account for the origin of life. It is concerned with the factors which operate in the development of life as a going concern. Our argument has now brought us to the issue of the nature of life itself. Can we speak of a distinctive ordering principle, or may an organism simply be a more complex form of matter understandable in terms of physics and chemistry? We must thus turn our attention to the questions of the origin of life, of its relation to physical energy, and of its relation to mind.

The difference between life and inanimate matter, between the organic and the inorganic, is most clearly seen when we recognize the distinction in structure. An inanimate thing is subject to mechanical law and is built up by external addition. Thus, in atomic physics we are dealing with neutrons, protons, and electrons as basic bricks, which enter into certain relational patterns to form the atoms of the various elements. These units do not themselves develop so that they perform special functions, and change is represented by their motions, not by any effect of their relationships upon their essential qualities. At the borderline of the living and the nonliving, new characteristics begin to appear. The virus has a molecular structure and yet is able to proliferate, like a living thing. Some elementary forms of organism still have characteristics of external addition but begin to disclose something quite different. This "something different" soon becomes evident at the organismic level. In organisms the parts cannot be treated as simple units unaffected by the relationships into which they enter. We are no longer concerned with simple identical units but with parts which serve specific functions in the whole. Organic wholes are unities of differences, not unities of identities. In them, change and growth cannot be represented by the motion of simple units. Rather they bring with them an increasing differentiation of the parts and a developing co-ordination between them. The character and function of a part is determined by its relationship to the other parts within the whole.

We may perhaps express this best by saying that life is characterized by a wholeness which is absent from inanimate matter. A crystal grows by adding atomic and molecular bricks externally, by external aggregation. It is built up from without. An advanced organism grows from within by internal differentiation. The crystal does not change its internal constitution by its addition. The organism grows by the internal development and differentiation of its parts, and yet it remains a unified and living whole. In the organism we have a hierarchy of parts, serving diverse functions but forming a single whole in which they function harmoniously and co-operatively. This suggests that, in the organism, the growth is directed growth. The whole seems to pervade every part and control its development. There is a directive self-regulation. The pattern of the whole would seem to be reflected in every differentiating element, and the organism moves ahead in a definite way until the end of the whole is attained. We see this in the development of the tadpole's egg.

This drive towards the end stage and its self-regulatory aspects are illustrated in the capacity of an organism to repair its injuries and to regenerate missing parts. If the pattern is interfered with, the organic whole readjusts itself to the new situation, reconstitutes the pattern, and moves again towards its normal realization.[31] Thus, in the case of a frog's egg, a cell separated from the rest will independently proceed to develop into a normal organic whole. Again, as Sinnott points out, the animal is so organized that, with altering circumstances, activities are set in train to maintain a "steady state" of body temperature and blood sugar.[32]

[31] Cf. E. S. Russell, *The Directiveness of Organic Activities* (Cambridge: Cambridge University Press, 1945), p. 44.

[32] E. W. Sinnott, *Matter, Mind and Man* (New York: Harper & Bros.), 1957, p. 38.

It is not only the physicochemical organization that manifests this inner teleological drive. It is seen not only in the development of structure and organs, but also in behavior. The animal grows certain organs, apparently without conscious intent and according to its inherent pattern. It also grows the faculty to use the organs. However much the debate may rage as to the extent and number of the instincts which guide behavior, no one can dispute the fact that, akin to the pattern guiding the growth of the structure, there is also a pattern or Gestalt that controls behavior and sets the goals which the organism is striving to attain. As Sinnott puts it: "In behavior, protoplasmic purpose grows to instinct, and with dawning consciousness this leads to thought and the higher elements of mind." [33] The chick pecking its way out of its shell acts by instinct, and actually is only carrying farther the movement which has brought it through its embryonic life. Instinct continues what the protoplasmic pattern has commenced. Conscious mind extends this still further. Here the phenomena associated with learning and animal memory come to the fore. As the organisms ascend the scale of complexity and of response to environment, rigid instinctive behavior gives place to a capacity to modify the details of action for a specific situation. This happens in nest-building and in the act of mating, for example.[34] The sequence of events by which a goal is attained in developed instinctive behavior is not always the same. The emphasis would appear to fall on the end rather than the means, and the word "purposive" becomes applicable. We can thus understand the comment of Dr. E. S. Russell:

> We recognize the fact that organic activities as manifested by organized unities such as cells and organisms, show characteristics, especially in their directiveness, persistency and adaptability which are shown also in in-

[33] Ibid. pp. 43 f.

[34] Cf. the investigations of the great field naturalist Fabre.

stinctive and intelligent behavior of ourselves and other animals.[35]

Attempts to reduce biology to biochemistry and biophysics are, however, regnant. They can at least be justified on the grounds that life does have a physicochemical basis. For one thing, the living cell is a highly complex organization of atoms and molecules, existing in many phases. It is by no means homogeneous. Within its enclosing membrane is the cytoplasm, a transparent fluid with oily globules forming a highly refined colloidal suspension. The oily globules differ in substance according to the function of the cell. Suspended in the cytoplasm are the centrosome, important in cell division, and the nucleus. The density of the cytoplasm is graded, and its density gradients are maintained by the "osmotic work" of the cell. This is supplied by the free energy of the cell which results from processes of anabolism and katabolism going on side by side. Protein molecules are built up to greater complexity and also broken down to provide the free energy of the cell. Now all these processes are understandable in terms of physics and chemistry. We know that metabolism involves the breakdown of the molecule of glucose into residual carbon dioxide and water. It is akin to the combustion of sugar at high temperatures at the inorganic level. But, in the cell, the energy is released by a complex cycle of processes at a much lower temperature. Many such processes are made possible and controlled by enzymes or catalysts, which, though minute in quantity, are sufficiently potent in action to direct the differentiation taking place within the individual cell and within the organism as a whole. Thus we find Sherrington urging that liv-

[35] E. S. Russell, op. cit. p. 179. Cf. J. Smuts: Mind "is a continuation, on a much higher plane, of the system of organic regulation and coordination which characterizes Holism in organisms. Mind is thus a direct descendant of organic regulation and carries forward the same task," *Holism and Evolution* (New York: The Macmillan Co., 1926), p. 224.

ing processes "are chemistry and physics."[36] Yet there is one characteristic of the physics and chemistry of the living system. The processes take place under different conditions and in ways that we cannot produce elsewhere, because they are within a living whole.

This brings us to the gene patterning of the cell nucleus. The latter consists of a chromatin network of chromosomes, which occur in pairs and which consist of carefully coded structures of genes. These carry both the physiological and the psychological characteristics of the organism. We are now learning much about the structure of these chromosomes and their constituent genes, as we unravel the mystery of the desoxyribonucleic acid molecule (DNA) with its duplicate helical stringlike structure and its coded orders of nuclectides—the purines and the pyrimidines. At this point it suffices to remind ourselves that this coding, through the mechanism of the ribonucleic acid molecular messengers (RNA), determines the physiological structure and the psychological structure of the organism. Like a molecular computer, the chromosomes and their coded genes form a chemical basis of living things. Yet even to solve their intricate structure does not finally plumb the mystery of the living whole within which they function.

A further physical aspect of the organism is that it is thermodynamically an open system. We have noted above that a closed system is one which is isolated from its surroundings. In it the energy available for useful work tends to a minimum and the entropy to a maximum, until thermodynamic equilibrium is attained. In an open system, there is a free exchange of matter and heat with the surroundings. In consequence there may sometimes in such instances be a decrease of entropy and an increase of available energy. Such is the case with living things. The processes of metabolism make possible both the storage of energy and its breakdown for the sustaining and

[36] Sir Charles Sherrington, *Man on His Nature* (Cambridge: Cambridge University Press), p. 291.

growth of the organism. The organism feeds on negative entropy. Organic beings are thereby able to stem what may be the inexorable *Götterdämmerung* of the universe to a heat death.

At the inorganic level, a flame is an instance of an open system. Here the chemical combinations that make the flame possible are conditioned by the ordering principles which characterize a stable flame. Once the flame is established, it stabilizes the event which elicits it and may feed on other material. If it be argued that a living thing differs by its capacities for procreation, regeneration, and self-stabilization, the same differentia apply at a more elementary level to the flame.[37] It can multiply and regenerate its form after outside disturbance. It can even change its substance and retain its form. Indeed, Polanyi[38] reminds us that it is a fundamental principle of open systems that they stabilize any improbable event that serves to elicit them. This holds of living things as well as flames.[39]

The stabilizing quality of a living or organic open system is manifested especially in the gene structure. These structures remain stable through generations, passing on the hereditary characteristics and sustaining the nature of a particular phylum or organic family. The cell divisions of the living organisms do not affect this gene structure nor does the process of reproduction. When new species emerge they are bound up with mutations in the same structure, in which the patterned atoms and coding of the chromosome/gene formation has been radically transformed. Now these molecular structures contain a relatively small number of atoms, and they should therefore be subject to the effect of the increasing entropy and disorderliness of the universe. As Schrödinger puts it: "That number is

[37] Cf. C. F. von Weizsäcker, *The History of Nature* (London: Routledge and Kegan Paul, 1951), p. 122.

[38] M. Polanyi, op. cit. p. 384.

[39] Ibid. pp. 383 ff.

much too small (from the $\sqrt{n}$ point of view) to entail an orderly and lawful behavior according to statistical physics—and that means according to physics. It is too small even if all these atoms played the same role, as they do in a gas or in a drop of liquid."[40] He points out that these molecules are such that every atom and every radical plays a distinctive part. Yet, subject as they are, throughout the generations, to 98° F temperature, they remain stable through those generations and are not perturbed by the disordering tendency of heat motion.[41]

Schrödinger suggests that the forces which are operative are not those described in the statistical laws of classical physics but those described in the models of quantum physics, since the molecules fall within this microcosmic range. Quantum physics gives us probabilities too. It cannot predict how individual particles will act at the small-scale level, but it can give us the probability. Thus it cannot predict a mutation in a particular gene structure, but it can give us the probability that it will take place. This probability can be shown to be much less than that which holds at the level of large-scale classical physics with its statistical laws (involving the square root of the number of particles involved). Consequently mutations are infrequent unless artificially induced (e.g. by nuclear explosions and the like). The probability of a change in gene or DNA structure and thus of a change of species is therefore slight. Von Bertalanffy suggests that "The induction of mutations is subject to the statistical laws of microphysics," but the organization of a living system turns this microphysical event into a macro-effect in the change of morphological structure or instinctive behavior of the organism.[42] We shall leave Schrödinger at this point and not deal with his pantheistic speculations.

[40] E. Schrödinger, *What Is Life?* (Cambridge: Cambridge University, 1948), pp. 30 f.

[41] Ibid. p. 47.

[42] L. von Bertalanffy, *Problems of Life* (New York: Harper & Bros., 1960), p. 166.

Once the requisite materials fall into the right combination, it is possible for organic life with its distinctive ordering principle to emerge and to stabilize itself on its physicochemical basis. We may, indeed, speak of the potentiality of a stable open system as its ordering principle. The potentiality becomes actuality when the requisite conditions are constituted in matter. This holds of life as it does of a flame. Granted the favorable physicochemical conditions, the right configuration of matter, the operations of the ordering principle of life are released and living things originate.

This would suggest that any mechanistic or reductive explanation of living things does not suffice. The behavior and organization of organisms cannot be fitted into a physical or mechanistic model without omitting much that characterizes them. We need to remember the affirmation of one of the great biologists of the last decades, Professor D'Arcy Thompson, that "one does not come by studying living things for a lifetime to suppose that physics and chemistry can account for them all." [43] The field naturalist becomes involved with living things as the laboratory experimentalist does not. He has a greater comprehension and his personal knowledge passes beyond a quantitative appraisal. Organisms have an integrative as well as a mechanistic aspect. They manifest a wholeness which physicochemical analysis ignores. Yet the latter is only undertaken because of a prior awareness of the comprehensive and integrated functioning of the whole. The parts function within and serve the ends of the whole. We recognize the functioning of certain operational principles. Thus physiology is a descriptive science in which we describe an organ and attempt to define its function within the whole. It is within such a framework that physicochemical investigation has meaning. Then, as Polanyi points out, we move from reasons to causes. But, as he remarks, "any attempt to replace physiology altogether by a

[43] D'Arcy Thompson, *Growth and Form* (Cambridge: Cambridge University Press, 1948), p. 14.

physicochemical chart of the living organism would completely dissolve any understanding of the organism." [44]

For this reason, we have advocated that biology should have its own concepts and categories as distinct from those at the physicochemical level.[45] This earlier argument both reinforces and is reinforced by what has just been said. It should be referred to at this point.[46] As we move up the scale of created things, we become more personally involved, recognizing something akin to ourselves. J. S. Habgood points out that, even at the mechanistic level, "all the time our physical description of it (a machine) surreptitiously includes our personal experience of purposive action and of our intentions in constructing machines." [47]

The alternative to reductionistic naturalism is not a form of Neo-vitalism as advocated by Driesch,[48] which tended to regard life as a kind of controlling intelligence or entelechy sitting above a machine. In postulating this "psychoid" factor in living things, a kind of "ghost in the machine," such thinkers fall into the error of the Cartesian dualism which set mind and matter in an unresolvable dichotomy. The psychoid factor is foreign to and yet activates the physical medium. Such a view is as fallacious as the mechanistic view, for it ignores the wholeness of the organism.

We have suggested that the idea of "emergence" may best describe the new and higher levels of evolution above the physicochemical. Since life at the physicochemical level is manifested as an open system, its emergence occurred when a

[44] M. Polanyi, op. cit. p. 360.

[45] Cf. J. H. Woodger, *Biological Principles* (London: Kegan Paul, Trench & Trubner Co., Ltd., 1929).

[46] See, Ch. II, pp. 62 ff.

[47] J. S. Habgood, "The Uneasy Truce Between Science and Theology," *Soundings* (Cambridge: Cambridge University Press, 1962), p. 36.

[48] Hans Driesch, *The Science and Philosophy of the Organism* (London: A. & C. Black, 1938), *passim.*

highly improbable but appropriate pattern of energy occurred. Thereby the ordering principle of life was released and living things originated. C. D. Broad suggests two ways in which emergence may be expressed. Either we may hold that in a vital whole, properties latent in the physicochemical constituents become actualized because of the new relations into which they enter in an organism. Or we may say that new laws of relationship hold for these constituents in the complex structure of an organism. He rightly points out that it makes little difference which way we express the idea of emergence, but we shall prefer the former alternative, namely that what is potential in energy becomes actual when certain levels of organization or structural relationship are attained. Here by energy we mean the primordial stuff which is undefinable except as activity but which is manifested at the physical level as either radiation or physical particles at various levels of organization. Thus energy may be more than the physical and material level discloses. Reductionism ignores such potentiality and endeavors to reduce the vital and the mental to the level of the physical.

The first emergence of life is an historical event. If we ask why we cannot produce living things now, the answer lies partly in the nature of the historical fact. History is unique. As von Weizsäcker has reminded us: "What has come to be through history, can be reproduced only by a repetition of its history." [49] But a billion or so years of time and change in the crust of the earth have made conditions different. This is not to say that we may not succeed in producing a living cell in a laboratory. Indeed we seem sometimes to be quite near doing so. The borderline between the living and the nonliving is getting more clearly defined as we consider intermediary structures such as the virus and the DNA molecule. Yet even should we do so, we should simply provide the physicochemi-

[49] C. F. von Weizsäcker, op. cit. p. 123.

cal conditions under which it is possible for the latent ordering principle of life to become actually operative. Energy exists to be the bearer of life and mind and it carries them potentially within itself, even when manifested at the physicochemical level. Aristotle may yet be nearer the truth than Democritus whose atomic naturalism is so favored by the naturalists!

At this point the metaphysical bias, which is present behind all scientific thought and which is evidenced once the scientist begins to move beyond positivistic description to interpretation, becomes evident. Already here we find scientists moving to their own metempirical standpoint. The naturalistic interpretation of the data would lead its scientific protagonists to postulate a different position from that just elaborated. We have to recognize that in speaking of emergents in the way we have, we are rejecting any purely reductionist hypothesis. Furthermore, we have to recognize that the naturalistic interpretation of the data is a live option, even though we may feel that it is less adequate. In the evolutionary process we have found new emergents, novelties which cannot be reduced to or explained by the lower levels of natural reality which have preceded them. In these new levels of the natural order new ordering principles would appear to be in operation. We can speculate that they may well have been latent in energy from the very beginning and were elicited when the organization at a lower level was ordered to a specific complexity. This, however, is to venture beyond the observable. Certain levels become clearly definable—those which we define respectively in terms of life, mind, and self-conscious mind or spirit. Evolution discloses a directed movement which culminates in the emergence of personal beings.

There are those who suggest that mind is coextensive with life and that life is simply the result of the operation of the unconscious mind. The self-regulating and goal-seeking qualities of life may well be the first indications of the presence of mind, and what we call life may be the first emergence of mind as an ordering principle within the sea of the matter.[50] E. F. Tomlin suggests that "it may be that mind . . . has not merely made its journey in company with life, but that the two started off together. Indeed, it may be that they are different words for the same thing." [51] Mind is not something alien to life or even to the stream of physical energy of which life is a higher organization. Energy appears to have been created to be the bearer of mind, and mind may well be nascent in the physical from the beginning of creation.

We should not, however, speak even scientifically of the emergence of life as a purely fortuitous happening, in which a fortunate chance collocation of molecules was matched by an equally contingent but happy environment. Here L. T. Henderson stressed, many years ago, "the fitness of the environment." [52] The environment is fitted to the emergence and maintenance of life. Henderson, himself a Darwinist and naturalist, examined the chemical factors in the environment and in living matter, especially the presence of the significant element carbon. After an exhaustive analysis, he concluded that "the elements carbon, hydrogen, and oxygen are uniquely and most highly fitted to be the stuff of which life is formed and of the environment in which it exists." [53] He even argued that "no other environment consisting of primary constituents made up of other known elements, or lacking water and

[50] See E. W. Sinnott, op. cit. p. 45; also Sinnott, *Cell and Psyche* (New York: Harper & Bros., 1961) and *The Biology of Spirit* (New York: Viking Press, 1955). L. von Bertalanffy in *Problems of Life* (New York: Harper & Bros., 1961) *passim,* takes a similar approach in advocating "organicism," but never comes to any explicit suggestion of an inner side to the organism and would appear to remain in the naturalistic camp.

[51] E. F. Tomlin, *Living and Knowing* (New York: Harper & Bros., 1955), p. 126.

[52] L. J. Henderson, *The Fitness of the Environment* (Boston: Beacon Press, 1958), *passim.*

[53] Ibid. p. 225.

carbonic acid, could possess a like number of fit characteristics or such highly fit characteristics, or in any manner such great fitness to promote complexity, durability, and active metabolism in the organic mechanism which we call life." [54] Such numerous coincidences cannot be put down to chance. The way in which cosmic evolution works step by step with biological evolution suggests that the two streams of evolution are in some sense one, and that what appear to be contingent happenings really constitute a single orderly development yielding "results not merely contingent, but resembling those which in human action we recognize as purposeful." [55] His mechanistic bias vitiates his further development of this judgment, but it also makes the judgment more striking and significant.

III. *The evolutionary process and the emergence of mind*

In speaking of evolution as a directed process and of ordering principles potential within energy but being released at certain levels of complex configuration of that energy, we have already indicated that mind may be latently present from the beginning. Indeed energy may have that quality of unrealizedness which Aristotle attributed to matter. Hence there are those, like Dalcq, Goldschmidt, Vandel, and others, who advocate an inner drive of directiveness which works harmoniously throughout the whole organism in the major evolutionary changes. Hence, too, there are those who accept more completely the mechanism postulated by Neo-Darwinism and yet speak of creativity in the process or of a strange co-ordination of the micromutations (e.g. Polanyi and Dobzhansky also to some degree). There does seem to be an inner nisus towards higher forms. Undoubtedly natural selection and random mutations play a part, but we have seen reason to look for something more. It is noteworthy that so ardent an advocate of the

[54] Ibid. p. 272.
[55] Ibid. p. 279.

Neo-Darwinian position as Sir Julian Huxley can write: "The primacy of human personality has been . . . a *postulate* both of Christianity and of liberal democracy; but it is a *fact* of evolution. By whatever objective standards we choose to take, properly developed human personalities are the highest products of evolution." [56]

When we look at the process of evolution in this way, we see a growing appearance of consciousness as more highly developed wholes emerge. If we reject the materialistic hypothesis and refuse to understand the higher in terms of the lower, what we find is an increasing control of the organism over its environment as the mental aspect of energy asserts itself. At the physicochemical level, the interaction between the constituent entities is describable in general and mathematical terms. Mechanical causation would seem to be the key. But once life makes itself evident we have a developing response of the organism to its environment soon manifesting itself in a self-movement in which the vital whole begins to free itself to some degree from its environment. It is at this level that the empathy of the observer begins to apprehend sensation and feeling; and, once the organism discloses a capacity to learn by experience, we can attribute more definitely to the organism a consciousness which accompanies its physiological reactions. The organic response at the conscious level is seen in self-motion and in a capacity to adapt itself to its environment. When self-consciousness emerges, we find a capacity in personal beings to adapt the environment increasingly to themselves. Thus we see in the evolutionary process the mental aspect slowly manifesting control over the physical until, with the emergence of man as finite self-conscious spirit, we find a capacity to understand and control his physical environment in an increasing way and to direct the natural process towards his self-chosen goals.

[56] J. S. Huxley, *Evolution in Action* (New York: Harper & Bros., 1953).

It is true, of course, that the advance is neither inevitable nor consistent and that there is evidence in the evolutionary process of degeneration in some lines of descent whereby the increased adaptiveness is lost. Yet as W. H. Thorpe suggests:

> . . . it is also true to say that students of the most diverse types and approaches have found in evolution an overall tendency to increases of complexity. We see the development first of increasing independence of, and then of control of, the environment. We see increasing elaboration of the animal's central nervous system and associated sense organs. And we find, of course, that these three tendencies very often go together.[57]

Hence the emphasis would tend to fall, not so much upon the mechanism employed which may be empirically Neo-Darwinian natural selection, but rather upon over-all progress and upon the final emergence of self-conscious mind or spirit. As Thorpe comments: "With the coming of self-conscious life the evolutionary process can be said to have become conscious of itself." [58] William Temple,[59] many years ago pointed out that, though minds and self-conscious minds are late arrivals upon the evolutionary scene, yet man's capacity to understand and direct the process betokens a kinship between man and the deeps of the process itself. If out of the developing order of nature, there emerges self-conscious spirit with its capacity to control and direct, we might postulate the activity of spirit

[57] W. H. Thorpe, *Biology and the Nature of Man* (London: Oxford University Press, 1962), p. 15.

[58] Ibid. p. 16.

[59] William Temple, *Nature, Man and God* (London: Macmillan & Co., Ltd., 1956), pp. 109–34. Temple offers an excellent analysis of the development of consciousness and self-consciousness in the organism with their differentiating characteristics and a defense of immanent spirit within the natural process. Temple's insights have been strangely neglected, probably in part because of the quasi-Hegelian framework within which he works.

throughout that order, giving it structure, meaning, and direction. If this be so, we move towards an understanding of the immanence of the Creator Spirit. The Christian theist moves, of course, beyond immanence to transcendence, and we shall consider such a transition later. It is sufficient here to note that Temple does this by his own characteristic dialectic based on the nature of the personal. Temple's comment is worthy of quotation: "*The more completely we include Mind within Nature, the more inexplicable must Nature become except by reference to Mind* . . . if, as science has disclosed, Mind is a part of Nature, then Nature (to contain such a part) must be grounded in Mind." [60]

W. H. Thorpe [61] has shown how the fully developed self-conscious spirit has its roots in the lower levels of biological and psychological structure. A discussion of the learning aspect of the behavior of animals discloses ideational processes not dissimilar from those in human experience, except that man displays a greater capacity to conceptualize and to develop a free ideation detached from specific objects. This ability to form and manipulate abstract symbols, in complete independence of the original perceptual objects which stimulated the conceptualizing process, would seem to have no parallel at the animal level. Man is able, in this thought, freely to manipulate universal ideas. This is possible because, again at the animal level, diffused centers of consciousness have been increasingly centralized in the cerebral cortex. Thus man is able to move quickly with a unitary mind from one type of sense perception to another and to co-ordinate his sensual observations, even though the cerebral cortex would seem to be, to some degree, specialized in various areas for certain sense organs. The mind of man is a unity.

Yet what marks man off most of all is his appraisal of absolute values. This, as Thorpe suggests, "seems to be a dividing-

[60] Ibid. pp. 133 f.

[61] W. H. Thorpe, op. cit. especially pp. 21–87.

line indeed." [62] Yet, even here, we can see a preparation at the lower animal level. Thorpe finds the roots of man's moral life in the developing gregariousness of animal life, although often what appear to be manifestations of self-sacrifice and altruism are at the level of the lower animals otherwise explained. With the higher mammals, however, he finds evidence for personal attachment and submissiveness which cannot be accounted for solely on the basis of dominance and inferiority. He suggests that inferiority characterizes the nonsocial animals, but that in submissiveness among the social animals we have a combination of inferiority and attachment. Considerable evidence is available for long-lasting "person" attachment of an animal to its mate. The evidence in such cases is not available by experimentation but by the field study and observation of animal behavior in its natural habitat.[63] We find genuine altruism among animals where such long-lasting personal friendships seem to be formed, as for example among porpoises and even chimpanzees. "There are . . . examples in chimpanzees of one animal deliberately putting herself in a position where she is in danger of attack, apparently solely for the purpose of shielding a less-experienced or more foolhardy animal from danger." [64]

Still more is there evidence of mutual aid and co-operation. The classic study of Kropotkin [65] may be cited here. During his exile in Siberia, this field naturalist cited many instances, and since his time the evidence has accumulated to indicate the high probability of a disinterested concern at the mammalian level. He argued that survival must be understood in terms of the group, not of the individual. There is no pitiless war for life within each species. Rather, in the struggle for

[62] Ibid. p. 59.

[63] For example, among wolves. Thorpe cites the work of the Crislers (L. Crisler, *Arctic Wild*, New York: Harper & Bros., 1958). Ibid. p. 63.

[64] Ibid. p. 66.

[65] Peter Kropotkin, *Mutual Aid* (London: Penguin Books, 1939), Chapters I and II.

existence, natural selection seems to seek for a way of avoiding competition as much as possible. Nature is an harmonious system in which living things are mutually dependent and co-operative. In his field studies, Kropotkin found evidence, not of pitiless conflict, but of co-operation and mutual dependence. Living organisms, as he saw it, form a vast co-operative society in which the best is achieved for all in a given environment.

All this suffices to indicate a continuity between the mental life of the animal order and that of man, but the radical break comes not only at the level of man's symbolic activity, but also at that of his appraisal of absolute values. Man's sense of obligation, his feeling of the claim of the absolute value, and his urge to pursue moral and mental excellence set him apart, however much of the ground for this may have been prepared at the mammalian level. Morality is not simply adjustment to a social environment, as C. H. Waddington [66] contends, suggesting that natural selection holds at the level of spirit. Man, at his highest, has a feeling of responsibility to his fellows, a pressure to follow a creative path at the mental level, an urge towards nobility of character at the moral level, which are *sui generis*. He reveres goodness for its own sake and not for its survival value. He pursues truth regardless of the cost. His vision of beauty is a perpetual taskmaster in his creative art. The passion for absolute and universal values arouses in him devotion and self-sacrifice which cannot be explained in terms of "survival value." Here we begin to touch the core of spirit.

If we follow the suggestions made earlier that living things, biological and psychological wholes, result from the stabilizing of open systems which emerge when matter attains a certain level of complexity, it would seem that, as Polanyi suggests,[67] some enlarged laws of nature become effective at this point.

[66] C. H. Waddington, *The Scientific Attitude* (London: Penguin Books, 1948).

[67] M. Polanyi, op. cit. p. 397.

These laws make possible the actualizing of operational principles which increasingly operate through consciousness. We would ourselves think of the laws of nature as descriptive rather than governmental and permissive. Polanyi is not sufficiently organismic, here. It might seem preferable to speak of an organizing activity which becomes effective in a new pattern. Such activity permits the development of consciousness within the physicochemical processes. Any changes in these processes would then be stabilized in the living and increasingly conscious open-systems which have emerged from them. The germ plasms of such systems, and particularly the gene structures, manifest this stability.

Biologists such as C. M. Child have long since suggested the concept of biometric fields in living organisms. By analyzing the system of metabolic gradients in an organic whole, they postulated the gradients as field-vectors operating in a way akin to the forces in electromagnetic fields of force. Polanyi would, however, postulate something less physicochemical. He speaks of a phylogenetic field that governs the entire process of evolution and in which the organisms are directed towards novel achievement. He writes: ". . . we are *driven* to assume that the maturation of germ plasm is *guided* by the potentialities that are open to it through its possible germination into new individuals."[68] The gradients of such fields are those of phylogenetic achievement. Thus Polanyi introduces the teleological factor. The field concept, at the biological level, represents the power of certain achievements to promote their own realization. Biology, in other words, must take note of the nature of life itself, and not allow its discipline to be reduced to the level of physics and chemistry.

In introducing the idea of achievement into the field concept, Polanyi reminds us that the gradients which provide the pathways to achievement have dynamic properties akin to

[68] Ibid. p. 400.

those at the physical level.[69] Biological fields are fields of opportunity and of a striving directed towards that opportunity. As such they have an active center from which such striving is directed. These field centers emerge within the process by increasing individualization. This develops from a purely vegetative character, as we have already seen, through active and perceptive wholes or selves until responsible personhood is attained. The risk of living and striving is undertaken by these centers throughout the process. At the top level of man, this center exercises responsible choices. Polanyi argues that "continuity demands that we should take the active component into account likewise down to the lower levels. The emergence of man . . . reflects the gradual rise of autonomous centres of decision." [70]

Once more we have a scientist moving to an interpretative and metempirical standpoint, pointing to consciousness and mind as the key to the evolutionary process, and suggesting that the latter has a directiveness. Man provides, for the present, the consummating achievement for which the myriads of centers have been striving, taking the risk of living and believing down the long evolutionary process. "We may envisage then a cosmic field which called forth all these centres by offering them a short-lived, limited, hazardous opportunity for making some progress of their own towards an unthinkable consummation." [71]

This idea of a heuristic field, while scientifically based and suggesting that biology should retain its own categories, including teleological ones, might be held to move slightly into the speculative realm. Still more is this true of Teilhard de Chardin, anthropologist and theologian. His outstanding reputation as an anthropologist must lend authority where he speaks at the scientific level. He has, however, presented, in his

[69] Ibid. p. 404.
[70] Ibid. pp. 402 f.
[71] Ibid. p. 405.

writings,[72] a somewhat bewildering fusion of the biological and the mystical in an attractive and challenging picture.

Teilhard believes that consciousness is latent in matter at a very early stage. Even before life emerges, he finds an aspect of consciousness, however rudimentary, in the physical. Life was, indeed, potential before it emerged. He holds that the realm of nature has a "within" as well as a "without," and that physical energy itself has two components, a tangential and a radial. The former is concerned with the outward aspect of nature, with its increasing complexity and with its measurable aspect. The latter is concerned with the inward aspect of nature, with the development of the inner side of life, with the emergence of consciousness, mind, and ultimately of self-conscious mind. With this inner side, science qua science is powerless to deal, and yet this has carried the secret of the whole process. More and more, in the process of evolution, the radial component of energy took over in a process of convergence which was directed toward the divinely ordained consummation of the whole process. To quote Teilhard:

> Beneath the "tangential" we find the "radial." The impetus of the world, glimpsed in the great drive of consciousness, can only have its ultimate source in some *inner* principle, which alone could explain its irreversible advance towards higher psychisms.[73]

The emergence of life from the physicochemical level is certainly so far a unique event. Teilhard suggests that there took place an explosion of "internal energy" which resulted in a fundamental super-organization of matter. That is to say, it occurred because the inner side of energy, that which ultimately manifests itself as mind, had converged sufficiently under the divine direction for it to direct and control the organization of

[72] Especially *The Phenomenon of Man,* trans. by Bernard Wall (New York: Harper & Bros., 1959).

[73] Ibid. p. 149.

matter in a radical way. Once this inner side thus asserted itself, protoplasm was formed, and the development of protoplasm betokens that the inner aspect of physical energy was more and more taking control and directing the outward or physical aspect. The inner aspect manifested itself more as conscious mind and ultimately emerged to full flower as self-conscious mind. Thus, we have both continuity and discontinuity, as the process is divinely directed. We have already moved beyond the scientific to the theological in quoting Teilhard's thesis. We must return to this next. Let it suffice here to point out his emphasis on a directiveness in the whole process. He is, however, too good a scientist to ignore the random elements also present. Much of Teilhard's thought, although his terminology is different, is very close to that of Michael Polanyi. The latter quotes him with approval,[74] later employing some of his categories.

All through the process of evolution we have seen evidence of emergents which are unpredictable in terms of what has preceded them. These emergents have marked the major steps in the upward movement of the natural order. The emergence of living wholes, of conscious beings, of self-conscious persons, are creative advances. Thorpe writes:

> I think we are perfectly justified in calling these events "miracles," divesting the term of its personal associations . . . I suggest that they may be regarded as miracles in the sense that they appear to be essentially unforseeable, while at the same time exhibiting overall consistency—the kind of general consistency that the evolutionary process itself had displayed.[75]

[74] M. Polanyi, op. cit. p. 388.

[75] W. H. Thorpe, op. cit. p. 18. William Temple, op. cit. p. 122, commenting on this situation remarks that the organism's necessity to adjust the environment to itself "can no more actually give birth to self-consciousness than self-motion can give birth to consciousness."

IV. *Creation and evolution— the Spirit as personal and creative presence*

We turn now from what scientists have to say and what they might say if the present models for the evolutionary process were modified in certain ways. We must now ask what interpretation we may give theologically to the evidence which science affords. Since we do not have to accept Genesis 1 and 2 literally, no trouble arises at this level. Indeed, from the very inception of Darwin's theory, there were theologians such as Calenso, Bishop of Zanzibar, who recognized that scientists might be unveiling the historical aspect of the divine creation.

Ever since evolution became an accepted part of the scientific description of the universe, metaphysicians have sought to make it a key for their understanding of the world process. Evolution taught them to take time seriously in a way that Hegel's Idealistic Monism had not. Hence we find a concern with emergent and higher wholes at the levels of life, mind, and spirit or self-conscious mind in the thought of Lloyd Morgan, S. A. Alexander, A. N. Whitehead, and J. Smuts. Lloyd Morgan and S. A. Alexander begin at the level of naturalistic description, simply accepting the new emergent levels with "natural piety" and agreeing that the new emergent qualities cannot be accounted for solely in terms of the lower levels. The concern for explanation, however, leads them to postulate in the process a "nisus" or drive by which the lower levels are driven on to greater and greater complexity and to higher qualities. Their naturalistic realism thus leads them to postulate an immanent nisus in the whole. Lloyd Morgan [76] finishes with a pantheism in which immanent spirit realizes itself as finite spirit at the apex of the natural pyramid. S. A. Alexander,[77] in a more embracing picture, begins with a

[76] Lloyd Morgan, *Emergent Evolution* (London: Williams and Norgate, 1927).

[77] S. A. Alexander, *Space Time and Duty*, 2 vols. (London: Macmillan and Co., Ltd., 1934).

primordial "space-time." In this unrealized stuff, there is a "nisus" towards ever more complex patterns within which new qualities emerge, the whole being driven towards the emergence of self-conscious spirit and ultimately of deity. A. N. Whitehead,[78] in his philosophy of organism, finds organism everywhere, even at the inanimate level. By taking organism as his basic metaphysical model, he shows an inadequate understanding of personal being, but he too paints a teleological universe in which God is the fellow traveler, realizing himself within the movement of the natural process towards higher evolving forms. Smuts [79] finds the key to the movement in an immanent holistic principle driving the process to ever more embracing wholes, with the human spirit at the summit.

It will be noted that all these thinkers endeavor to find some deeper explanation than scientists offer. They end with the postulation of the immanence of something akin to spirit, most actualized at the level of human personal being or else moving towards actualization in deity. The process is teleological, directed by an inner "nisus." Yet the metaphysical system that results is pantheistic and immanental. This is as would be expected. If we begin with the empirical and thus the immanent, it is doubtful whether we can ever, by reasoning, reach the transcendent. Indeed, by its very definition, the transcendent is beyond such rational discovery. The ultimate and transcendent mystery, if it be, must disclose itself to us. As Marcel continually reminds us, it cannot be solved by logic, like a problem. It is known only as we become involved with it, as we live with it, in disclosure and commitment.

We have continually reiterated that such disclosure of the transcendent is of the essence of the Christian revelation, but

[78] A. N. Whitehead, *Science and the Modern World* (Cambridge: Cambridge University Press, 1932); *Process and Reality* (Cambridge: Cambridge University Press, 1929).

[79] J. Smuts, *Holism and Evolution* (reprinted; New York: The Viking Press, 1961).

we have also noted that such transcendence is not inimical to the immanence of the divine being. This is the affirmation of Christian theism and it is built into the Trinitarian structure of the divine mystery. In this volume we see no need to apologize for the acceptance of the orthodox Trinitarian position. We have sought to do this in earlier books.[80] Historically the divine creative act has been associated most intimately with the Second Person of the Holy Trinity, the Son. The Logos Christology of the Prologue to John's Gospel, also found in certain aspects of Paul's thought (I Cor. 5:6 and Col. 1:15–17), stresses the divine Word as the creative principle, while the Holy Spirit is almost entirely confined in New Testament thought to the redemptive activity of the risen and ascended Lord in the life of the believer and in the church. Yet the Old Testament witness opens in Genesis 1:1 with the picture of the Spirit brooding or hovering like a bird over the chaotic deep out of which God the Creator brought forth his ordered universe.

This at least seems clear in most theological formulations of Trinitarian doctrine—the Holy Spirit represents the immanence of God in his universe. The Father is God as the ground of creative and redemptive power; the Son or Word is the personal activity of God coming forth in creative and redemptive love; and the Holy Spirit is the immanent aspect of that love effecting the divine purpose in nature and history, and especially in the life of the redeemed man. Thus we may describe the Holy Spirit as the immanence of God within his creation, effecting the divine intention of the Father as this is expressed in creative, sustaining and redemptive activity through the Son. It is significant that at the Incarnation, the Holy Spirit is described in the New Testament witness as he who effects the divine intention within the womb of the Virgin,

[80] See E. C. Rust, *Towards a Theological Understanding of History* (New York: Oxford University Press, 1963); pp. 141 ff.; *Salvation History* (Richmond: John Knox Press, 1963), chs. V & VI.

whereby the Word becomes flesh and pitches his tent among men. But it is often forgotten that, in the imagery of the creation story of Genesis 1, the Holy Spirit broods over the primeval chaos from which God calls forth order by his creative Word, as if to suggest that the Spirit effects and sustains the creative plan within the cosmos. Too often this creative activity of the Spirit has been left on one side in Christian theological understanding.

The New Testament witness itself is not always transparently clear in its differentiation of the Spirit from the Son. Paul can speak of "the Lord, the Spirit" (II Cor. 3:17) in the same breath, as if they are identical, and yet speak of them as distinct in most of his letters, carefully distinguishing the Christ from the Spirit. Thus, in many respects the activity of the two is so identified that theological reflection has to make some clearer differentiation. This may well account for the way in which the work of the Holy Spirit is, often unintentionally, confined to the life of the believer and of the believing community, and also for the comparative neglect of the doctrine of the Holy Spirit in much Christian thinking.

The Prologue of John's Gospel can describe the Word as the creative as well as the revelatory agent, him through whom the Godhead effects both creation and redemption. It might be better, in the light of current thought, to describe the Word as the Cosmic Christ, whose Incarnation in the historical Jesus sums up the long process of creation and revelation in the movement of the divine purpose. For we need to remember that the Word, the Cosmic Christ, is he who is the source of life and also of the light which lightens all men. Wherever and at whatever level of understanding some light of meaning has dawned in the minds of men, there the eternal Son has been active.

Yet the Biblical testimony is also clear that such divine disclosure, coming to men from beyond themselves, can be grasped by them only if there is an inner illumination of their minds. This immanent presence of God illuminating men's minds, as he is also sustaining them and their material environment, is the Holy Spirit. It should be noted that the Christian revelation is given to us through God's creatures, that the divine Word comes to us in self-disclosure through the created order, the order of nature and the movement of human history in all its intrapersonal relationships. It is a mediated self-disclosure and yet it is also immediate, because the mind is illumined to grasp that which is "given." Such preparation of the human mind is, at every level of understanding, the work of the Holy Spirit, the *testimonium intus spiritus sancti.* The Cosmic Christ is God coming to us, and the Holy Spirit is God opening our blind eyes and releasing our imprisoned souls that we may grasp his coming. He takes the things of Christ and makes them plain unto us, but the things of Christ embrace not only the redemptive activity of the incarnate Lord, but also the creative, sustaining, and revelatory activity of the Cosmic Christ who is Son of God from all eternity.

In these days, when our somewhat disintegrated culture is dominated by the tremendous success of the scientific method and the technological processes which result from it, it may well be that we need to stress more than ever this role of the Spirit as the divine immanence. For the very success of science puts an emphasis on the empirical and tends to discount the transempirical. Psychologically this supports a philosophy of immanence, with little emphasis on transcendence. Increasingly, therefore, the Church is having to justify its faith in the transcendence of God, and it may well need to approach such validation by an emphasis on that divine immanence which is characterized as the activity of the Holy Spirit.

One consequence of the lack of any deep concern with a doctrine of the Holy Spirit has been a continuing tendency to refer to him as if he were not a personal presence but a kind of impersonal spiritual force. This can be traced back to Old Testament thought, where "spirit" (*ruach*) was regarded as an extension of the divine activity, a kind of invasive force which could take possession of men, like Elijah, turning them into prophets; kings, like Saul, throwing them into prophetic ecstasy; heroes, like Samson, giving them feats of superhuman strength. In the early days, spirit was not regarded as a permanent aspect of the human constitution, but as one which temporarily took possession, energizing men and conferring special gifts and insights. With the Exile, however, spirit became a permanent aspect of the human person and was especially associated with the intentional and intellectual aspect of man. Furthermore, in the pre-Exilic period God could be described as spirit in contrast to man's finitude and fleshliness. But God discloses himself as personal, and man in his psychosomatic wholeness is personal. Thus spirit was now understood as taking on personal qualities and became synonymous ultimately with personal being.

This becomes very evident in the New Testament. Here "spirit" seems to be regarded by Paul as the upper aspect of human personality. Indeed, Bultmann would identify spirit (*pneuma*) in the Apostle's thought with the self in its voluntary and conscious aspects.[81] So the divine spirit bears witness with our spirits, making us aware that we are the children of God (Rom. 8:16).[82] Confusion arises because the word "spirit" carries a double connotation of the divinely given Holy Spirit and also of the human spirit as a willing and conscious agent. Paul's thought oscillates between the two.[83] We can

[81] Thus in II Cor. 12:18, Paul uses the phrase "walk in the same spirit," which could be rendered "conduct ourselves in the same attitude or intention," R. Bultmann, *Theology of the New Testament,* trans. by K. Grobel (New York: Charles Scribner's Sons, 1951), I, 206 f.

[82] Bultmann. ibid. p. 207. Cf. I Cor. 2:11: "man's spirit knows within," a phrase set in comparison with God's spirit which alone knows the things of God.

[83] Eduard Schweizer, "The Spirit of God," *Bible Key Words,* III, 54–88, trans. from G. Kittel, *Theologisches Wörterbuch zum Neuen Testament* (New York: Harper and Bros., 1960). Schweizer holds that in

understand the ease with which his mind moves from one usage to the other. If the human spirit especially describes man's conscious and intentional attitude, his pursuit of a goal, it is that aspect of his personal being which gives him kinship with God's Spirit and a capacity to respond to the divine approach through the Holy Spirit. Paul is drawing "an explicit analogy between the self-consciousness of man and the profoundest being of God in His deepest self-awareness and self-manifestation." [84] The Spirit makes men's spirits alive because of righteousness (Rom. 8:9–10). As spirit, man is made in the image of God who is spirit.

The human spirit is in New Testament thought, therefore, the unifying center of personal being, its innermost core. Man is a psychosomatic whole for the Biblical writers. There is nothing akin to the Greek idea of the soul as something dwelling in a prison house of a body. Man is a unified whole; and the latter's prevading pattern—the purposive center of human life, the seat of free decision for or against God, the focal point of the commitment of faith—is his spirit, what Polanyi calls its active center. Spirit in man connotes his personal presence and power.

What holds of finite, embodied man holds more of "spirit" when used of God. He is personal, and he is spirit. The Holy Spirit is God's immanent personal presence and power, and it is as such that we must think of the divine activity within the creative process. Furthermore, if we understand God the Holy

Paul's true thought, the soul is never thought of as finding its completion in spirit. Where spirit is thought of as an organ in man for receiving God's spirit, he argues that it is thought of as something given man by God, ibid. p. 86. It may well be that his Reformed theology is here read overmuch into his understanding of Paul's thought. Bultmann offers a more balanced interpretation. Even Schweizer has to confess that "the thesis that Paul knows nothing of a human spirit cannot be sustained." Ibid. p. 84.

[84] A. Come, *Human Spirit and Holy Spirit* (Philadelphia: The Westminster Press, 1959), p. 81. Professor Come offers an excellent criticism of Schweizer's position and an elaboration of the position here adopted.

Trinity in his unity, on the basis of the social model, as a perfect communion of personal love,[85] we may see that in all divine activity the triune God acts as one personal whole, even though a particular "person" is associated with a special activity within the divine economy. When the Spirit acts, he always does so with the Father and the Son, even though the divine purpose becomes focalized for the time being in his distinctive activity. The Father, who is the ground of creation, issues forth in the Son, his creative Word, to effect his purpose, and the Spirit, as immanent presence, fulfills that purpose within the creaturely order.[86]

One might be acccused at this point of almost identifying the Spirit with the Creative Word, the Cosmic Christ; and, indeed, careful distinction is not always drawn, even at the redemptive level, between the Spirit and the risen Lord. It is noteworthy that the earliest post-New Testament writers, the Apostolic Fathers, tended to identify the Spirit with the Logos,[87] yet the Prologue to the Fourth Gospel and the development

[85] I have discussed this at length in *The Review and Expositor,* Vol. LXIII, 2, and used H. W. Robinson's suggestion of a mutual indwelling of the three "Persons" in a perfect harmony of being, so co-inherent that their will is one because God in his organic personal wholeness is love. Cf. H. W. Robinson, *The Christian Experience of the Holy Spirit* (London: Nisbet & Company, Ltd., 1930), pp. 271–81.

[86] Cf. Prenter's interpretation of Luther's thought: "The Son is the Word by which that which is created is brought forth from nothing. The Spirit is the sanctifying and preserving love of God by which he takes creation into himself and preserves it in the Word." Regin Prenter, *Spiritus Creator,* trans. by J. M. Jensen (Philadelphia: Muhlenburg Press, 1953), p. 192. Cf. also H. B. Swete, *The Holy Spirit in the Ancient Church* (London: Macmillan & Co., Ltd., 1912), p. 15: "Apart from the Spirit, the Cross stands inert, a vast machine at rest, and about it lie the stones of the building unmoved. Not till the rope has been attached can the work proceed of lifting the individual life through faith and love to the place prepared for it in the Church of God."

[87] H. B. Swete notes that "it is common to find the titles of the Holy Ghost assigned to the Logos." *On the Early History of the Doctrine of the Holy Spirit* (London: George Bell & Sons, 1873), p. 15. H. R. Wolf-

of a Logos-Christology by the Greek Fathers ensured that the creative aspect of the work of the Son/Word should be retained.[88] The fact that the Holy Spirit dropped into the background after the suppression of Montanism, with its pneumatic emphasis, and during the Christological controversies of the first centuries, should not blind us, however, to his importance in theological thought. The Nicene Creed retained the description of him as the "Giver of Life," and the Western tradition, in its technical jargon, described him as proceeding from both the Father, the Creator, and the Son, the Redeemer. There would seem to be here some effort to retain the significance of the Spirit outside the narrow realm of the Church and redemptive experience.

It remains true, of course, that the creative activity of the Cosmic Christ seems to fill the picture of creation. Yet two points need to be borne in mind. For one thing, the Christ, as cosmic Word, incarnate Son, and risen and ascended Lord, still retains in Christian thought a measure of transcendence which cannot easily be reconciled with the immanent aspect that the divine creative activity would demand. Secondly, the Godhead acts as a personal unity, so that Father, Son, and Spirit are present at every level, creative and redemptive. Thus the close association of the Son with the Spirit at the level of the divine creative activity is in keeping with a true Trinitarian theology. At the same time, it safeguards that immanent aspect of the divine creative work, whereas the emphasis on the Father safeguards the transcendent aspect of the divine being, the depths of divine love in which the creative urge originates. Trinitarian

son, *The Philosophy of the Church Fathers* (Cambridge, Mass.: Harvard University Press, 1956), p. 191, notes that at the end of the period of the Apostolic Fathers the Holy Spirit is identified with the pre-existent Christ.

[88] H. Wheeler Robinson, *The Christian Experience of the Holy Spirit* (London: Nisbet and Co., Ltd., 1930) p. 21*n*. He regards it as "interesting to speculate on the consequences for Christian theology if the Logos idea had been linked to the Spirit instead of the Son."

theology sought historically to safeguard this by defining the Father as the eternal source of the Godhead, and by speaking of the Son and the Spirit as being eternally begotten and as eternally proceeding respectively. The language is outmoded and, of course, logically odd, as is to be expected. In addition, such theological speculation is frowned upon in these pragmatic days. But the emphasis needs to be remembered. H. P. van Dusen expresses this well:

> THE NEVER-FAILING AVAILABILITY OF GOD—of this, we are made sure in the Holy Spirit. But that PRESENCE—so near, so intimate, ever about us and within us—that very self-same PRESENCE pervades the whole Universe, and determines its every atom and motion; and, that PRESENCE often so hauntingly vague and mysterious, is —the Spirit of Jesus Christ.[89]

The whole picture now becomes meaningful on the basis of the model for transcendence and immanence that was suggested in the preceding chapter.

The divine immanence must be described in language other than that required for empirical science. Furthermore, there must be no attempt to fill up gaps in scientific knowledge by introducing such theological concepts, for it is of the essence of science that it lays claim to the whole realm of observable nature at its own level of explanation. The theologian must be careful not to mix up theological statements with scientific statements. In so doing he lays himself open to justifiable attack. He may, in the light of his own theological understanding of nature, call in question some theories, but he must produce evidence at the scientific level which would invalidate them. If this is not possible, he must call to mind that science is concerned with the observable aspects of nature and with empirically verifiable invariants (such as laws or regularities)

[89] H. P. van Dusen, *Spirit, Son and Father* (New York: Charles Scribner's Sons, 1958), p. 177.

which observation discloses as permanent relations between observable entities. Whereas his own task is concerned with the "depths" of the natural order, the hidden and divine forces which sustain the relationships and invariants that science studies and which guide them to their appointed goals. Thus he is concerned with teleology and purpose in nature, whereas science, by its very method, ignores such concepts. It is concerned with relations between observables and not with unobservable potencies, with accidents and not with substantial forms, as medieval scholasticism expressed it—*accidentia,* not *substantia.*

The last reference is no advocacy of the old Aristotelianism or of Neo-Vitalism. Rather we are suggesting that the theologian is concerned with an immanent teleology inherent in the very process itself, by which the Creator Spirit works in and through the psychophysical medium, effecting his purpose. Outwardly we may expect to see signs of this presence which sometimes are manifested in scientific observation and sometimes not, since science, for its own purposes and because of its techniques, ignores their presence. We must think of this immanent Creator Spirit as leading and organizing nature from within, until, at long last, finite spirit may emerge within the process, with all the possibilities of free responsible personal being, and thereby be gathered into the greater whole of the divine community of love, what has been called the "hyperpersonal."

Perhaps no contemporary thinker has been more concerned with this understanding of evolution than Teilhard de Chardin.[90] He sees a developing inner side to the evolutionary process as well as the outer aspect with which empirical science is primarily concerned, and he offers what he calls a phenomenological study of the natural process. He sees an increasing proliferation or divergence as the evolutionary move-

[90] Teilhard de Chardin, op. cit. *passim.*

ment moves from the physical to the vital and as the earth becomes metaphorically covered by a skin of life which he terms the "biosphere." He sees a movement of matter towards more and more complex states and to this degree states that they are increasingly improbable. Yet, within this growing complexity of the cosmic stuff, self-consciousness emerges, and the earth is covered by yet another skin, that of mind (*nous*) the "noosphere." He is careful to explain that by complexity he does not mean mere aggregation but an organized heterogenity, a developing "wholeness." At the level of the noosphere, the divergence gives place to convergence. The inner side of the process seems to take over. The proliferation of species begins to cease as the movement passes to the anthropoids and hominoids. We come to an increasing convergence which issues in the emergence of one self-conscious species, *Homo sapiens*. Then evolution undergoes a radical change, as what is passively borne moves into "auto-evolution." In man consciousness turns in upon itself and becomes thought. "When for the first time in a living creature instinct perceived itself in its own mirror, the whole world took a pace forward." [91] Indeed, the earth finds its soul.

Teilhard sees this increasing convergence, as it works out in man in its sociological aspect, directed upon an Omega Point. Here the mystical element in his thought differentiates itself increasingly from the scientific. The Omega Point is a personal transcendent center towards which the whole evolutionary process moves. Here the process becomes involuted as the convergence reaches its center and the whole is integrated into the life of God. Such union of the personal must preserve the personal differentiation. It must neither fuse nor dissolve the personal. Hence it must be distinct from them, and so the Omega point can be described both as transcendent and as possessing its own personal being. Phenomenological analysis

[91] Ibid. p. 181.

ends here, but the Christian faith takes over, and Teilhard finds the Omega Point already actualized in the Incarnation. The whole creative process is thus brought to a focus in Christ and in the unified society which is gathered into his representative humanity, his Body which is the Church. This is the hyperpersonal goal.

Once more we find a vision of God the Holy Spirit as immanent within the process, an immanent will quickening and guiding the whole until it becomes conscious and finally self-conscious. R. C. Zaehner has a tendency to a pantheistic emphasis in his stimulating book *Matter and Spirit,* but he is, within this limitation, seeking to express the same truth. He points out that even the Marxists admit that the universe is being propelled towards self-consciousness by a force which they attribute to the "inner laws of nature." He argues that this is simply an evasive way of talking about "an immanent will pursuing the ends of a mind innate in nature herself." [92] He would identify this with the Holy Spirit. His further comment is significant and creative:

> We cannot understand how the Holy Spirit can *both* operate in matter, thrusting it forward to consciousness and perhaps beyond to what Teilhard de Chardin calls the "hyper-consciousness" of the whole phylum, *and* remain outside it all as the bond of unity that welds together the Godhead itself. We cannot understand this at all unless we can imagine that it would please an absolutely perfect being not only to raise up to himself children who should in the end become "like him" in that they should share in his eternal mode of existence, but also to assume to himself their very nothingness and weakness that he might himself bring them back to his own perfection.[93]

[92] R. C. Zaehner, *Matter and Spirit* (New York: Harper & Row, 1963), p. 189.

[93] Ibid. pp. 189 f.

v. *The kenosis of the Spirit*

By speaking of the immanence of the Spirit, we are not implying any pantheistic interpretation. He is not to be identified with the process in which he is creatively and dynamically at work. He is certainly not to be identified with the potentialities present, as we have suggested, in the primordial energy itself. Rather it is he who by his immanence directs the process, creatively making it possible for the new qualities to emerge within that structure. In other words he provides the nisus or creativity evident throughout the evolutionary development. He is the holistic principle manifested at every level, indwelling the whole process and leading it towards its consummation, a blessed community in which the love of God is fully realized. At this point we may find help for our understanding, as always, in the Incarnation, for does not Paul remind us that the Son emptied himself and made himself of no reputation and took upon him the garb of a slave (Phil. 2:6–8)? Outwardly Jesus of Nazareth walked among men so evidently human that few discovered his incognito, and then only when the eyes of faith were opened. The deity was veiled in the humanity, in all its phases—birth, childhood, manhood, and death. The hiddenness of the divine activity is always the concomitant of the divine revelation. God hides himself as he gives himself, and never more so than in the Incarnation. But then his revelation always is mediated through his creatures, and those who fix their eyes upon the creatures may miss that disclosure which awaits those who look through the creatures with the eyes of the spirit. Outwardly our Lord manifested the same physical, biological, physiological, and psychological behavior as his fellows, but inwardly there was that perfect union of God with man which faith alone can affirm.

So too with the presence of the Spirit in and with the order of nature. May we not here also, as H. W. Robinson [94] suggests, affirm a kenosis, a self-emptying? Just as the Son poured his deity into the vessel of humanity and freely accepted the limitation of a historical human personality, so the Spirit has freely accepted the limitations of the natural order at all levels within which to exercise his creative and directive activity. Furthermore, we may not expect that the natural process will disclose his presence at the empirical level, even though, as we have seen, signs of creativeness and directiveness may present themselves. Rather we may expect that the analyses of scientific method and theory will provide a descriptive explanation at their own level without any reference to the divine presence. For this is what kenosis means: "self-emptying and humiliation of spirit when it expresses itself, as it always must, in 'degrees of reality' lower than itself." [95] Even at the human level, finite spirit, the core of personal being in its self-consciousness, is limited as it seeks to express, communicate, and disclose itself through the outward medium of the body and the natural order. So always the spiritual must lay aside "some of its own attributes and powers when clothing itself in the material." [96] Only that can be manifested which is consonant with the behavior, structure, and laws operative at the level of reality of the medium.

Yet the kenosis may also mean a "Calvary" of the Spirit! If this natural order with its interplay of physical and vital forces is to provide the environment within which free incarnated spirits, personal beings, may freely choose to love God for himself, such freedom would not be possible in a totally determined universe. The continual references in modern science, at all levels of investigation, to probability, chance, and randomness may indicate an aspect of reality which even the theo-

[94] H. W. Robinson, *The Christian Experience of the Holy Spirit* (London: Nisbet and Co., Ltd., 1930), pp. 87 ff.

[95] Ibid. p. 87.

[96] Ibid. p. 87.

logian should not dismiss. Too much ought not to be made of indeterminacy in the subatomic and atomic orders; and it may well be, as we have suggested, that the Neo-Darwinian emphasis on random mutations presents but half of the true picture, yet we might expect to see systems in tension and conflict within the orderliness of nature. An element of contingency may well be anticipated, always within and overruled by a framework of orderliness, for this would leave an area in which the human spirit could freely express itself in outward behavior.

Any observer of the vast process of evolution cannot evade the signs of deterioration and degeneration in certain species which form branches of the tree of life, nor the unexpectedly evil and unaesthetic twists which the very fecundity of nature produces in its children, nor the waste and suffering that underlie the upward surge of the process. Evolution does not advance in a straight line. It seems, at times, to advance along blind alleys, to grope until the right complexity for creative advance opens up before it. Technically we cite this as the dysteleological aspect, but it should not blind our eyes to the way in which life and thought, the appraisal of beauty, and the moral consciousness have emerged within the whole. We may see here the activity of the Creator Spirit who gives play to contingent elements and rival natural systems while exercising over them a control which finds expression in the orderliness of nature and the nisus of the process of evolution. Might we not say that the self-limitation of the creative Spirit carries the agony of creating an aspect of disorder within the order that he may guide the whole to be a true environment for free and finite spirits? If this be so we might see even a creation groaning and travailing for the unveiling of the sons of God and within it listen for the travail of the indwelling Spirit himself groaning with groanings that cannot be uttered.

This should not surprise us if the whole creative process is to find its culmination in the Incarnation. Such a process is costly to God, yet he has willed to share his blessed love and life with his creatures too! Just as, in our human experience, error, frustration, disobedience, and rebellion in those we love bring suffering and often redemptive suffering to the human heart, so we may see a cross that God bears in his essential being from the moment of creation. That cross is borne in the immanence of the Creator Spirit and finds its culmination in the Incarnation and Cross on Calvary's hill. "If Christ crucified be the one perfect manifestation of the Godhead to us, then we shall expect to find foreshadowings of it at every preliminary stage of the creative process."[97] Any doctrine of creation and providence has a cross at its heart.

VI. *The Creator Spirit and finite spirit*

Modern man has a long prehistory. Skeletons of creatures walking erect with structures resembling man have been discovered in Africa and Asia, especially the former, dating back to hundreds of millennia. Such skeletons may not be those of true man, but rather of that psychophysical organism which God was preparing for activation by the human spirit. Actually the time span need not disturb us, if we recognize that the whole process is under the divine creative activity and that God was patiently making ready an organism in which self-conscious spirit should be actualized. When man did emerge in his fullness as spirit, he manifested the threefold capacity to worship God, to relate himself morally to his fellows, and to control the lower nature in his own and higher interests. This kind of evidence from the remote past is so difficult to attain that we cannot say when this happened.

With this emergence of free personal being, the creative activity of the spirit reached its climax, yet it also reached its

[97] C. E. Raven, *Natural Religion and Christian Theology*, Vol. II: *Experience and Interpretation* (Cambridge: Cambridge University Press, 1953), p. 157.

final obstacle—human freedom. God, who mysteriously and wonderfully creates finite spirits to share in his own freedom, must bear the cost of that God-given freedom. With the appearance of man, free to decide under the sense of the divine claim, the process reaches its crisis. The long upward process with its joy and its travail issues in a rebellion which the immanent Spirit sustains, accompanies, and bears in love. He strives with men, still guiding the movement of human history and encompassing their sinful rebellion within the circle of divine claim and the divinely instituted orders of relationship. Finite spirit, in attaining to self-consciousness and thus to self-transcendence, not only becomes aware of itself, but also aware of the all encompassing, unconditioned presence of God. Everywhere the human spirit encounters the divine Spirit. Emerging in the ascending process with a capacity for apprehending absolute values, created with a conscience capable of experiencing the pressure of the divine claim, possessing a freedom to decide for his own interests or for the encompassing personal presence, man chooses himself, and the calvary of the Creator Spirit reaches its climax.

Through his Spirit, God strives with men, sustaining them in their rebellion and pressing his claim upon them in judgment and in mercy, convicting their consciences and granting them visions of his love. Moreover, he illumines their understanding that they may grasp something of his created order. From the days of rudimentary science mingled with magic to the days of a highly developed science, the great advances in man's understanding of and control over his environment have come with intuitive insights that bear all the signs of personal disclosure. The movement of the Spirit in the order of nature has been matched by his illuminating presence in the minds of men. Despite man's sin, God has unlocked to man the mysteries of natural structure and of his own bodily form. Man in his misuse of his freedom has often misdirected the knowledge, and yet the Spirit has patiently guided the movement of human history as he has guided the evolution of the natural order.

Through the millennia of preparation the immanent Spirit brings human history to its climax in the Incarnation. The Gospel insight describes his presence in the womb of the Virgin making possible the miracle of all miracles, the redemptive presence of "God with us." In Jesus of Nazareth our torn and broken humanity is gathered up into the life of God, and the travail of the Creator Spirit issues in the agony of Calvary and the glory of the Resurrection morn. Here the process is redirected. Here man finds his true personhood by the commitment in faith to the God-man. Here he learns that he is truly free only as he surrenders his freedom to God. Here the Spirit takes up his dwelling in a new way, and a man truly lives, as the Spirit, who is now the Spirit of Christ continuing the work of the Incarnation, dwells in him. Here our scientific knowledge finds its true framework in that wisdom which is the knowledge of God. Here the "hyper-personal" goal is manifested already in the body of Christ, the Church. We have already spoken of man as free spirit. To speak in this way, we must examine what science says about man and correlate it with the Christian understanding of man.

V

The Nature of Man as a Psychosomatic Whole

With the nature of man scientific knowledge and theological understanding have a frontier situation. Scientific method is concerned with what is observable and thus fundamentally with man's outward, somatic aspect—hence it is concerned with the body's physics and chemistry, with its biological structure and functioning, and with the observable aspects of psychic and mental behavior. At the level of neurophysiology and especially in the functioning of the cerebral cortex, the issue of the nature of mind and its relation to the brain becomes very real. Furthermore, the causative structure of the physical sciences raises serious problems with regard to the reality of freedom and the nature of human personality. When psychology ventures within the mind and moves from its behavioristic forms to a preoccupation with the depths of the conscious and unconscious mind, new difficulties arise. For here too, the attempt to retain a scientific approach necessitates the retention of a causal structure, and hence the attempt to account for man's spiritual ideals and personal qualities on a naturalistic causal basis. The challenge of behaviorism on the one hand and such theories as those of Freud on the other thereby become living issues in the defense of the Christian understanding of man.

1. *The Christian understanding of man*

It is well that we should begin very briefly with an analysis of the roots of the Hebrew-Christian view of man in the Biblical testimony. In Old Testament thought the word for "soul," *nephesh,* has a totally different connotation from that in Greek thought and in much of current usage. For the Greek the "soul" was essentially rational, and it was imprisoned in the bodily structure. The rational soul, the *nous,* had appetitive appendages because of such somatic imprisonment, but the reality in man was his reason, and this alone was immortal. The Greek stress on "reason" is matched by the Hebrew emphasis on "will." A static conception of reality as an unmoved rational structure stands over against the Hebrew dynamic understanding of reality as living and personal—God is personal will and love. Correspondingly, reality is known for the Hebrew not by rational contemplation as it is for the Greek, but in obedience and personal trust. The Hebrew was consequently much more concerned with man as a personal being in his totality. He did not despise the physical order, the realm of becoming. It was good because God had created it. It was no shadowy realm, no moving image of reality. It was real and man's bodily state was not something from which he must long to escape.

We are not surprised, therefore, to find that the Hebrew is concerned with man as personal being in his psychosomatic wholeness. The word for soul, *nephesh,* has various shades of meaning. At its simplest level it means "life," the animating principle which animates the personal totality and is specially associated with the blood and the breath. At a deeper level it stands for the personal being, the "I," and here the emphasis does not fall upon some inner ego but upon the self in its outward appearance as well as its inward aspects. It signifies all the elements which constitute a living person. As such it may also stand for some of those elements and in particular the psychic functions associated with feeling and desire. Thus the "soul" can also denote the emotive side of man's life.

This personal totality is a whole constituted of many elements. Man is not to be differentiated from any of them, for they together make up personal being, a living *nephesh.* Man is "flesh" or "dust" and as such is distinguished from God. The flesh is a reminder of his creatureliness and betokens his oneness with all other created things, for all creatures have this in common. Yet the flesh is not wholly material in our modern sense, for it may manifest psychic characteristics—a man's flesh may long for God (Ps. 84:3). Evolution only serves to bear out such a point of view. Within the bodily whole, the "heart," *leb,* also performs psychic as well as physical functions. It is associated with willing and knowing, and is indeed the controlling instrument. In it the springs of life rise up (Prov. 4:23). It is the seat of understanding (Prov. 23:12), and thinking is described as "saying in one's heart" (I Sam. 1:13). Here the conscience is grounded (I Sam. 24:5), and from the heart man's will is directed (Eccles. 11:9). Thus the "heart" in a real sense is the measure of a man's personal being, and yet it is only a part of his totality. He *has* a "heart," and he *is* a "soul." In exilic and post-exilic usage "spirit," *ruach,* becomes also a constituent and permanent element of man's personal whole. Originally an invasive element and regarded as a divine agent, God's power taking possession of the individual, it now became a constituent of man's nature serving psychic functions akin to those performed by the "heart." It is especially bound up with the personal activities of thinking and willing, of knowing and obedience, and in such activity it provides the instrument for man's communion with God.

In all this we are not to think of man as a kind of dissociated trichotomy of body, mind, and spirit. The Hebrew had no word for body except "soul," *nephesh,* and occasionally "flesh," *basar.* A corpse was described as a dead soul (Num. 6:6). Rather, we are to think of a personal whole which in its totality as soul, involves, as well as its concrete and outer bodily aspect to which "soul" is especially applicable, an inner and personal integrating core of willing and thinking which is particularly associated with "heart" and "spirit." Yet the inner and outer constitute one psychosomatic whole, and it is as such that man must survive death. Hence the understanding of such survival is in terms of resurrection.

One other term used to describe man is the "image of God" (Gen. 1:26 f.). Entering Hebrew usage about the same time as the human element of spirit, the term represents man's unique relation to God. And yet, it involves also his relationship to his fellows. The priestly writer can describe man and woman as made in the image of God, selecting the most intimate of personal relationships as a type for all. Such responsible personal relationship is conjoined to the ability to subdue and direct the lower order of nature. Thus man as a responsible being under God is created both a social and a tool-using creature.

In the New Testament Greek influence has been felt to some extent, but the basis for the Christian understanding of man lies still in the Hebrew tradition. The word "body," *soma,* now comes into usage, but, like Hebrew "soul," it stands for personal being in its concrete aspect, and thus to speak of the resurrected "body" is really to speak of resurrected personal being. "*Soma*" represents the corporeal totality of man and thus means more than his physicobiological aspect. It is used of man as a personal whole.[1] Again, "soul," *psyche,* as in the Old Testament usage, is used to describe man in his entirety. He is a living being, and soul describes him as such a being in his outer bodily aspect and in his inner nature as consciousness, a being who thinks and wills. The "heart," *kardia,* continues to be associated with man's reflective and voluntary life, but it is conjoined to "mind," *nous.*[2] Here we reach the inward aspects of human personality, the area of decision and conscience, of thought and judgment. Man is a self-conscious, rational, morally responsible being, and it is, as such, that he is an "I." Perhaps this inward aspect of the personal totality, the "I," is described most significantly in the Pauline use of "spirit." Despite a current exegetical fashion to associate "spirit" al-

[1] Note especially Paul's usage in Rom. 12:4 ff. and I Cor. 12: 12–26.

[2] E.g. Rom. 6:17; Luke 6:15; Rom. 12:2; 14:5. "Heart" is more confined to intention and willing, whereas "mind" stands more for knowing, the intellect.

ways with a divinely given element in the redeemed man, we shall follow Bultmann's interpretation of it as a permanent constituent of human personality, fallen as well as redeemed.[3] Just as "body" and soul can take the place of the personal pronoun "I," so also can "spirit" (II Cor. 2:13, 7:13). In distinction from "soul," "spirit" refers, however, to the conscious aspect of the personal whole and is thus approaching "mind." It also connotes intentional and voluntary aspects of personal being (II Cor. 12:18). Thus "spirit" denotes the self in its self-conscious and voluntary totality, and as such is especially bound up with the activity of the Holy Spirit in the believer's life. This continues the developed Hebrew usage.

Man's psychosomatic existence is in the "flesh," *sarx,* but again the "flesh" is not just physicobiological. It possesses psychical characteristics and can dominate the mind and the heart. It betokens man's creatureliness and, in the New Testament, can be the special seat of sin. Man is in the flesh, but, as a redeemed person, he will not walk after the flesh (Gal. 2:20; Phil. 1:22; cf. II Cor. 5:16, 10:2; Rom. 8:5).

The total picture which emerges is one of man as a self-conscious person capable of willing and thinking, of loving and choosing, existing in responsible relationship to God and to his fellows. As such, man is constituted a psychosomatic unity around an inner self-transcendent "I" which is expressed in the outer somatic condition. There is no thought of an imprisoned soul, of the body as alien to the spirit, of an unreconcilable dichotomy between mind and matter. Rather, the body is the outward expression of personality which has its roots in the heart, the mind, the spirit. All are within a psychosomatic totality, and it is as such that man is a self-conscious subject. He is a living self-transcendent whole who has the capacity freely to respond to God in love.

This picture is gathered to a focus in the Incarnation. In

[3] See R. Bultmann, *Theology of the New Testament,* Vol. I, trans. K. Grobel (New York: Charles Scribner's Sons, 1951), pp. 205 ff. This is shown in I Cor. 7:23, 2:10 f.; I Thess. 5:23. See also above pp. 187 f.

Christ we see man as he should be, living in intimate communion with God and in self-less and self-giving relationship to his fellows. Christ is *the* man for all men, and yet his every act manifests an inner freedom which is brought to clarity in Gethsemane. He found his perfect freedom in doing the Father's will, and yet the choice before him was clearly a real one when he set his face, like a flint, to go to Jerusalem. He was concerned with the whole man as his healing miracles show. Healing of the body and forgiveness of sins might be two ways of describing the same mighty act of the Kingdom through his own person. For him man was a whole, and as such he was the child of God to whom the Son of Man must show compassion.

Yet this picture of man is marred by man's alienation from God. He has mishandled his freedom, fixed his eyes upon himself and his physical environment. In his pride he has built his life around himself and his own powers, instead of around his Creator.[4] He has used his God-given powers to make the lower orders of creation serve his own ends, and his relation to his fellows has become subservient to selfish motives. His estrangement from his Creator leads to estrangement from others. Nature and society have fallen apart because of man's sin. The Biblical analysis of this estrangement describes it as rebellion, the rebellion of the creature against his Creator. Yet, because it is creaturely rebellion, it is rooted in both pride and fear, as the saga of Genesis 3 discloses. On the one hand, there is man's trust in his own powers and thus his tendency to God-almightiness. On the other, there is a creaturely insecurity, a fear that drives him to rely upon himself lest this invisible God fail him.

In the Biblical picture, the Incarnation is not just a picture

[4] Bultmann points out that the phrase "after the flesh" is ambiguous. Used to modify substantives, it indicates, like the phrase "in the flesh," man's creaturely mode of existence (Rom. 9:3; I Cor. 10:18). But used to modify verbs, it indicates *sinful* existence (II Cor. 1:17), op. cit. pp. 236 ff.

of man as he ought to be, but also a redemptive act in which God reconciles estranged humanity to himself and straightens out its misdirected life. The healing miracles of our Lord and his compassion indicate an understanding of man's sin which embraces his psychosomatic totality. Nor can we forget his dying words: "Father, forgive them; for they know not what they do." Our frail creatureliness is such that we cannot put ourselves right and often we do not realize the implications of what we do. Even our responsibility for our deeds can be measured aright only by our Creator!

II. *The physical basis and physiological substructure of personhood*

The psychosomatic nature of the human person has been borne out increasingly as science has progressed. Evidently our personality, our selfhood, has its roots deep down in the physical and physiological aspects of our bodily structure. More and more we are made aware of the interrelationship of a body chemistry and our personal characteristics, of the intimate bond between the brain and our mental activity, of the implications of our genetic structure for our personal development.

The relation of our behavioral patterns and personality traits to the secretions of the endocrine glands is an immediate indication of our psychosomatic wholeness. These glands with their hormone secretions form a balanced cycle mutually influencing one another through the blood stream and also influencing the development of somatic organs and functions. The effect of the pituitary gland secretions upon bodily development, the relationship of oversecretion of its growth hormone to initiative, courage, and aggressiveness in human personality, the way in which its activity affects sex development so that overactivity can produce the nymphomanic—all these are significant evidence of the physical roots of personal being. They show that many of the problems raised by human behavior can be traced back in part to the chemical constitution of the human body.

To these should be added the significant effect of the thyroid gland secretions upon man's mental life. A placid or a highly strung temperament is related to the state of the parathyroids with their influence upon calcium metabolism. A thyroid excess or a parathyroid deficiency can often lead to emotional instability and to an apprehensive attitude towards life. An underactive thyroid can be associated with lack of concentration, mental backwardness, and indecision. The whole area is mysterious still in many ways, and temperament is not completely decided by endocrine secretions. But it is apparent that a proper balance of the endocrine glands is important for the energy, social aggressiveness, tenderness, and sex interest of a person.

It is also increasingly evident that the interaction between the nervous system and the glands is mutual, so that patterns of adjustment in the nervous system exercise an influence upon the endocrine balance. As Gardner Murphy puts it: "We are dealing with no one-way street from glands to external traits; excess thyroid activity may lead to apprehensiveness but it may also arise from it."[5] A. P. Noyes cautiously notes that "inherent differences in size and reactivity of endocrines may be among factors producing individual differences in temperament" and warns that ". . . the relation of personality structure and mental disorders to endocrine disturbance is only indirect."[6] Thus we cannot say that these glands and their hormones *determine* certain aspects of the personality, especially those associated with affective response, which we describe as temperament. But we can say that they provide a

[5] Gardner Murphy, *Personality* (New York: Harper & Bros., 1947), p. 98.

[6] A. P. Noyes, *Modern Clinical Psychiatry* (Philadelphia: W. B. Saunders), p. 73.

chemical base within which the personality and its traits have to operate. The delicate chemical balance of our physiological structure has effects on our personality.

Yet more primal than our body chemistry at this level is the genetic structure which is ours by heredity. Every living cell of the human body, except for the seed cells, possesses in its nucleus forty-eight paired chromosomes, twenty-four from each parent. These chromosomes, as previously discussed, are highly complex organic molecules, coded by genes. We now know their structure better because of our work with desoxyribonucleic acid. They carry not only our physical traits but also our behavioristic ones. Much of our psychology would appear to be bound up with these strange entities. As the RNA molecules are sent out from their coding, these messengers penetrate every part of the developing human being and help to shape his physiological and psychological machinery. We cannot escape our heredity, which we carry inside every cell of our body, like a molecular computer properly programmed to effect the required developments in our psychosomatic whole. This means that many personal characteristics which seem bound up with our mental and spiritual life are inherited by and bound up with a physiological structure which has a chemical base. Our conscious life with its peculiarities, and our character traits, are tied in with the physicochemical forces which are basic in the development of the embryo. It is the Hebrew rather than the Greek understanding of soul that we are concerned with here.

Because man is one with the mammalian order, he carries with him in his bodily structure the same instinctive reactions and impulses similar to those of other living creatures. The structure and functioning of such inherent modes of behavior is undoubtedly carried within the coding of his genetic structure. They consist of unlearned and inborn structures and as such must be distinguished from modifiable and learned behavior. At the lowest organic level we have the simple reflex action in which a single somatic organ or a system of organs responds immediately to a simple stimulus. There would seem here to be no conscious accompaniment and thus no evidence of what we would normally describe as mind. But the higher animals have much more complicated systems of reaction in which an elaborate chain of responses involves a close co-ordination of various bodily organs. Here reflex actions play their part, but the whole is more than physical and appears to be on the border line of the psychical. It is instinctive, in the accepted sense of that term, an inborn urge, and would seem to have emotional accompaniments. It is evoked in its totality, given the appropriate stimulus and physiological condition, and, when its behavioristic expression is inhibited, intense emotional reaction results, such as frustration and anger. This tension would seem to indicate that some degree of conscious feeling is basic in such instinctive drives. As W. H. Thorpe puts it, ". . . emotion is the boiling over of a heated instinct."[7] Thus already mind is beginning to make its appearance, although we must beware of associating all instinctive activity with conscious feeling.

At the level of the higher animals, mental processes akin to our own seem to be evidenced in instinctive behavior, but this does not hold throughout the animal order, and "modern analaysis of sense-organ function and brain function, and the structure of the nervous system and the spinal cord, is tending to provide a reasonably adequate physiological description of much of such behavior."[8] What we call mind or consciousness does, however, become more evident as we move from instinctive to learned and modified behavior.

Now man, because of his evolutionary heritage, does show in his own behavior the deposit of the behavioral types just discussed. In him, too, we find the instincts of self-preserva-

[7] W. H. Thorpe, *Biology and the Nature of Man* (London: Oxford University Press, 1962), p. 30.

[8] W. H. Thorpe, op. cit. p. 30.

tion, sex, aggression, and gregariousness. Often he behaves not as a result of mental reflection and conscious decision, but as a result of inborn drives and instinctive urges. These are built into his psychosomatic wholeness, and they lie at the borderline of the physical and the psychical.

As we ascend the scale of animal life, we find such instinctive urges increasingly flexible and more and more modified by learned behavior. This variation reaches its climax in man and is bound up in the evolutionary process, with an increasing centralization of the nervous system and its association with a developing brain structure. Here consciousness comes to occupy the center of the stage, and the mystery of mind confronts us.

III. *Mind and the cerebral cortex*

Conscious mind and mental processes are now known to be restricted to that part of the brain known as the cerebral cortex, a thin layer of gray matter. Certain parts of the cerebral cortex would seem to be associated with particular sense organs, but in the case of man there is a co-ordination between them. Thus artificial stimulation of certain areas of the brain can produce certain sensations. The thalamus at the neural entrance to the brain appears to be a relay and sorting station through which the various sensory impulses are transmitted to their appropriate corticle area.[9] Le Gros Clark suggests that these groups of cells also "allow for the resorting of the incoming impulses so that they are then projected on to the cerebral cortex in a new kind of pattern." [10] If the corticle area associated with any sense organ be destroyed, any consciousness of the associated sensation ceases.

[9] See W. E. Le Gros Clark, "The Structure of the Brain and the process of Thinking," *The Physical Basis of Mind,* ed. Peter Laslett (Oxford: Basil Blackwell, 1957), pp. 18 f.

[10] Ibid. p. 19.

It may well be that in the earlier stages of evolution living organisms had more than one center of consciousness, but, at the human level, there is the functioning of a unitary consciousness. As Thorpe points out, however much lower organisms may possess multiple minds, "the mind of man is a unity," although this is a later evolutionary development and "is far from perfect even now."[11] Memory is carried apparently in any part of the cortex, and the memory capacity is a function of the size of the brain rather than of the location.[12]

The intimate relation of man's personal life to the cerebral cortex is indicated by the operation known as lobotomy, performed sometimes on persons suffering from such mental disorders as schizophrenia and melancholia. In this, the large bundles of nerves connecting the front part of the brain with the rest are cut. The prefrontal area of the cortex is associated with the thought processes, and in this operation the connection is broken between thought and emotion. In consequence emotional tension is eliminated and anxiety disappears. An excitable patient becomes quiet and reasonable.

Unfortunately the operation, while eliminating overanxiety, may also lead to inconsiderateness and sometimes to a loss of planned initiative. Since the operation is performed on mentally ill people, the actual effects are somewhat in dispute. Similar conditions arise when there is injury to the frontal lobes of the brain. An energetic person can become listless, and good nature can give place to touchiness.

The brain functions only as the blood supply with its blood sugar content is functioning normally. Here the glands, the brain, and consciousness are often bound together. Anxiety arising in the consciousness may send stimulation down the nervous system, upset the secretions of the suprarenal glands,

[11] W. H. Thorpe, op. cit. p. 58.

[12] See Ibid. p. 56. Lashley's experimental removal of brain tissue shows that the amount of forgetting is dependent on the quantity of brain tissue removed and not on its location.

cause changes in blood pressure and heart beat, lead to changes in blood sugar, and result in physical upset.

How then does the brain function and what is its structure? Here we have been helped considerably by the tremendous developments in the construction and use of calculating machines. Electronic computers have certain inbuilt elements which enable them to function. They are constructed to observe certain rules; they are then able to store information in their "memory," and this information is so stored that it can be "scanned" and made into available data for calculation. Finally, we have the control unit which governs the whole process. The similarity to the brain has led many to regard the latter as just a highly complex "thinking engine" and to regard "mind" as an unnecessary term, possessing no distinct actuality as a separate entity.

Let us look at the brain itself. It acts as an integrating center for the complex nervous system of the human body which feeds its messages into the spinal cord and thus transmits them to the brain. The mechanism of the latter is centered, as we have seen, in the gray matter on its surface, the cerebral cortex. Here we have a complicated pattern of intertwining nerve fibers, which connect about ten billion nerve cells or neurons. Sherrington once likened the brain in action to "an enchanted loom where millions of flashing shuttles weave a dissolving pattern, always a meaningful pattern though never an abiding one." [13] A more sober and scientific description is offered by Adrian:

> The essential activity seems to consist in a sudden change in the cell surface which allows a momentary escape of some of the molecules. This surface change can be repeated at very short intervals so that the cell may become active and inactive as often as fifty times a second, and each time it becomes active an impulse will

[13] C. Sherrington, *Man and His Nature* (Cambridge: Cambridge University Press, 1946), p. 225.

> pass out from the cell to its neighbors or further afield to other parts of the central nervous system.[14]

Thereby we have rapid changes of electric potential in the brain, electric discharges between the nerve cells. These can be observed and recorded on an electroencephalograph chart. We find that the brain shows certain characteristic rhythms. When a person is relaxed, a large part of the brain maintains a steady rhythm termed the alpha rhythm. But these regular waves between the nerve cells are broken once signals arrest the attention and thinking begins. Different types of people manifest characteristic reactions in this alpha rhythm when attention or thought takes place, depending apparently upon the ability to visualize things. All this bears strong similarity to the functioning of an electronic computer, although much more complicated. The alpha rhythm can be likened to the "ticking over" of the machine. The brain cells are marking time until called into use. It would appear that consciousness is connected with an irregularity in the activity of the cells or neurons. As messages come in from the sense organs or from other parts of the brain, and some part of the cortex reacts, consciousness is manifested and the rhythm is broken. So long as all the cells observe the same rhythm and engage in the same activity, consciousness recedes. W. S. Beck remarks that "it is now recognized that the patterns of movement of these excitation waves (impulses)—their rhythm, arrangement, timing, and spatial distribution—are the phenomena which somehow we must learn to correlate with consciousness."[15]

What of memory? Somewhat as the computer is programmed, so the brain stores up our mental data. Education and training contribute here. The suggestion has been made that memory is bound up with a cyclic grouping of neurons.

[14] C. Adrian, "What Happens When We Think," *The Physical Basis of Mind,* ed. Peter Laslett (Oxford: Basil Blackwell, 1957), p. 7.

[15] Cf. W. S. Beck, *Modern Science and the Nature of Life* (Garden City, New York: Doubleday and Co., Anchor Books, 1961), p. 297.

Arranged in a circular network, an impulse introduced into them would circulate indefinitely so long as the electrical energy was available. In this way memories are stored up in "permanent reverberating circuits." [16] Russell Brain reminds us how words stimulate the brain:

> The word "dog" for the nervous system is not simply any of the thousand and one ways in which it can be pronounced: it is also an electrical pattern which is called up by each and all of them and of which we are not even conscious. The function of this electrical pattern is to arouse other patterns—those underlying ideas, feelings, and perhaps memory-images, which is what the word means to us and through which we know what it refers to.[17]

Purely at the physical and physiological level we may regard the brain on the model of a highly complex electronic computer. Undoubtedly as our knowledge of computers increases these artifacts will enable us to penetrate more deeply into our cerebral processes. Yet they are analogies and we must not press the analogies too far. In the next section we shall see how dangerous a literal identification of the two may become.

Let us, at this point, notice certain factors which need to be taken into consideration. First of all, the nature and mechanism of the brain draws to a sharp focus the psychosomatic nature of human personality. Personality and consciousness are especially bound up with the brain, but not with this alone. A random mutation in one of the hereditary genes may alter the brain structure of an offspring and produce mental defects. The nerve centers outside the brain and the gland secretions can have repercussions on our conscious life. The organization and regulation of the hormone cycle may influence a man's

[16] Ibid. p. 297.

[17] Russell Brain, "Speech and Thought," *The Physical Basis of Mind*, p. 54.

personality as much as the structure of his brain. Here the computer analogy breaks down.

Secondly, the electronic computers are human artifacts. The pattern of stimuli to which they respond has to be built into them by their makers. A computer can do only what it is instructed to do, and such instructions serve some specific purpose in the minds of those who construct it. There is no doubt that such machines can duplicate the actions of the human brain—and they often perform more quickly. But they have to be programmed. They cannot program themselves. As S. Zuckermann reminds us: "The patterns to which a real brain responds are . . . established through past experience. A living brain is thus self-organizing, establishing its own connections, its own patterns of memory, and the feed-backs necessary for the maintenance of an equilibrium." He wisely adds, however, and on this fact the analogical theme is based: "The difference between the real and artificial brains is . . . ceasing to be absolute, since machine-brains have been made which, even if in only a rudimentary way, are also dynamically responsible for the establishment and working of their own controls." [18]

Thirdly, this means that we ought not to set limits to the outward behavioristic aspect of machines, with which after all we are alone concerned. Behavioristically we might define consciousness as evidenced by response to certain stimuli. In the same way, we may well construct machines which in behavior simulate our feelings and emotions. But the distinctive aspect about human consciousness and human emotions is the aspect described by the personal pronoun "I." Outwardly I

[18] S. Zuckermann, "The Mechanism of Thought: The Mind and the Calculating Machine," *The Physical Basis of Mind,* p. 34. Cf. Magnus Pyke, *The Boundaries of Science* (Harmondsworth, Middlesex: Penguin Books, Ltd., 1963), pp. 142. Pyke cites machines constructed at the Burden Neurological Institute in Bristol which "exhibit some extraordinarily human traits," including moods of sulkiness or excitement.

may be described as a "he," and my conduct may be simulated by an IBM computer. But inwardly I know that I know, I am self-aware, and I know that *I have* emotions. When someone is unconscious and does not respond to stimuli, like I do, I know that he is not like "I" in an important way. Objective language, such as science uses, does not fully describe or explain the "I" whom I know from within. I. T. Ramsey, in a valuable discussion of this issue, comments: ". . . whether we could say that the machines 'had' the emotions as we might say 'I had' the emotions, is the point at issue. Could a machine display genuine, i.e. self-disclosed, ownership?" [19] We shall return to this later.

Fourthly, the fallacy of such arguments lies in the presupposition that the only way of knowing is the empirical and objectifying way which is sharply delineated in scientific method. But we have argued that this ignores a primary and intuitive awareness of wholes and its development in the knowledge that comes through love and sympathy. It is in this way that we come to know and understand other minds, other "I"s. Paul Weiss, in a searching analysis, argues that though I might, on the ground of behavior, attribute minds to machines which behave like I do, yet they are not human. They fail on two counts—they cannot be loved by one who can love and they cannot love what can be loved. He writes: ". . . a machine is an artifact whose parts are united so as to enable them to act together, whereas man is a unity in which the whole governs the behavior of the parts. Only such a unity has a self, with feelings, mind, will, and the rest." [20] Once again, the same resort is made in this argument to the inner and subjective aspect of the "I," which can truly be penetrated only by love and the "I"s capacity to love in response. It is here that ma-

[19] I. T. Ramsey, *Religion and Science: Conflict and Synthesis* (London: S.P.C.K., 1964), p. 59.

[20] P. Weiss, "Love in a Machine Age," *Dimensions of Mind*, ed. S. Hook (New York: Collier Books, 1961), p. 180.

chines are not on a footing with men. Pyke concludes that "the working of the brain with which we think out our science is, therefore, a combination of physics, chemistry, and biology, but it goes beyond this. It can, in fact, pass beyond the boundary of science." [21]

IV. *The nature of mind—the thesis of naturalism*

We have already indicated our own conviction that man is more than a machine and that the human personality and consciousness with its quality of self-transcendence is not to be reduced to a biochemical and physiological level. A further defense of this position must be undertaken, but prior to this the naturalistic thesis must be more carefully examined. The chemical and physiological substructure of personality lends considerable support to such a position at first sight, and those who are concerned solely with an empirical approach will often tend to embrace it.

Psychological behaviorism is to some degree outmoded in its original form. In modified forms it is now much more consonant with an epiphenomenal view of mind. It would reduce mind to external somatic behavior and internal physical changes. What we call "mental" becomes a matter of mechanical reflex actions, and even the most complicated human activity is reducible to a causal nexus of such reflexes in the nervous system and the brain. Thus the physical and mechanical are sufficient to account for mental behavior. C. D. Broad has described this as an instance "of the numerous class of theories which are so preposterously silly that only very learned men could have thought of them." [22] The utter disparity between a

[21] M. Pyke, op. cit. p. 144.

[22] C. D. Broad, *The Mind and Its Place in Nature* (London: Kegan Paul, Trench, Trubner and Co., 1947), p. 623. Broad continues: " . . . it is more important to remember that a theory which is in fact absurd may be accepted by the simple-minded because it is put forward in highly technical terms by learned persons who are themselves too confused to know exactly what they mean." Ibid. p. 624.

sensation and a movement in the brain is sufficient to indicate the ridiculous nature of such a position. Thinking is not just a pattern of somatic behavior. If a surgeon could investigate surgically the operations of my cerebral cortex during a moment of awareness, he would still observe only the physiological activity but he would not see my state of awareness. I know this from within. For the behaviorist, even his theory has no significance, since it too is a physiological operation!

Behaviorism did, however, set a pattern just here; in its rejection of introspection. It is true that introspection opens the door to subjectivity and is fallible. But then it is an open issue how far we may speak of objective or public knowledge. The attempt to differentiate between public and private knowledge is very much open to question, and the boundary line between them is by no means clearly drawn. All knowledge is personal knowledge. We are to some degree interpreting as we perceive. Even the behaviorist can only record behavior *as it appears to him.* When observing behavior, he is intelligently aware of it, that is to say, he is considering its relevance to some hypothesis and approaching it with his premises. It is true that introspection is concerned with private events not open to public observation, but even the latter is much more subjectively conditioned than we are prepared to admit.

Furthermore, we do live through an experience and apprehend it from within. Even if introspection is largely retrospection when we investigate this experience, we are relying on short range memory and that is still introspection, for we are still investigating our own experience. If we say that this does not give us genuine information, but rather alters the original experience, such an assertion can be made only on introspective grounds. We have no more reason to doubt such memory judgments than any others about equally recent events. As C. D. Broad points out:

> Like all such judgments, it cannot be defended by argument against a sceptic who chooses to doubt the trust-

> worthiness of memory *in general.* But there is no *special* reason for doubting the substantial correctness of this particular kind of memory-judgment; and therefore no special reason to doubt that perceptual and other referential situations have substantially the structure and the constituents which we assign to them on the ground of introspection and memory.[23]

The fact that we lived through the experience from within is so evident that to deny it is to deny the obvious. That our examination of this experience is open to fallibility means that the method should be cautiously used and that the observer should train himself and develop a skill. But then this applies to any other method of gaining information, including the so-called public and objective ones of behavioristic science. As H. H. Price comments: ". . . if someone alleges that there is a procedure in which mistakes are impossible one supposes that it is not really a way of obtaining information at all. When one cannot be wrong, one cannot be right either."[24] He argues, therefore, that introspection *is* a form of cognition.

Already we are moving over to a much more popular view of mind, that of epiphenomenalism. Broad describes this as "emergent materialism."[25] It regards mind as emergent from matter and consequently derivative from its material base, so that it is materialistically determined and, in some sense, a manifestation associated with matter. It accompanies and is the product of physiological processes, so that every event in the human consciousness is a correlative of a physical event in the somatic structure. It can and does initiate no physical or physiological process. Rather it reflects such processes, which

[23] Ibid. pp. 313 f. Broad's searching analysis should be consulted at this point. It is by no means outdated.

[24] H. H. Price, "Some Objections to Behaviorism," *Dimensions of Mind,* op. cit. p. 83.

[25] C. D. Broad, op. cit. p. 610. "Materiality is a differentiating attribute, and mentality is an emergent characteristic."

are purely causal at the material level. Like a mirror, consciousness shows what is happening in the somatic and cerebral processes. Causal connections exist solely at the physiological level, and they do not apply to the relation of the consciousness to its physical base. Thus mind is still reduced to a manifestation of matter.

Now it is true that mind has emerged from matter in the course of the evolutionary process, but this by no means supports the idea that mind is a refined form of the material order, a reflection of its processes. To say this is to fall in the position attacked by Aristotle centuries ago—that of identifying an entity with its origins instead of its ends. That mind emerges from matter and discloses in its own thought a rational order in the physical realm might conversely suggest the immanent but hidden organizing presence of mind from the beginning. We have just as much reason to adopt this teleological interpretation as the epiphenomenalist's argument from efficient causation.

It is equally true that mind, where we meet it in our natural order, is always associated with a physical and physiological base. But here the fact that the latter is always present with mind in human experience does not imply that matter *determines* the functioning of mind even though it provides the condition in which mind emerges. An artist's vision is not determined by the medium of oils, water colors, or pastels in which he expresses it. All the latter do is to condition the expression. Furthermore, the phenomena of parapsychology offer at least enough verifiable evidence to indicate that the understanding of the human mind is not dependent wholly on physical principles. Parapsychological investigation has established to the satisfaction of some the reality of telepathy and also that telepathic communication is not a matter of any presently-known physical radiation. We have not yet found a cerebral organ which could be a receiving or transmitting center for such radiation, and the communication is in no way weakened or inhibited by spatial distance. It would seem that telepathy points to mind being more than an epiphenomenon. As Rhine suggests, ". . . to comprehend the role of human personality in the natural order, it is necessary to deal with certain properties and operations that are part of the personal living system although they are non-physical in character." [26]

Perhaps the widest acceptance of the epiphenomenal view of personality is in the Marxist context, where mind is described as due to a higher organization of matter. Marxism accounts for man's ideal values, religious faiths, and apparent freedom solely in terms of material forces and, in particular, as arising out of economic determinism. "Man is what he eats," as Feuerbach had declared.

An attempt to move beyond epiphenomenalism has been made by H. Feigl in his identity theory.[27] He rejects the reductive tendencies of radical behaviorism and does not deny that we have "well-confirmed knowledge . . . concerning the mental states of other human beings." [28] He argues that he can retain a thoroughgoing naturalism and reject any metaphysical transcendence while avoiding the errors of phenomenalism. He does this by suggesting that we have a body-mind identity, in which the neuro-physiological terms and the corresponding phenomenal terms, though they differ widely in sense or meaning, yet have identical referents. The fact that they differ in meaning will result in different modes of confirming statements which employ them. The referents will be either immediately experienced qualities or their configurations in the various phenomenal fields. Thus every mental event is identical with some state of the brain.

U. T. Place and J. J. C. Smart [29] support this position and

[26] J. B. Rhine, "On Parapsychology and the Nature of Man," *Dimensions of Mind,* p. 78. Cf. J. B. Rhine, *New Frontiers of the Mind* (Harmondsworth, Middlesex: Penguin Books, 1950).

[27] H. Feigl, "Mind-Body, Not a Pseudo-Problem," *Dimensions of Mind,* op. cit. pp. 33–42.

[28] Ibid. p. 39.

[29] U. T. Place, "Is Consciousness a Brain Process?" *The Philosophy*

argue that the thesis "consciousness is a process of the brain" means the identity of the two classes of events. We have not a separate class of mental events distinct from the physiological events. This, all such exponents argue, is the error of epiphenomenalism. This theory postulates a physical causal law in the physiological context and another law of psycho-physiological correspondence. According to it the mental states are dependent variables connected with the physiological and observable phenomena but not causing them. Smart[30] describes such mental states as "nomological danglers" and dismisses the idea. He and Place argue that *is* in the thesis "consciousness *is* a process of the brain" means identity.

Place dismisses as mistaken the "assumption that if the meanings of two statements or expressions are quite unconnected, they cannot both provide an adequate characterization of the same object or state of affairs."[31] He argues that, in the case of introspection, it is a "phenomenological fallacy" to suppose that "the descriptions of the appearance of things are descriptions of the actual state of affairs in a mysterious internal environment."[32] There is no internal screen, no phenomenal field, on which images of objects and events are cast. Our conscious experience is directly of objects and events in our environments, and we do not have to infer that the real properties of the latter form the phenomenal properties of images cast upon a mythological screen. Color concepts for example cannot be properly applied to brain processes.

There are connections between this kind of thought and the refined neo-behaviorism of Gilbert Ryle.[33] The latter is con-

of Mind, ed. by V. C. Chappell (Englewood Cliffs, N.J.: Prentice-Hall, 1962), pp. 101–9. J. J. C. Smart, "Sensations and Brain Processes," *The Philosophy of Mind,* pp. 160–72.

[30] Ibid. p. 161. Feigl uses the expression "dangers" for the laws rather than the entities. *Dimensions of Mind,* p. 35.

[31] U. T. Place, *The Philosophy of Mind,* p. 103.

[32] Ibid. p. 101.

[33] G. Ryle, *The Concept of Mind* (New York: Barnes and Noble, Inc., 1949).

cerned to eliminate mind as any kind of stuff whatsoever. He wishes to eradicate the Cartesian dualism of mind and matter from thought, and refers to the Cartesian concept of mind as "the ghost in the machine."[34] He concentrates upon observable human behavior and analyzes "overt intelligent performances," arguing that such are not clues to the activities of mind but are those activities.[35] Hence he offers a kind of refined behaviorism, and we should have dealt with him earlier, except that some of the points he makes are related to the arguments just studied. He himself acknowledges his behaviorism at the end of his work.[36] He denies that man is compounded of an immaterial thinking substance, mind, and a material extended substance, matter, which, though incompatible somehow mysteriously interact. Thus we do not have mental processes as distinct from physical processes. There are mental processes such as making a joke, but they are really descriptions of certain types of physical process. A description in mental terms and a description in physical terms have different meanings but they both refer to the same physical process. The mistake of Cartesian dualism is one of category. The name "mind" does not refer to a thing, but it and cognate terms are simply a description of certain types of human behavior.

We should expect that Ryle's difficulties will arise at the level of introspection. In his treatment of "the elusiveness of the I," he naturally denies any inner aspect to self-knowledge and seems to indicate that such arises from listening to our own words and studying our own behavior.[37] In this way he endeavors to demonstrate that self-awareness is not in reality a mode of knowing distinguishable from knowledge of other people.

[34] Ibid. p. 15 f.
[35] Ibid. p. 58.
[36] Ibid. pp. 327 f.
[37] Ibid. p. 169.

John Wisdom[38] deals in cogent criticism with this aspect of Ryle's thought, arguing that the peculiarity of the soul is not that it is visible to none but that it is visible only to one. He contends that this need not lead to skepticism about knowledge of other minds, but that this knowledge is a fact and thus telepathy has to be considered.

Ryle at least follows Descartes in a passion for clear and distinct ideas as the sole basis of knowledge. Awareness and apprehension of wholes is, as we have already argued, a way of knowing which awakens a desire to comprehend and know more clearly, but which in the beginning may be quite vague. Descartes ignores this, and Ryle, with his analytical approach, does likewise. The "elusiveness of the I" leads him to dismiss on such grounds "the ghost in the machine," yet even he has to confess that people are only "relatively easy to understand."[39] Despite all his argument, the myth of mind remains to haunt him. Indeed, he often uses in his thinking the very logic of this myth which he is so anxious to banish.[40] H. D. Lewis cogently remarks that

> the proneness of Professor Ryle's "ghost" to make a fresh appearance at the moment it has been thought to be finally laid, is not, as some suppose, merely because it has been built into the structure of our language or is unavoidable in descriptions of overt behavior, but because we are directly aware of ourselves as non-material beings, and there is also involved in this a quite irreducible difficulty of knowing what it is like or means to be another mind.[41]

[38] J. Wisdom, "The Concept of Mind," *The Philosophy of Mind,* pp. 53 ff.

[39] G. Ryle, op. cit. p. 114.

[40] Cf. the criticism of Stuart Hampshire in his review of Ryle's book, *Mind,* Vol. LIX (1950), pp. 237–55.

[41] H. D. Lewis, "God and Mystery," *Prospect for Metaphysics,* ed. Ian Ramsey (London: George Allen & Unwin, 1961), pp. 208 f.

Ryle's argument is logical, granted his behavioristic premises, but often one feels that he is hard put to it to include certain aspects of mental experiences within them.

Ryle and the brain-mind identity thinkers alike offer brands, however refined, of materialistic reductionism. It is true that the former concentrates on the physical aspect of overt human behavior and the latter on the physiological processes of the brain, but each in their own way would deny any distinct substantial status to mind. Ryle and the other group are not crudely materialistic. Indeed Ryle argues that man is not a machine. He writes: "Man need not be degraded to a machine by being denied to be a ghost in a machine. He might, after all, be a sort of animal, namely, a higher mammal. There has yet to be ventured the hazardous leap to the hypothesis that perhaps he is a man." [42] On this, C. B. Daly's comment bears repeating:

> Gilbert Ryle, near the end of *The Concept of Mind*, remarks that philosophers may yet come to recognize that man perhaps is, after all, man. But this is not, as he seems to suggest, the end, but the beginning of philosophy. To resist all pretenses to explain man in terms of the non-human; to strive for ever deeper realization of the human; but to know that there is always more to know about man than can be known, that is the task of metaphysics.[43]

v. *The views of the neurophysiologists*

The naturalistic schools of all types fail to recognize that mind is more than the aggregate of its manifestations. Our argument for the a priori nature of our awareness of wholes before the analytical investigation of their parts has suggested

[42] G. Ryle, op. cit., p. 328.

[43] C. B. Daly, "Metaphysics and the Limits of Language," in *Prospect for Metaphysics*, p. 200.

a transcendence, a mystery in other minds and our own self-awareness, which we can never express in clear-cut form, but which is nonetheless real. Neurological models and computers are not minds, and in our primary awareness, we know this. Mind is associated with the grasping of meaning, with commitment to a proposition, with interpreting mechanisms in relation to purpose, with critical appraisal of reflective thought and creative originality within it. In every act of thinking and scientific investigation such personal powers are being employed. When the neurologist or another thinker constructs a neurological model of man and identifies man with it, he is denying to the being that he is interpreting the very powers which he is employing in the act of interpretation.[44] This may be true of the physical and physiological levels, but man is more than these, and the investigator is demonstrating this in his own mental activity.

Despite all the arguments of the naturalistic thinkers, the distinctive status of mind remains. The interaction theory has not been demonstrated as untenable. Nor is it necessarily bound up with the Cartesian "dualism of incompatibles." Tacit to much naturalism is the assumption that the physical order forms a closed system, and that the physiological chain of events associated with mental events constitutes a continuous chain of cause and effect in which there is no place for the intervention of any nonphysical agent. One element in the argument is the appeal to the principle of the conservation of energy. It is argued that if the "mind" intervenes in the physical system, it should impart energy. This should be observable in the total balance of energy in the bodily system. The difference between the intake of energy by food and oxygen should differ from the output in physical activity by this amount, and such a difference is not observable. Allowing for the openness to error of such physical measurements, the

[44] Cf. M. Polanyi, *Personal Knowledge* (Chicago: University of Chicago Press, 1958), p. 263.

argument fails in its basic assumption that even in a closed system effects cannot be caused without a flow of energy from cause to the effect.

C. D. Broad [45] reminds us that when a weight is suspended by a string from a fixed point, changes in the distribution of the energy of the system between kinetic energy and potential energy occur as the weight swings in its path. The changes in distribution and in the movement of the weight itself are caused by the pull of the string, but the string makes no difference to the total energy of the weight. Here we have a conservative system at the physical level in which the cause of a movement only changes the distribution of the total energy, not the amount. We have no grounds for holding that "mind" may not do the same thing.

Now, here, it may be argued that, in the illustration, we are concerned with a physical system in which cause and effect are both physical, but that the real difficulty in the brain-mind problem lies in the unlikeness of the cause and the effect, whichever way the causation operates—brain to mind or mind to brain. Yet there is nothing paradoxical or illogical in an ontological distinction between cause and effect. Broad [46] argues that, though the criterion of a cause-effect relationship between two events should be more than concomitant variation, yet he is not prepared to believe that this criterion *must* involve their quantitative likeness. Ducasse likewise points out that "the causality relation . . . does not presuppose at all that its cause-term and its effect-term both belong to the same ontological category, but only that both of them be *events*." [47] So long as body/brain and mind be constituent aspects of a psychosomatic whole and there be events in that whole describable solely in terms of one or the other category, this by

[45] C. D. Broad, op. cit. pp. 107 ff. I do not believe that Broad's analysis of the interaction issue has been bettered.

[46] Ibid. p. 98.

[47] F. J. Ducasse, "In Defence of Dualism," *Dimensions of Mind*, p. 88.

no means rules out such events from being causally related.

It would seem that if "mind" is distinct from "brain" but is causally related to it, what we have is not an injection of "physical" energy into the physiological system by some mental event, but rather a transformation of the energy in that system from one form to another, for example, from a chemical form to that of bodily activity. As Broad suggests, the objections just considered "suggests that all the energy of our bodily actions comes out of and goes back into the physical world, and that minds neither add energy to nor abstract it from the latter." [48]

Now, whereas naturalistic philosophers are seeking to banish the idea of mind as a distinctive aspect of personal being, many leading neurologists have been led to just the opposite view out of their own experience. They thus support the position to which our argument has been pointing. W. H. Thorpe writes: ". . . although I believe there to be an extremely close interrelation between mind and brain, I can only conclude that they are in some sense two things." [49] Here we need to remember that the neural system and the physiological structure of the brain do function as a series of reflexes which may be artificially stimulated so that the resulting behavior is outwardly identical with that which has been "consciously willed." Again there are large numbers of our bodily activities and adjustments which are controlled by such chains of reflexes through the cerebral cortex, and which the brain executes without any consciousness on our part whatsoever—such as the muscles *et alia* which operate to keep the head vertical or which keep the body balanced and erect.[50] Yet the consciousness can also intervene and alter the operation.

Are consciousness and will illusory terms? Do "I" do any-

[48] C. D. Broad, op. cit. p. 109.

[49] W. H. Thorpe, *Biology and the Nature of Man* (London: Oxford University Press, 1962), p. 21.

[50] Cf. C. Sherrington, *Man on His Nature* (Cambridge: Cambridge University Press, 1946), pp. 175 ff.

thing? Wilder Penfield, the noted neurologist, has concerned himself much with this issue. The brain, as is well known, is divided into two hemispheres, which are mirror images and which control the operations of the opposite halves of the bodily organism. If an electrode is applied to the appropriate motor area of the right hemisphere, it will cause the left hand to move automatically. A conscious subject cannot prevent this happening by the exercise of his "will," but he can put his right hand over and hold the other hand still. As Penfield suggests, "he doubtless makes use of the motor area in the cortex of the untouched hemisphere. The effector-mechanism employed by him during voluntary activity is denied him in one cortex but is still available to him in the other." [51]

Penfield cites another instance in which there is artificial interference with the speech mechanism of the brain. When a butterfly was presented, the patient could recognize the object. His memory circuits were intact and called up the concepts of "butterfly" and "moth." He tried to utter "butterfly," and, failing that, he tried "moth"—according to his report after speech was restored. But neither idea caused the speech mechanism to operate. Penfield comments:

> *Here is an example of the operation of the mind.* Action in the brain accompanied the thought part way, but when words were called for, the brain failed. He expected an automatic response, expected the word to flash up in consciousness reflexly. It was not that his lips and tongue were paralyzed. It was the idea of the word that was not forthcoming.[52] [author's italics]

There are mechanisms which form the physiological basis of the mind, but at this frontier we come upon some agency

[51] W. Penfield, "The Cerebral Cortex and the Mind of Man," *The Physical Basis of Mind*, pp. 60 f.

[52] W. Penfield, "The Physiological Basis of the Mind," *Control of the Mind,* Part I, ed. S. M. Farber and R. H. L. Wilson (New York: McGraw-Hill, 1961), p. 15.

which "calls upon these mechanisms, choosing one rather than another." [53] Mystery faces us, although we dare not say that it is beyond our increasing understanding. But, as Penfield comments, "there is as yet no scientific proof that the brain can control the mind or fully explain the mind. *The assumptions of materialism have never been substantiated.*" [54] [author's italics]

Russell Brain [55] likens the brain and the nervous system to the threads which are woven into a tapestry and suggests that with the mind we perceive the patterns which have been woven. In the brain we have complicated nervous patterns which the mind perceives. But we still have to ask whether the mind shapes the pattern and directs the weaving. Penfield believes that it does, and Eccles, the famous neurologist, concurs. The real problem is how a seemingly deterministic pattern of nervous reflexes and sensory motor connections can be directed by "will." Where does mind fit into the causal scheme of things? One hint has already been made—namely, in the transfer of energy from one form to another and not in the injection of new energy. We have further argued that unlikeness of cause and effect is no barrier. But the mysterious inbreak of mind into a nervous and cerebral mechanism, such as Penfield describes, still raises problems.

Here Eccles helps us considerably.[56] He argues that though our self-consciousness is private, yet it becomes public by means of linguistic communication. The mutual reporting of inner and private experiences makes us aware that such are not hallucinatory, and thus they achieve objectivity and validity. Hence these experiences have as much right to scientific investigation as "things" which are perceived in sense experience; and mental phenomena are open to scientific investiga-

[53] Ibid. p. 16.

[54] Ibid. p. 16.

[55] R. Brain, "Speech and Thought," *The Physical Basis of Mind,* p. 55.

[56] See J. C. Eccles, *The Neurophysiological Basis of Mind: The Principles of Neurophysiology* (Oxford: Oxford University Press, 1953).

tion. Because this is so, it is his opinion that we should investigate the way in which mental and physiological events are correlated, and where exactly the human consciousness interacts with the somatic processes. It is evident that he will reject any naturalistic solution, although he is quite clear that Cartesian dualism is crudely stated.

We have already seen that conscious activity is related to breaks in the regular electric rhythms of the cerebral cortex, that is to say, to special states of the system of neurons with their interconnections. Lord Adrian has shown that the regular alpha-rhythm in the cortex gives no liaison with mind, but that the liaison occurs when the electroencephalogram is irregular and rapid. Eccles holds that, in such states, the dynamic patterns of activity among the neurons have a distinctive character which is not comparable with any state of the cortex when not so activated or with anything in the behavior of physical energy in the natural order. The latter will, of course, reflect the macro-laws of statistical physics.

Eddington, on a purely theoretical basis, suggested that possibilities for understanding the relation of mind to brain might be opened up by Heisenberg's indeterminacy principle.[57] If energy changes of an order embraced within the principle occur, there would be no infringement of the causal laws of macrophysics, which are based on statistical averages. Eddington suggested that the cerebral area where the physical effects of volitions begin consists of matter which is not "identical in all respects with inorganic matter, for that would reduce the body to an automaton acting independently of consciousness." [58] Hence he believes there is an undetermined element in the behavior which lies within the area of the indeterminacy principle. He points out that, at the inorganic level, there is no correlation of the undetermined behavior of the

[57] A. S. Eddington, *The Philosophy of Physical Science* (Cambridge: Cambridge University Press, 1939), pp. 180 f.

[58] Ibid. p. 181.

individual particles. He dismisses as nonsense the hypothesis that the consciousness decides the exact behavior of any one particle within the limits of Heisenberg's uncertainty relation. Instead he postulates that in "conscious matter," there *is* a correlation of the behavior of the particles and that "if volition operates on the system, it does so without regard to the Heisenberg limits." [59] He argues that there is no halfway house between random behavior, as in the Heisenberg principle, and correlated behavior to which the Heisenberg limits do not apply.

It would seem that Eccles is much more prepared to lean upon the Heisenberg principle, because of his specialized knowledge of the cerebrum, not available to Eddington. The brain cell or neuron is the center of a complex network of nerve fibers which have synaptic contacts with the fibers of other neurons. The receiving processes of neurons are termed "dendrites," and the process along which a nerve impulse passes out of a neuron is named the "axon." Now the nerve fibers impinge on the dendrites and terminate upon the neuron in "synaptic knobs." At a conservative estimate each neuron has, on the average, at least three afferent or intake branches and three efferent or output branches. Allowing for the extreme density of the neurons in the cortex and for the large number of synaptic contacts in which their nerve fibers intermesh and nervous impulses pass between them, Eccles argues that a small energy excitation of one synaptic knob in a neuron will suffice to excite very rapidly the other neurons in a large area of the cortex. Thus a large-scale effect could result from a small energy change.

Eddington had dismissed the idea that a small energy variation within the Heisenberg range could be effective. He had postulated the correlation of the behavior of particles. Eccles argues that such minute effects could lead to a cortical excitation sufficiently intense to produce bodily changes and movement. He notes that the synaptic knob of a neuron has

[59] Ibid. p. 183.

a mass of about 5×10^{-13} gram. Therefore, it cannot be treated in terms of the deterministic laws of classical physics but falls within the range of Heisenberg's principle. In consequence unusual behavior at this level involves no infringement upon the physical laws. Eccles suggests that an act of "will" shuts down one synaptic outlet from a circuit in the cortex and opens another. In this way the impulse is redistributed in the adjacent branches, travels rapidly through the system, and becomes sufficiently intense to cause bodily movement or change. If, moreover, the act of will influences not one single mode but a whole spatiotemporal pattern of them, then, in a matter of seconds, a considerable cortical modification can result. Here we have something akin to Eddington's theoretical idea of correlation. The picture which emerges is of a nervous system possessing a degree of sensitivity which is of a different kind and order from those of any physical instrument. This sensitivity enables detection of minute "fields of influence" spread spatially and temporally over the cortex, and leads to consequent integration which can produce large-scale bodily change. As Eccles puts it:

> Thus, the neurophysiological hypothesis is that the "will" modifies the spatio-temporal activity of the neuronal network by exerting spatio-temporal "fields of influence" that become effective through this unique detector function of the active cerebal cortex.[60]

We are asked to envisage the correlation of a spatiotemporally patterned series of excitations of synaptic knobs. Each excitation in itself would fall within the area of quantum phenomena and might be attributed to chance. But the chance element recedes into the background as the correlation of such excitations looms in the foreground. For the fact that, again and again, such a pattern of small excitations produces movement at the bodily level would indicate more than random

[60] *Eccles,* op. cit. p. 277.

happenings. At the quantum level the regularity would have a low probability, and its actual occurrence points to some controlling presence. Mind has taken over from physical law, and volition has replaced probability by certainty.

Sir Charles Sherrington has vividly described the functioning of the brain as it moves from unconscious to conscious states:

> Suppose we choose the hour of deep sleep. Then only in some sparse and out of the way places are nodes flashing and trains of light-points running. Such places indicate local activity still in progress. At one such place we can watch the behavior of a group of lights perhaps a myriad strong. They are pursuing a mystic and recurrent manoeuvre as if of some incantational dance. They are superintending the beating of the heart and the state of the arteries so that while we sleep the circulation of the blood is what it should be. The great knotted head-piece of the whole sleeping system lies for the most part dark, and quite especially so the roof-brain. Occasionally at places in it lighted points flash or move but soon subside. Such lighted points and moving trains of lights are mainly far in the outskirts, and wink slowly and travel slowly. At intervals even a gush of sparks wells up and sends a train down the spinal cord, only to fail to arouse it. Where however the stalk joins the headpiece, there goes forward in a limited field a remarkable display. A dense constellation of some thousands of nodal points bursts out every few seconds into a short phase of rhythmical flashing. At first a few lights, then more, increasing in rate and number with a deliberate crescendo to a climax, then to decline and die away. After due pause the efflorescence is repeated. With each such rhythmic outburst goes a discharge of trains of travelling lights along the stalk and out of it altogether into a number of nerve-branches. What is this doing? It manages the taking of our breath the while we sleep.

Should we continue to watch the scheme we should observe after a time an impressive change which suddenly accrues. In the great head-end which has been mostly darkness spring up myriads of twinkling stationary lights and myriads of trains of moving lights of many different directions. It is as though activity from one of those local places which continued restless in the darkened main-mass suddenly spread far and wide and invaded all. The great topmost sheet of the mass, that where hardly a light had twinkled or moved, becomes now a sparkling field of rhythmic flashing points with trains of travelling sparks hurrying hither and thither. The brain is waking and with it the mind is returning. It is as if the Milky Way entered upon some cosmic dance. Swiftly the head-mass becomes an enchanted loom where millions of flashing shuttles weave a dissolving pattern, always a meaningful pattern though never an abiding one; a shifting harmony of subpatterns. Now as the waking body rouses, subpatterns of this great harmony of activity stretch down into the unlit tracks of the stalkpiece of the scheme. Strings of flashing and travelling sparks engage the lengths of it. This means that the body is up and rises to meet its waking day.

Dissolving pattern after dissolving pattern will, the long day through, without remission melt into and succeed each other in this scheme by which for the moment we figure the brain and spinal cord. Especially, and with complexity incredible, in that part which we were thinking of, the roof-brain. Only after day is done will it quiet down, lapse half-way to extinction, and fall again asleep. Then at last, so far at least as the roof-brain, motor acts cease. The brain is released from the waking day and marshals its factors for its motor acts no more.[61]

[61] C. Sherrington, *Man on His Nature* (Cambridge: Cambridge University Press, 1946), pp. 224 f.

Thus we have a picture of the brain as "the organ of liaison"[62] between the mind and body. Nor need this lead to a crude Cartesian dualism, for, as we have already shown, the evolutionary emergence of mind within the physiological organism has meant that the roots of the human mind lie back in our animal ancestry and that there is an intimate relationship between the mind and physico-physiological machinery. Our powers of perception have, for instance, been shaped by our heritage. There are ranges of sound and radiation to which our own sense organs are not sensitive and which in consequence convey no messages to the organ of liaison. Yet if we are to understand the process by which mind has emerged and been shaped in the give and take of the developing organism with its changing environment, there is no justification for a retreat into either skepticism or solipsism.

Now the cerebral cortex is patterned by messages from the sense organs. Likewise, we might suggest that mind, just as it voluntarily directs the cortex, may also abstract messages from the cortex and come to know the rational structure of its world. Accidental damage may mean the reception of messages from one sense organ, such as sight, in the area of the cortex reserved for another sense organ, such as hearing. This will lead to hallucinations, but there is no reason to mistrust the whole mechanism or to retreat into a private world which has no relation to the actual order of nature and other persons. It is much more reasonable to believe that the physico-physiological and the mental are so wedded by the long process of development that the sensory excitation of the cerebral cortex does convey to the mind perceptions which enable it to grasp the rational structure of the world.[63] It remains true, however, that the structures of our sense organs and of our brain "do determine what kinds of tasks and correlations the brain is

[62] Cf. C. Sherrington, op. cit. pp. 236 ff.

[63] Cf. Sherrington, op. cit.

able to perform," and that the "brain exerts a major influence on what the mind can do and how it can express itself." [64] Brain and mind are not incompatibles. One has emerged creatively within the structure of the other, and the physical order has a rational structure which the mind is able to grasp and which gives it a kinship to the mental.

We are left at the neurophysiological level with the picture of mind as an aspect of personal being which cannot be reduced to the level of cerebral, physiological, or material structures. It is an interesting point that differences in the sizes of brains cannot be related to differences in intellectual ability. Le Gros Clark reminds us that

> no anatomist . . . has yet been able to show any consistent difference between the intrinsic structure of the brain of a genius and the brain of a man of average intelligence.

He concludes that the genius has "the knack of using the ordinary kind of human brain much more efficiently than most of us are able to do." [65] Once more we are reminded that man is more than brain.

We have already indicated that the reality of mind as a distinctive constituent of human personality is borne out by the phenomena associated with telepathy and extrasensory perception. Undue claims are often made by exponents of E.S.P. and they often lead to a type of Cartesian dualism, but the evidence is sufficient to indicate that there are elements in man's mental life which are not physically mediated.[66] The telepathic communication of thoughts between persons having no physical contact in any way have been substantiated by a multitude of experiments, in which the probability of mere

[64] W. H. Thorpe, op. cit. p. 27.

[65] W. E. Le Gros Clark, "The Structure of the Brain and the Process of Thinking," *The Physical Basis of Mind*, pp. 23 f.

[66] See J. B. Rhine, op. cit.; G. N. M. Tyrrell, *The Personality of Man* (London: Penguin Books, 1946).

chance coincidence has been overridden. A sender receives a pack of cards with symbols on them, and a receiver, completely isolated from the sender, endeavors to write down the cards and symbols in the order in which the sender concentrates on them. In this way the deviation from chance expectation has been measured, and, in the case of telepathic subjects, reveals remarkably high odds against chance. Evidently some unknown positive factor is at work here, and we cannot explain it in terms of brain structure and radiation, as we have already indicated. It would appear that telepathy discloses the reality of the mental in distinction from the physical. Rhine, with whose somewhat Cartesian point of view we should disagree, argues that ". . . the acceptance of the occurrence of nonphysical operations in personal action as an established finding of parapsychology today is necessarily to abandon any view of human nature dependent wholly upon physical principles." [67]

VI. *The issues raised by depth psychology*

The naturalistic attack on mind has taken place on many fronts, and we must now turn our attention to the approach of depth psychology, especially as developed by the Freudian school of psychology. Freud's approach ties in mind with the physiological and biological structures of human nature. His understanding of mind has no contact with the sharp and crude dualism of the Cartesian school, and his psyche is not equivalent to "soul" as this word is used in dualist circles. He regards man as a psychosomatic whole and would describe *psyche* as an abstraction from that whole, its separation from which is an artificial device. We would agree that mind and consciousness function within the personal totality and ought not to be separated from it. They are within the personal

[67] J. B. Rhine, "On Parapsychology and the Nature of Man," *Dimensions of Mind*, p. 77.

whole. The real issue is which has the priority and whether we can speak of mind as distinctive in its own right and not merely derivative. It is one thing to indicate that the roots of mind lie back in the evolutionary process and quite another to hold, as Freud does, that mental life is a function of the physiological apparatus of the nervous system and the brain.[68]

Freud introduced into psychology, in this connection, the concept of the unconscious. This concept was already in the air in philosophical thought of his time, although the identification of mind with consciousness at first made the description "unconscious mind" appear somewhat anomalous. William James was already using the term, while behaviorism with its reflex mechanisms was suggesting something of the same idea. Freud identified the depths of the unconscious with innate drives or biological instincts which provide the emotional energy of human personality and which are directed upon the satisfaction of some particular biological or physiological need. These instinctual drives or impulses form a primitive undirected mass, prior to the development of consciousness. Freud calls this impersonal complex of interacting energies the id.[69] The id constitutes the structure of the unconscious. It lies beneath the processes of the conscious life and, according to Freud, *determines* these processes. Here we come to the naturalistic interpretation he offers. Man is a victim of his unconscious, and his conscious acts are causally connected with his id. The vital impulses which activate the id are generally termed the libido. Originally associated with the sex impulse, and especially so in Freud's thought, it came to stand for the general life energy, although Freud always put the sexual aspect in the center.

Out of this id, the conscious life of man emerges as the ego. The latter is a modification of the impulsive forces, conditioned

[68] See S. Freud, *Outline of Psycho-Analysis.*

[69] Cf. S. Freud, *The Ego and the Id,* trans. Joan Riviere (New York: W. W. Norton and Co., Inc., 1962).

by sense experience. It is, however, still subject to the determinative influence of the hidden instinctive drives, even though it consists of a controlled selection of these. Consciousness is thus an epiphenomenon. Even our reason is a function of the ego. We use it to justify conscious activities which are actually determined by hidden motives lying deep down among the urges of our unconscious mind. Reason is thus a conscious justification of our unconscious desires.

Beside the modifying influence of sense experience in the shaping of the ego, Freud postulated that the pressure of society introduces a second modification of the id, the superego. The aggressive and irresponsible expression of the primitive impulses is frowned on by organized society, which, from the beginning, sought to curb it by taboos and prohibitions. The latter were taken into the conscious life as the "conscience" or superego. The superego is thus parents and larger social groups imposing their will on the ego, but doing so within a structure of the consciousness itself. It rises from the ashes of the Oedipus complex.

On the basis of this trinity of id, ego, and superego, Freud built a naturalistic and deterministic theory of mind. At every level man's conscious life is causally determined. Its causal roots lie deep in the complex jungle of interacting impulses in the unconscious. Indeed, for Freud, our human development reflects the childhood stage of experience, when the id begins to be modified by the emergence from it of the ego. As the babe develops, its infantile sex instincts are directed on the mother. There is a desire to possess the mother and oust the father. This situation becomes intolerable, a guilt feeling appears, and the male child seeks a new live object, identifying himself with the father. This identification involves taboos which the father presents, so the child's ego divides, and the superego is formed in which the father's standards are taken into the self and become inner commands. The father provides security, but when the father fails or becomes otherwise unavailable, the father image is projected on the heavens as God. Thereby the object of religion takes over the functions of the father and guarantees the moral laws and rules which are now given supernatural sanctions. For Freud, therefore, the conscience and religious belief are alike products of the development of the infant mind.

Freud's study of neurosis led him to postulate that such mental illness means a return to some childhood state through which the subject has not passed successfully. The complex relationships with the parents in the early years lead to conflicts which are repressed, because they are unbearable, and completely eliminated from the conscious memory. Thus the unconscious contains those aspects in which we do not want to grow and which try to pull us back from reality to the sheltered and irresponsible status of the mother's arms. The unconscious contains the forces which would drag us back to our mother's womb. It harbors our Peter Pan. In the crisis moments of life, as anxiety is awakened in the ego, such forces reassert themselves in the conscious life, and the adult resorts to infantile behavior.

Freud's later analysis developed the thesis of a tension between what he regarded as the two basic instincts: the life instinct or Eros and the death instinct or Thanatos. The life instinct is compounded of the sexual urge and the self-preservation drive. Really it is the libido with a strong sexual flavor. The death instinct was a new development in Freud's thought. It was quite separate from the libido and represented an innate destructiveness and aggressiveness against the self. It was directed to a return from all tension and striving to the primitive state. This second element has been much criticized —it probably arose from a false identification of the aggressive impulse in man with the natural fact of death.

Freud locates religion in the recession to the infantile stages of life. He can describe religious belief as neurotic, for it means that the individual has never really developed beyond an

arrested stage in his childhood development. The inadequacy of a parent led him to project an adequate righteous father image on the heavens. The religious believer has not really grown up. His religious beliefs are not the result of a rational study of the universe. They are his flight from the brute realities of his own existence. He creates a fantasy universe over against the brute realities, a universe in which his father image can provide him with the security that reality lacks.

This contention that religion is a neurosis is part of Freud's doctrinaire attitude. He does not argue logically. We should not expect him to do so, since he identifies reasoning with rationalization. He presents his conclusions from clinical experience dogmatically and attacks his opponents on the ground that their attitude arises from unconscious inhibitions.[70]

His position is immediately open to criticism, however, apart from this. His description of religion as a neurosis would imply a similar history of psychological development in all believers and especially similarities in their upbringing, but there is no evidence to support this. Further, we should expect to find more evidence of neurotic upbringing among believers than among unbelievers. But this is not the case, and actually the sharing within a believing community helps to mitigate some breakdowns. Again, neurosis tends to isolate and shut up the subject in his own private fantasy world, and this is just the opposite to what makes a religious community possible. Finally, there is no evidence that normal people are generally atheistic and that the neurotic are religious. Rather, as Yellowlees has indicated, "it is a matter of plain historical fact that religion in its highest manifestations gives not only peace of mind but great and increasing powers of endurance, qualities in which the neurotic is sadly lacking." [71]

Freud's strength lies in his indication that the human mind is

[70] Cf. S. Freud, *New Introductory Lectures on Psycho-Analysis.*

[71] D. Yellowlees, *Psychology's Defence of the Faith* (London: S.C.M. Press, 1936), p. 103.

very much open to forces which surge up from the unconscious. His mistake lies in his naturalistic contention that man's religious and moral life are determined by such hidden urges. Actually, to be consistent, he should also hold that man's scientific ideas are likewise determined, and then his own theories are open to the criticism of being wish fulfillments also. Even science may be an illusion. The truth is that psychological criticism is not sufficient to dismiss man's religious beliefs any more than any other aspect of his intellectual and valuational structure. Such truth must be dealt with on rational grounds, such as coherence. Irrationality at this level might indicate the validity of the psychological attack.

There are instances where religious beliefs are held by mentally unbalanced persons, and doubtless the expression of such beliefs is influenced by the neurotic disturbance. But the insanity of the believer does not thereby discredit his beliefs. The fact that some unbalanced and insecure persons find refuge in religious faith does not invalidate the truth which is involved in such a commitment. Some beliefs, such as ideas of grandeur or hallucinations, can be explained away psychologically. Yet even in such cases of mental illness, the basis of the beliefs must be removed on other grounds in order that they may be established as part of the mental disorder. Alastair MacIntyre reminds us that "the truth or reasonableness of any assertion is independent of the sanity or normality of the person who utters or believes it." [72] As we have pointed out earlier, there is a difference between determining and conditioning. The influence of upbringing and the strength or weakness of the unconscious may sometimes be seen in a narrowing or other limitation of faith's expression in thought and deed, but they do not doom an individual to a particular type of religion or to irreligion. Human nature is not mecha-

[72] A. MacIntyre, *Difficulties in Christian Belief* (New York: Philosophical Library, 1959), p. 95. MacIntyre's discussion is particularly helpful.

nistic, and man's values and faiths are not determined by the jungle of his unconscious. Freud is helpful in assisting in removing the accretions and distortions to which religious faith and practice are subject because of our psychological structures.

Man is a responsible being. He is not an automaton or a being mounted upon a strong steed that he is powerless to control. To explain all guilt as a complex due to repression is not really to account for man's sense of responsibility. Undoubtedly some guilt feelings are abnormal and associated with repressions due to narrow moral rigor and severity in childhood. Neurotics are often morbidly moral, and, if religious, they interpret their inner conflicts and tensions in terms of sin. Often also they stand more in need of an analyst than a priest, because of the abnormal state. A man who is religious may interpret his symptoms in religious terms, whereas the real problem is not religious but psychological. On the other hand, normal morally responsible people betray no neurotic symptoms. Indeed, the conscience of such people is no emotional upsurge of conviction and feeling from the unconscious, imprisoned in a superego, but rather is associated with an intuitive sense of right and wrong and subject to rational judgment. We shall consider this issue of responsible freedom later.

Jung, at first Freud's disciple and later his critic, developed a psychology of the unconscious much more friendly to the Christian faith and much less naturalistic. Whereas Freud had made the libido almost exclusively sexual, Jung included more openly all unconscious emotional energy. Furthermore, although Jung accepts the influences of the unconscious, he does not make them determinative. He makes a place for freedom of will and choice. Whereas Freud was concerned with efficient causation and thinks in terms akin to physical science, Jung recognizes a teleological element. Life is a movement forwards, and Jung is concerned with future goals. The roots of neurosis do not lie for him in the past but in the present situation. He writes: "I no longer find the cause of neurosis in the past, but in the present. I ask what is the necessary task which the patient will not accomplish." [73] Jung is not so much concerned with repression as with regression. The basis of neurosis is not repression of infantile maladjustments, but regression into a more primitive past from present failure to cope with a situation.

Here we are helped by Jung's analysis of personality. He finds three levels of the *psyche:* the conscious, the personal unconscious, and the collective or racial unconscious. At the conscious level, that of observable personal being, he divides persons into types. There are two attitude types: the predominantly introvert and the predominantly extrovert.[74] Along with these we have the function types which are characterized by the predominance of one or more of the psychological activities of thinking, feeling, intuiting, and sensing. Usually these activities are paired into thinking/feeling and intuition/sensation. The full personality should have a balance of what both types of classification represent. It is here that the personal unconscious comes in. This is formed in the process of development in infancy. It constitutes a mirror image or opposite to the state of the consciousness, and thereby it exercises a compensatory role. A person who is extrovert and thoughtful at the conscious level is introvert and emotional at the level of the personal unconscious. Hence some possible personal attitudes and functions lie submerged in the unconscious. If they could be lifted into the consciousness and used, the self would be more integrated. Here conscious will is usually at a loss and here neuroses tend to arise. When a situation arises with which

[73] See J. A. C. Brown, *Freud and the Post-Freudians* (Baltimore: Penguin Books, 1963), pp. 49 f.

[74] For the extrovert life is adventure and opportunity; he is outgoing. For the introvert life is responsibility and problem; he is cautious and detached.

the conscious attitude and functions fail to cope and in which the compensating powers, neglected and relegated to the unconscious, could help in adaptation, there is a tendency for the personality to regress to a more primitive pattern of behavior. Sometimes the conscious personality may voluntarily learn from this and make a fresh creative advance. At other times, this may lead to a neurotic state.

Jung's "libido" is driving towards integrated wholeness. The personality develops as it moves to the assimilation of hitherto unconscious potential. Violet de Laszlo, commenting on Jung's theory, reminds us that

> the introvert who can establish a fuller relationship with his environment and the extrovert who can discover the reality and wealth of his inner life will both be immensely richer than before, and so will the thinking man who gains access to his formerly unknown feeling values, or the factual sensation person who previously found himself excluded from the sphere of the intuitive imagination.[75]

It is here that the collective unconscious comes in, for it has reserves of wisdom not available at the conscious level. This racial unconscious is universal and primary. In it are stored the primeval racial memories, so that it is an epitome of the mental evolution of the human race. Here are the symbols expressed in the myths and aspirations which have been central in that process of development. Such repressed memories are accompanied by other material which is nascent, has never been expressed, and is available for those moments when the time is ripe for its conscious expression. The latter, too, can only be expressed symbolically.

Hence Jung finds in the collective unconscious a repository of the wisdom of the race and of possibilities never yet harnessed to reality, all stored in symbolic form. It is the home of

[75] From the introduction to *The Basic Writings* of C. G. Jung, ed. by Violet Staub de Laszlo (New York: The Modern Library, 1959), p. xvi.

the great archetypal images—the mother and father symbols, the image of the old wise man, the hero image, and so on. Some of these have arisen originally from sexual association, but they have gathered much wider significance at the spiritual level and apply to many higher areas of the conscious life. Since such symbols appear in dreams, Jung's dream interpretation, as opposed to Freud's, does not follow the path of reduction to sexual problems. He holds that dreams may have prospective and higher significance. The archetypal images of the collective unconscious may become vehicles of profound spiritual insight. Thus the image of rebirth and its accompanying symbols points to the possibility of a new adaptation to the issues that beset human existence. An original sexual symbol has deeper implications than its literal significance. This means that in the collective unconscious are resources that will enable men to cope with the situations which might lead to neurosis. The task of the psychotherapist is to harness such forces more fully, although at every stage of human existence they are exercising their influence.

Jung's position is by no means generally accepted. Often it is colored by philosophical presuppositions. His idea of a collective unconscious suggests a kind of panpsychism and goes much further than the old Hebrew idea of social solidarity and its cognate Christian concept of man as being "in Adam." There is undoubtedly a mental atmosphere and a corporate nexus of relationships into which we are born, but this is quite different from the kind of presupposition which postulates a racial recapitulation in the individual at the level of ideas. Furthermore, Jung's view relies at the mental level upon the idea of the inheritance of acquired characteristics, a view generally rejected at the organismic level by evolutionists.

Again, Jung bases his analysis of religion upon this idea of the collective unconscious and its contents. The archetypal images express the general primitive attitudes to the world and its problems, and as such they are religious. They influence our conscious attitudes and take in our religious life. Jung writes: "The religious character of these ideas proceeds from the fact that they express the realities of the collective unconscious; hence they also have the power of releasing the latent energies of the unconscious." [76] He believes that the revelations which come to any founder of a religion flow up from the collective unconscious and are concretizations of the archetypal images. Thus the deity is a mythical deity, and God becomes a psychological function of man, man's child.[77] Jung quotes Scheffler's verses:

I know that without me
God can no moment live.
Were I to die, then He
No longer would survive.

I am God's child, His son,
And He too is my child;
We are the two in one
Both son and father mild.

Evidently God is at best the collective unconscious, and the latter is the true "ground of being." God becomes objectively, however, my projection. This may satisfy the pantheist, but it does not account for the theistic religions with their emphasis on the over-againstness of God and man, on the "otherness" of God, and on the creaturely status of man. Indeed if God is for Jung a projection, consistency demands that other persons and the realm of nature be projections also. Pantheism would concur.

Jung does, at any rate, give the spiritual aspect of man's mental life a place, while his emphasis on the consciousness and on voluntary action saves him from the naturalistic determinism of Freud. Finally, Jung is concerned with man as a

[76] Jung, *Psychological Types,* trans. H. G. Baynes (New York: Harcourt, Brace & Co., 1938), p. 271.

[77] Ibid. p. 300. For the quotation from Scheffler see pp. 317 f.

psychosomatic whole. For him the self comprises the full reaches of the personality, including the unconscious, and thus ideally it transcends the present existing personality. The archetype of wholeness, of the self, dominates the whole process of personal development. There is a kind of inherent integrative plan which is experienced symbolically where the image of wholeness is present. It is here that the archetypal God image plays its part. In a significant statement, Jung says:

> Too few people have experienced the divine image as the innermost possession of their own souls. Christ only meets them from without, never from within the soul; that is why dark paganism reigns there, a paganism which, now in a form so blatant that it can no longer be denied and now in all too threadbare disguise, is swamping the world of so-called Christian culture.[78]

One final point needs to be made. Religious faith is neither confirmed nor denied by psychological investigation. It is one thing to investigate how faith arises and quite another to answer the question: Why? In the case of Freud, just because men find it satisfying to organize their existence and their world about a religious faith by no means proves that such an organization is false and religion an illusion. In the case of Jung, just because men find that religious faith helps in the integration of the psyche does not demonstrate the reality or unreality of God. Jung himself confesses this:

> The competence of psychology as an empirical science only goes so far as to establish, on the basis of comparative research, whether for instance the imprint found in the psyche can or cannot reasonably be termed a "God-image." Nothing positive or negative has thus been asserted about the possible existence of God, any more than the archetype of the "hero" proves the actual existence of a hero.[79]

[78] C. G. Jung, *The Religious and Psychological Problems of Alchemy*, included in *The Basic Writings* of C. G. Jung, p. 442.

[79] Ibid. pp. 444 f.

The danger is that people should use psychological processes as reasons for rejecting religious faith, since the validity of such faith is not established at the psychological level.

We have ranged from Freud to Jung and excluded later and more currently popular exponents of depth psychology, because the former raise in an acute way issues that are still raised by many of their successors. Both feel that mental processes should be considered in their own right and not merely as other ways of presenting the physiological processes of the brain. For them, mind, conscious and unconscious, is an important element in the personal whole, but neither fall into the trap of Cartesian dualism. Mind has its roots down deep in the evolutionary movement and is intimately bound in with the physical, physiological, and biological processes of the human organism. If man is to be an integrated self, that self is compounded of an inner and an outer aspect, and one may not be reduced to the other. So we come to a discussion of man's subjectivity in the light of the current position of the sciences.

VII. *The subjective aspect of pyschosomatic wholeness—self-conscious spirit and personal being*

The picture of man which is being developed is neither a radically dualistic one nor a monistic one, neither materialistic nor idealistic. That mind should emerge creatively within the physicochemical and biological levels is at least a reminder that the physical and physiological are not inimical to the mental, and we have seen enough reason at the scientific level to support the separate status of mind. Whatever matter may be (and the nature of physical energy remains an enigma!), it must, as we suggested earlier, have the potentiality for bearing mind. Indeed, the mathematical structure which the physicist is continually discovering within the physical order suggests that there is rational structure in nature. We are almost, if we cared to speculate in this direction, where the Aristotelian schools rested their case.

In a sense, man is a microcosm of the macrocosm. We may picture man as embodying in himself the whole evolutionary process. The physicochemical base of his psychosomatic whole is integrated successively at the biological level and the level of mind, being brought to a focus in self-conscious mind or spirit. If life is the point at which mind first emerges within the sea of energy, howbeit in unconscious form, we may see a link between life and mind in the new temporal aspect common to both. In this aspect the physicochemical basis is integrated temporally in a new way. It is characteristic of self-conscious mind that it pursues goals and that its temporal dimension is directed and integrated in a characteristic way. Past and future are influential in the present as memory and anticipation. This is what differentiates history from nature.

In the living organism we find the beginning of such a differentiation. At the inorganic level we have a movement based on efficient causation. If we were to take any physicochemical system at any moment, we should find that, at this level, its state would be understandable solely in terms of preceding events. It is characterized by succession, before and after, with every "after" determined by its "before." When we turn to a living whole, we find succession too, but here the "after" is more important than the "before!" The living thing and its parts are definable finally in terms of the stage of mature growth, and not in terms of beginnings. The process of growth would seem to be governed by the final stage which the whole attains and all the internal relations subserve this end.

It is true that feedback mechanical brains can be constructed, as we have already indicated, and yet the feedback mechanism is a creation of thinking man, and its direction is dictated by the purpose for which it is made. This could be taken as an indication that, at the level of the artifact, mind in its creative and directive capacity is still a necessity. Only so does a man-made machine manifest direction. What we find in a living organism is a temporal process in which the "befores" are drawn up into and included with the "afters," rather than being mere causative antecedents. Indeed all "befores" are adjustments to "afters," which have yet to arrive. A. A. Bowman suggests that "the movement of life is not like the movement of a projectile in space, but like that of a snowball gathering substance as it goes." [80] Thus already in living things we see a reflection of the temporal characteristics of mental and spiritual life.

It would seem that in life we have the emergence of a new organization of energy which prepares it to serve the capacities of mind and spirit. We might say that the time form is transformed that it may bear meaning. Life provides the spatio-temporal patterned energy within which mind and ultimately human personality may flourish. When mind does make its presence evident, already physical energy has been adapted to enter into functional relationship with it. As the vital supervenes upon the physical, the characteristic temporal form of mind and personal being is manifested in living organisms. Again to quote A. A. Bowman:

> Life . . . transforms the time of physics into another kind of time; and the time of life, like the time of experience, is characterized by the distinctions of past, present and future. It is this fact above all, which distinguishes the living body from other corporeal structures, and fits the former to enter into a single ontological system (*a heterogeneous system, of course*—editorial comment) with the spiritual mode of being, and to be the vehicle for the moral purposes of mankind.[81]

We are left with a duality rather than a dualism, for the two components of the physical and the mental are always within a whole, both in the natural order and in human society. When

[80] A. A. Bowman, *The Sacramental Universe* (Princeton: Princeton University Press, 1939), p. 363.

[81] A. A. Bowman, op. cit. p. 363.

we come to man, we can say that man *is* a person but that he *has* a mind and a physical body. Thus "person" is the description of man as a whole, in which the duality of the physical and the mental is integrated at the level of self-conscious mind or spirit. All the physical, biological, and mental factors are thus brought to focus in self-awareness. Buber has aptly expressed this, when he defines spirit as "man's totality that has become consciousness, the totality which comprises and integrates all his capacities, powers, qualities, and urges." [82] The human mind differs from the animal mind at just this point. The higher animal knows, but man both knows and knows that he knows. He is a part of nature, with all the material and physical elements that constitute the natural order, and yet he is not *merely* a part of nature, for he transcends it. He is not reducible to the animal level. He is not just a higher mammal. He is a subject with all that the word implies. He is in the objective order and yet he transcends it since he is the one who knows, orders, and controls it.

In speaking of man we therefore use two language categories. On the one hand, we describe him in terms of his bodily behavior: "He is doing something." On the other hand, we can describe him in terms of his mental life: "He is thinking." The first form is based on direct observation and is public. The second form is based on inference from observation or on communication by the subject himself. It is private and known only to the person whose inner life it is. It is experienced, not observed.

It is often suggested nowadays that the Born complementarity principle in quantum mechanics might be applied to these two forms of language. Just as we may speak of the atomic particles in language employing the wave picture or in language employing the particle picture, and just as both enable us to penetrate into the mystery of the subatomic

[82] M. Buber, *Israel and the World* (New York: Schocken Books, 1948), p. 175.

world, so also we have to employ the two forms of language to penetrate the mystery of personal being. Our only difficulty is that the similitude breaks down somewhat since both the wave and the particle categories apply to the same atomic entity, whereas the mental and behavior categories apply to two distinctive aspects of personal being which are mysteriously related in the personal whole.[83] We could, of course, make the principle apply much more happily if we held to the identity theory which we have already dismissed. As Sherrington aptly puts it: ". . . nothing known of mind brings mind within what we conceive as energy. Mind refuses to be energy, just as it has always refused to be matter." [84]

What binds the two languages together is the first person pronoun "I." "I am doing something" and "I am thinking" are both significant dynamic aspects of personal being. But let us note that directly we introduce "I" we move to the subjective realm. Neither of these sentences means the same with the first person employed as when the object "he" is used. The objective approach by observation can know nothing of the inner life of the one whose bodily actions are being described. The knowledge is indirect by inference and by communication of mental activity by the person under observation. But when "I" is used, immediately there is open directly to the speaker the inner world of motivation, reasons, and free choice which is closed to all observers. "I" experience where others observe.

This means that the logical use of "I" in any statement gives it a distinct logical basis. Bertrand Russell once wrote: "I hold

[83] Cf. C. Sherrington, op. cit. p. 350 f.:
"There is no more of course than mere analogy between this mind-energy complex which teases biology and that other, the wave-particle dilemma which has been teasing physics. In the latter case both of its terms are at least assimilable in the measure that each is describable by space into time. Both are, in short, physical. The biological dilemma is of another order. In it the two terms are divergent to the degree that while the one is sensible the other is insensible."

[84] C. Sherrington, op. cit. p. 348.

that whatever we know without inference is mental." [85] "I" involves consciousness and self-awareness. It is a word that cannot be public. It has a distinctive significance when related to objective language, for "I" am more than what can be publicly observed. I. T. Ramsey points out the logically hybrid character of the sentences "I am asleep" and "I am dead," for the words "dead" and "asleep" have meaning which are solely and inevitably bound up with such objects as "he." He argues that "a first person singular activity word tells of more than 'objects'" for "my 'free' activity is more than the public behavior which expresses it." [86] The two languages thus attain a peculiar status when the subject "I" replaces the objective description "he." It is here that brain/body and mind meet in the personal whole which is typically expressed in the first personal pronoun.

When we try to express "I" in objective categories we tend to use the observable, physical category and to dismiss the "ghost in the machine" along with Ryle. After all, our knowledge of other persons comes to us partly through sense observation. For us, at the level of observation, they are bodies performing activities, and we are strongly tempted to accept the empirical estimate and to reject any mysterious mind or spirit. Sherrington reminds us that "mind, for anything perception can compass, goes . . . in our spatial world more ghostly than a ghost. Invisible, intangible, it is a thing not even of outline; it is not a 'thing.' It remains without sensual confirmation and it remains without it forever." [87] The inner world of other persons, if they have one, is private to them and not open to our observation.

The dilemma is met if we remember that intuitive awareness

[85] B. Russell, *Human Knowledge, Its Scope and Limits* (London: George Allen and Unwin, 1948).

[86] I. T. Ramsey, *Freedom and Immortality* (London: S.C.M. Press, 1960), p. 87.

[87] C. Sherrington, op. cit. p. 357.

and personal disclosure are also involved. The inner world of others becomes public to the degree that observation and communication confirm our own intuitive awareness of their personal being. For it is this with which our knowledge of them commences. Through a sensible awareness of their somatic appearance and behavior we have an initial apprehension of their personal being. We then proceed to fill in this apprehension by inference from their actions and by seeking to understand them through their communicating words.

Yet all such understanding of others, knowledge of them rather than about them, is possible because of our own self-awareness and self-understanding. Because we know ourselves as persons from within, we are able by empathy and sympathy to understand their inner world. We know what it is to be a subject, and so we can extrapolate something of our inward life to them. Though let it be noted that such understanding has an empirical basis. There is nothing mystical about it, and it is fulfilled in the fellowship and mutual communication born of love.

What remains mysterious is the "I" itself. It is here that the linguistic analyst with his empiricist approach presents his challenge. Following Descartes and yet rejecting his dualism, he refuses to accept as knowledge anything that is not a clear and distinct idea. Hence there is Ryle's rejection of the elusive "I" for, as we have seen, the "I" cannot be clearly expressed in objective categories. "He" is always less than "I," and the latter makes objective sentences logically odd.[88] The peculiarity of the "I" in the epistemological process is that it is always the knowing subject, even in introspection. The consequence is that it is never able to turn itself into an object, for what

[88] Cf. J. R. Jones, "The Two Contexts of Mental Concepts," *Proceedings of the Aristotelian Society,* 1958–9, Vol. VI, p. 124: " . . . a 'ghost' is built into grammar, and it will not be laid." Quoted by I. Ramsey, "The Possibility and Purpose of Metaphysical Theology," *The Prospect for Metaphysics,* ed. Ian Ramsey, p. 166.

knows is always marked off from what is known by an uncrossable barrier. I always put myself over against that which I seek to know and to express objectively, including my own empirical ego. I think about myself thinking, and going deeper, I think about myself thinking about myself thinking, and so on, but "I" always eludes me in this dimension of knowing. I know myself as knowing. The self that I know is never identical with "I," for I am also the one who knows. So in trying to understand myself by turning myself into an object, I never discover my innermost self which is still knower. I am both knower and known, and thus there is in every "I" the quality of self-transcendence. I am always more than I comprehend.

It is here that Ryle's attack on the "ghost in the machine" takes on some measure of validity. For directly I fall into objective language I begin to speak about mind or spirit as substance and thus to suggest that it is a quasi-physical entity. But in the dimension of self-awareness, although aware of myself, I cannot define exactly what consciousness is. We know what consciousness is in our own self-consciousness, but there is a *sui-generis* quality which makes it irreducible to or expressible in physical and objective categories. "I" include my body and its physiological machinery and my mental states, but "I" also transcends them. Yet, mysterious as self-conscious mind or spirit is, I do know it in being a mind, and, as H. D. Lewis reminds us, this "is as direct a way as any." He points out that to know ourselves as subjects must not be allowed to lead us "into the false presupposition that the self is real only in some formal or highly tenuous way . . . I know myself as a real being, although what I know here is not primarily body." [89] We may accept this statement without concurring in his evident idealistic bent. My awareness of my self is an apprehension which cannot be fully expressed.

But the mystery should not bother us, for directly we move

[89] H. D. Lewis, "God and Mystery," *The Prospect for Metaphysics*, ed. Ian Ramsey, p. 210.

from the observable to the imponderable we cease to deal with problems and become involved in mystery, as Gabriel Marcel has reminded us. A problem may be solved by logical analysis and may be expressed with clarity. It belongs to the objective realm and to the region of clear and distinct concepts. Yet a great deal of our experience at the personal and suprapersonal levels is concerned with mysteries which are known only by disclosure and sympathetic imagination. The other person may be treated as an object, and we may adopt the impersonal objectifying relation to other persons. That is to say, we may concern ourselves with what is observable and dismiss the inner personal being. But the other is truly known only as we involve ourselves with him and seek, to use Marcel's phrase, to participate in the mystery of his being.[90] For mystery he is, and mystery he remains, even when from his own personal disclosure and by our own sympathetic imagination, we have sought to understand him. We can give no clear and distinct statement about his consciousness anymore than we can give one of our own. Depth psychology may help us to understand something of its structure, but we can no more grasp his "I" than we can grasp our own. Directly we turn him into an object the reality evades us as it does with ourselves, for we set him, to use Buber's idea, at a distance from ourselves.[91]

This distance is, as Buber points out, necessary for us to enter into relation. It differentiates us from the other, for we can enter into relation only when the other is set at a distance from us. Furthermore, the objective knowledge that comes when we set him at a distance may help in the understanding that issues from personal involvement with him. "The "I-It" relation is thus contributory to and interacts with the "I-

[90] G. Marcel, *The Mystery of Being. I. Reflection and Mystery* (London: The Harvill Press, Ltd., 1950), especially pp. 197 ff.

[91] Cf. M. Friedmann, Martin Buber: *The Life of Dialogue* (Chicago: University of Chicago Press, 1955), pp. 80 ff.

Thou," but although it is inevitable that we should withdraw from personal involvement into such objective contemplation, we never understand the other if we remain in this dimension of knowing. The other ceases to be a "Thou," an "I." If we thus depersonalize the other, we also depersonalize ourselves. Erich Frank suggests that "as long as man interprets himself merely in terms of objective nature and shapes his life and his world according to this concept, he estranges himself from his real self, and his soul becomes empty." [92] It is the unifying wholeness in man which makes him a person.

Indeed, self-consciousness is fully realized only as we are actively involved with the other in personal relationship. This is to be expected, since it would appear that self-consciousness comes to birth in us along with the consciousness of others. "Individuality," writes Buber, "makes its appearance by being differentiated from other individualities. A person makes his appearance by entering into relation with other persons." [93] The antenatal life of the child rests in the womb of the mother. As the child develops, so this relationship at the level of spirit differentiates into self-consciousness and consciousness of the "Thou." Buber can say: "I become through my relation to the *Thou;* as I become I, I say *Thou.*" [94] We find ourselves beset by personal mysteries in which we can participate but which we can never express with the precision and clarity possible at the level of scientific and empirical observation.

The key to the mystery of the other is love. It is by love that we become truly involved with other persons and spirit may meet spirit. The other comes to us always in a personal disclosure in which claim and sympathy are commingled. He challenges us to involvement. He calls on us to forsake the

[92] Erich Frank, *Philosophical Understanding and Religious Truth* (New York: Oxford University Press, 1945), p. 15.

[93] M. Buber, *I and Thou,* trans. by R. Gregor Smith (Edinburgh: T & T Clark, 1937), p. 62.

[94] Ibid. p. 11.

enthronement of our own person in an objectified world which we seek to order and control. He bids us be open to him and to other persons. He evokes love, commitment, responsible decision.

It is precisely here that man begins to achieve his true destiny, for in the claims of others he experiences the claim of God. He meets God in this world with all its claims and possibilities, and above all in the claims of his fellows. To this theme we must continually return. Our very environment, natural and social, calls us into encounter with encompassing reality, with God. And once more we face mystery. If we cannot clearly express human personhood how much less can we clearly express God who is infinite Spirit! We know him as we become involved with him in trust and commitment, but always he passes beyond our understanding and we touch but the outskirts of his ways. As with the elusive "I" and "Thou," so God too is the final mystery which encompasses our life. But this does not mean the absence of knowledge, it rather means that the inner world of spirit is not so open to the objectifying process as is the empirical order with which science deals.

In talking of disclosure we find ourselves facing two aspects of personal being. Disclosure, first of all, involves communication, and the signal mode of communication is words or language. Even some higher mammals communicate by signs to a degree; and here we may see the evolutionary preparation for the emergence of self-conscious, self-transcendent mind. Man is a symbolizing creature. Somewhere and mysteriously, where self-conscious mind and cerebral cortex express their unity, a symbolizing process goes on. Sensations become apprehensions, apprehensions are conceptualized, and man's symbolizing faculty takes over. He is not only conscious of messages from his world, but also he is able to put them at a distance, to order and compare them, to formulate concepts which have been freed from any particular perceptual situation, and to organize his bodily signs that these may become communicative symbols to his fellows. He is a maker of language. By his words, he organizes and symbolizes his experience and communicates it to other minds. He transcends his signs so that he is able to develop them grammatically and order their usage. Man's capacity for free ideas, his gift for rational ordering and critical judgment, his ability to symbolize and communicate by language are all facets of one aspect of his self-transcendence—his ability to find meaning in his world.

VIII. *Freedom and determinism*

The second aspect of personal being involved in disclosure is man's sense of responsibility and freedom. It is here, perhaps, that the language of science and the language of faith seem to become especially involved. For science deals inevitably in efficient causation and a deterministic scheme, whereas faith is concerned with teleological causation and the inner freedom of spirit. Naturalism, as we have seen, takes the scientific evidence and makes man into a causative structure. Mind is either another way of talking about the causative processes of the cerebrum or it is an epiphenomenon cast around the cortex, reflecting and not influencing its processes.

When naturalistic thinkers go further with Freud and admit the reality of mind, they turn consciousness into something that is entirely determined by hidden forces in the jungle of the unconscious, especially sex and hostility. The picture they present is one of man as a creature who at every level of his being is determined by the natural forces which are involved in his personal structure. Freedom is an illusion. The conscience, which Kant had made the keystone of such freedom, is at best but a superego thrown up by unresolved conflicts which have been repressed into the unconscious. Man's behavior is either a matter of conditioned reflexes or a reflection of natural impulses determined in expression by social pressures and often perverted by unconscious forces.

We have seen that many neurologists would not concur but would regard mind as a distinctive aspect of personal being, influential in initiating and controlling action. Hence we have Eccles's able formulation of the way in which mind can operate within a causal framework which is fundamentally statistical, while observing the principles of quantum mechanics. This, at least, allows for the operation of personal freedom within the scientific scene. But let it be noted that we are not mixing the two languages, since all we can speak about scientifically is an ordered excitation of the neurons within the quantum mechanical framework, and thus we still speak in terms of scientific concepts. And, incidentally, we must be careful not to take our model too literally. Here freedom and consciousness still go their ghostly way. We are dealing with means and not with ends, with the instrument and not with the purpose that may activate it, with efficient causation and not with teleological.

This differentiation still remains true at the psychosomatic level. The instrument, physical, physiological, and even psychological, can have no purpose of its own. The purpose belongs to the directing agent, and we should expect that the instrument would possess its own determinate character, if it is to be effective in the service of the "I." As the "I" retreats and objectifies process after process within the psychosomatic whole, we would expect such determinate character to be manifest, for freedom remains ever in the inner deeps of subjectivity. This would hold of other persons, whom we may study objectively, as well as ourselves. And, insofar as they voluntarily become the instruments of our intentions we may expect to find a determinate character in their behavior. This is the basis of all propaganda, suggestion techniques, and brainwashing tactics—to impose ideas upon the other which will determine his intentions. Or, even more dangerously, to loosen in some way the contact between inner freedom and the objectifiable instrument so that the other becomes a means to our ends.

Empirically of course, we observe only behavior. Freedom belongs to the inner side of personality. It is private primarily. We have, in fact, from the empirical standpoint to ask what constitutes a situation in which freedom and responsibility are experienced by the subject. Here we can be grateful for the careful analysis undertaken by I. T. Ramsey.[95] At the moment of free decision, there is present something more than the mere objective behavior pattern—the transcendent aspect of personal being associated with "I." "I" know that I am not limited to the objective behavior which I show to a scientific observer. The chemical, reflexive, instinctive, inhibitive, and unconscious movements and urges which he analyzes are all transcended. In my free decision I realize myself as something more than scientific language can describe. As Ramsey puts it: "My behavior, to me, when deliberate or decisive, is 'objects' *and more.*"[96] Thus events might outwardly fit completely into a causative framework so that even my activity may appear to be the result of causes beyond myself. Yet, even in such events, I can declare that they have "my backing" and that they express my decisive activity.

From the moral and religious standpoint, no description purely in terms of causal events will ever be adequate. This standpoint claims that the sense of responsibility implies freedom to choose. If I have an obligation, then I also have the capacity to evade it. We are not creatures under compulsion from efficient causation, but we have the gift of *responsible* decision.

[95] I. T. Ramsey, *Freedom and Immorality* (London: S.C.M. Press, 1960). The first two chapters of this book should be consulted in detail by the interested reader.

[96] Ibid. p. 28.

Ramsey finds two transcendent elements in any "duty-situation," as he terms it. Objectively, in the first place, I am aware of a challenger. I discern an obligation in the situation which transcends the observable "objects." He writes: "It is this 'transcendent' reference which makes the challenge moral: to be aware of such a challenge is to recognize a moral obligation."[97] Thus the good Samaritan might, according to the rules of his national group, have ignored the injured Jew, as the priest did before him. Then the situation would have been impersonal, and he would have conformed to the expected behavioral pattern. But instead, the situation became personal, and he became aware of his obligation as a human being. So he was moved "inwardly" by compassion.

This brings us, secondly, to the subjective aspect. Here we find a free decision in response to the challenge which transcends normally expected public behavior. It is conduct which rises above any "specific determination." A "natural" or "impersonal" act will be causally connected with and determined by the objects alone. But in the free decision there is no restraint expressible in causal language. Thus a man may decide to get married because of circumstances. He may want a wife to "see him through college," or he may decide to marry money and relieve himself of pecuniary embarrassment. There is here an external causative structure—college education or lack of funds. On the other hand, he may marry because he sees something worthy of his total commitment and love in the woman. In such a decision he freely decides to marry and to accept the obligation that such commitment brings with it and which is expressed in the marriage vows. Outwardly the behavior will appear the same, but an impersonal, causative act will give place to a personal and responsible decision.

What we have in acts that have a moral and responsible nature is not necessarily expressed as a different pattern in observable behavior—this may occur or not. The crux of the

[97] Ibid. p. 33.

issue lies in the "I," with its sense of obligation as it discerns a certain moral challenge in the objective situation, and with its free and responsible decision in the light of that challenge. As Ramsey remarks: ". . . the determination of my decision when there is free will, is no causal determination. It is a peculiar kind of response to a peculiar kind of challenge."[98]

Against the sovereignty of the deterministic and objective way of thinking, the existentialist revolt must be understood. The existentialist turns to the inner bastions of personal being and declares man's essential freedom. For him the distinctive mark of man is freedom and responsibility. He is realistic in his analysis of man's somatic state and his natural and social environment. He recognizes man's historicity, his position in space and time. He offers no retreat into any idealistic ivory tower. Man is characterized by his "thrownness." He is here and not there. He is now and not then. His life is marked by birth, by death, by temporal transience. He is limited by his somatic condition, by his social pressures, by his historical placing. He is not unconditioned. Yet within this area he is free to determine his existence.

As here used, existence has a peculiarly distinctive meaning. It expresses man's free decision about the nature of his personal being. Christian existentialists, such as Kierkegaard and Marcel, argue that man's essential being is ontologically prior to any decision on his part. Then his existential choice may lead to the actualization of that being or may lead to an existence in which he is estranged from his true nature. Atheistic existentialists, such as Camus and Sartre, would hold that each determines his own being in his existential choice.

All emphasize the centrality of freedom and decision. The categories they employ are inevitably associated with this inner aspect of personal being. They speak of responsibility and guilt, of fear and finitude. They bid man look downwards into his innermost being and consider the decision that he must

[98] Ibid. p. 38.

make in the deeps of his spirit. The pressure of conscience, the anguish and sense of guilt which beset man, his conditioned nature, his finitude and historicity call for decision. In the light of his finitude, of his thrownness in space and time, of the claims of his fellows, and of the pressure of the Unconditioned, of God, he must decide what kind of man he is going to be. Above all, for Christian thinkers, it is the last pressure which is ultimately significant, as it is God who in creation gives to man the divine image with its innate freedom. Once such an existential choice has been made and a man has decided his destiny, the initial commitment is reflected in every subsequent choice. A man may decide what kind of man he is going to be, for or against his divinely given destiny, and that choice will set the direction of his inner personhood.

This last statement means that man's inner decisions are not indeterminate. The freedom of which we are speaking is not indetermination. True freedom is found for the Christian only in commitment to God, the Unconditioned. Here, too, to return to Ramsey's analysis, man discerns a certain pattern in the objective order and apprehends a personal presence which lays claim upon him and challenges him to responsive love. As he commits himself in free decision at this point he finds his true freedom in doing God's will. Such commitment determines his character, the central direction of "I." Around it are increasingly integrated all his psychosomatic urges, and the forces of his life tend to flow along channels which become more and more habitual. His specific acts of choice may vary, but their general trend will be in line with that continuity of personal being, character, which the primal existential choice has directed. His personal being becomes increasingly integrated and reflects his inner commitment. Within that initial commitment he remains free and responsible, but this is not indetermination. It is self-determination. It reflects his inner being, and the less integrated he is, the less dependable will his decisions be. It would seem that Ramsey has left his analysis open at just this point. William Temple reminds us that "*freedom is not absence of determination; it is spiritual determination, as distinct from mechanical or even organic, determination. It is determination by what seems good as contrasted with determination by irresistible compulsion.*" [99]

But such a decision is not a universal one. Man may refuse to be a singular one, a true person—to use Kierkegaard's phrase. Man's historical state is not one of conscious and acknowledged relation to God. As Kierkegaard saw it, he may live at the level of desire, in which case he chooses a naturalistic mode of existence, and such a choice will mean the enslavement of his freedom. His "will" will be subject to lower desires, and the challenge of the higher in *most* situations will be rejected. He may, at a higher level, center his life in himself and determine his existence by commitment to certain moral principles. Yet the mystery always is that his existence remains egocentered. He is placing himself or his natural urges and desires in the place of God. He either regards himself as self-sufficient or merges himself in his natural environment. In so doing he becomes alienated from his true destiny as a spiritually directed person existing in relation to God. Fundamentally it means that man turns his eyes from God and from his fellows upon himself. He turns his world into an "It," an instrument to serve his own purposes. He regards his fellows, not as ends in themselves, but as means to his own ends. He, the creature, arrogantly claims for himself the sovereign powers which rightly belong to his Creator.

Yet man cannot escape responsibility for this free decision. Anthropologists and sociologists have made us aware of the variation of moral standards across the world and down through historical time, but this does not remove from man a sense of obligation to live up to the standards of behavior which hold for his social group. Nor can such an awareness of

[99] W. Temple, *Nature, Man and God* (New York: The Macmillan Co., 1956), p. 229.

claim be causatively connected with social pressure, as naturalistic sociologists love to postulate. Often the prophet and the saint, the seer and the wise man, the Amos and the Socrates, will go beyond the accepted duty and set themselves against society in what they see to be morally compulsive challenge and obligation. Further, the attempts of Freudians to ascribe guilt feelings to an unhealthily produced superego would make us all abnormal people. In any case, if all thoughts and theories are but rationalizations of unconscious impulses, even Freud's theory can have no more claim to truth than any other, and the whole position is reduced to absurdity. So guilt and the sense of obligation beset man's path, even when he has chosen against his destiny. His alienation from his true destiny produces a feeling of insecurity and besetting creaturely anxiety.

But when men are thus committed, how can they change? At the theoretical level it is equivalent to a change in the absolute presuppositions which determine our logic. If a man has committed himself to false standards and unsatisfactory ideals, it will be the tensions, contradictions, and insecurities that they introduce into his existence which will begin to set him free from his false existence. The loss of meaning in life and its accompanying insecurity, the contradictions and tensions which may arise in moral decisions and personal relationship will begin to "pry him out of his shell."

Ultimately, however, it is the "expulsive power of a new affection" which will release him and lead to a new and decisive commitment. It is here that the love of God moves into the deepest strata of personal being and in the inner decision of faith brings us to a new and real integration of our personal wholeness. The Incarnation points to man as he should be, living in openness to God and openness to his fellows. It is in this personal disclosure of God that man finds the integrating center of his own life and must make his existential choice. The core of self-conscious mind or spirit is the capacity to love, and without such utter commitment to others, life and thought can be empty. M. Buber puts it: "The Single One is the man for whom the reality of relation with God as an exclusive relation includes and encompasses the possibility of relation with all otherness, and for whom the whole body politic, the reservoir of otherness, offers just enough otherness for him to pass his life with it." [100] In being related to God, I am related to all others, and in their claims and companionship I know the companionship of God.

[100] M. Buber, *Between Man and Man,* trans. R. Gregor Smith (London: Kegan Paul, 1947) p. 65.

VI

The Incarnation and a Sacramental Universe

The attack upon divine transcendence which characterizes much of our contemporary radical theology requires of us a new understanding of the nature of transcendence and of the meaning of sacrament. Modern science, with its success, has fixed our attention upon the natural order including the outward and observable aspects of human nature. Its empirical emphasis has tended to support immanentism rather than transcendence in our theological interpretation and to look for the practical rather than the mystical in the expression of the Christian faith.

An other worldly emphasis will not, therefore, make any contact with the modern scene. Equally a Christology which ignores the humanity of Jesus and concentrates on his deity can refute the true meaning of the Incarnation—"God with us." If God became man, then he accepted our "thrown-ness," our positioning in this order of space and time. Thereby he sanctified our human existence and, in making it possible for us to become real persons, redeemed us as incarnated spirits, as human flesh and blood. When our Lord asked of man: "Wilt thou be made whole?" he manifested his gracious concern for man's total well-being, physical as well as spiritual. Thereby he showed that this natural environment in which we are set and of which physically and somatically we are a part is not alien to God's purpose but involved in his redemptive plan. To know Christ's love and reconciling power is not to turn our back upon this world or to develop an "other worldly" attitude. Rather it is to share Christ's life here and now in our own "thrown-ness" and to find in our social relationships and natural environment the area in which we may fulfil God's purpose for our lives.

But this is exactly what the Christian doctrine of creation also implies. The creation saga of Genesis 1 does not teach asceticism and other worldliness. When the Creator contemplates his creation, he declares it to be very good, and Hebrew realism, throughout the travail of Israel's history, believed that it was in this world that men could be found by God and enjoy his fellowship. Furthermore, to serve God and obey his will meant to control nature in the interests of his purpose and to reform society at all levels of relationship so that in it his rule might be manifest. When God's people failed to serve him, such failure was manifested, at the social level, in the injustice and selfishness which broke society asunder, and at the natural level, in the divorce between man and his natural environment which played havoc with the natural forces that God had created. The Old Testament men saw one outcome of man's alienation from God as estrangement from nature. His natural environment failed to co-operate when he sought to exploit it for his own ends. Only as he learned its laws and co-operated with the divine will which was active within it, could he live in God's world as a son and not as an alien.

Hence if man was to know God he must know him as personally present in the social order and natural environment which provided the setting for his life. But this is exactly what the Incarnation means for us today. Christ came into just this setting and, through his Spirit, meets us still in the midst of the social relationships and natural forces which press in upon us and shape and mold our human existence. This requires of us an understanding of the natural order, in relation to man, and of man's bodily existence.

1. *The significance of the natural order and of man's somatic existence*

We live in a physical order which underlies our own somatic structure as well as providing the basic framework of our environment. This physical order is constituted by the enigmatic stuff which is known in its measurable aspects as "energy." Whatever "energy" may be, it is characterized by a dynamic potentiality and indeterminateness. It has a capacity for being determined in a manifold variety of ways, of being knotted up into increasingly complex wholes, in which the patterned structures are associated with new and distinctive modes of activity. Furthermore, at every such level of determination or wholeness, there remains potency for yet further change and advance to more complex patterned wholes. This alone can account for the continuity and change within the evolutionary process, the products of which in their abundant variety at all levels, inanimate and animate, constitute our environment.

As such this basic stuff, with its capacity for spatial separation and temporal succession, provides a medium in which free personal beings can enjoy a relative independence of one another and of God. God as Creator sustains the whole process, and sustains them within the process, but he creates beings in a natural environment and in a psychosomatic form which ensure that neither will they trespass radically on one another's freedom nor will he infringe upon that freedom of decision which he has given to them. The natural order makes separation and quasi-independence possible.

It also makes communication possible. The psychosomatic structure of personal being makes finite persons both continuous with and discontinuous from the natural order in which their existence is actualized. Their bodies are instrumental for the creative activity and vision, and through their bodily structure they communicate with other persons. Yet such communication is possible only because nature itself becomes instrumental to the bodily senses, for light and sound are aspects of our physical environment. We assimilate our media of communication, our tools and instruments to ourselves as extensions of our personal being, and pour ourselves into them. Just as the body is part of ourselves, so they too become a part of us in moments when we are communicating with others or expressing our creative vision and imagination.

If we concentrate on the body or on the media employed and cease to be concerned with that meaning which we are seeking to express through them, then we shift our attention to the scientific and analytical level, and cease to concentrate upon the personal wholes with whom we are communicating. But normally we tacitly accept our body as part of ourselves and also the media which nature provides as extensions of our personal being. In the same way, we know others as they communicate with us using their bodies and natural media as symbols through which they may disclose themselves to us. In their case too, concentration by us upon their bodies and the nature of the media that they employ will destroy the meaning which they are seeking to convey. Michael Polanyi, in a careful analysis, writes that "a man's mind may be known *only comprehensively, by dwelling within the unspecifiable particulars of its external manifestations.*" [1]

Finite person is concrete being, always both mental and physical in nature. It is through nature that we encounter other persons, meeting them on the physical periphery of their being. It is their traffic with the natural order which discloses them to us. Their body and their environmental activity become the outward manifestation of their inward being. I know myself as self-conscious person or spirit, and the other seems to be body, but as W. E. Hocking reminds us,

> . . . as I think it through, there seems to be nothing about that body which conceals the spirit—body seems to do no more in separating than to fix and define the simple otherness of that Other from myself; in all other respects it does but give me that Other Mind in more

[1] M. Polanyi, *The Study of Man* (Chicago: University of Chicago Press, 1963), p. 33.

> tangible form than by experience of its inner life on its own grounds alone, I could have it.[2]

Thus the other person may be aware only in a subsidiary way of his bodily and environmental activity for he is concentrating upon his own self-disclosure through it, while I so concentrate upon comprehending his inner being, that I too am only aware of that activity in a subsidiary way. As Polanyi points out: "He and I may be mutually comprehending each other, by dwelling within one another's external mental manifestations." [3] We meet through the foregrounds of experience and thereby share our inner being.

In a very real sense our body is an intrinsic symbol of our inner state. It presents externally so often what the mind is internally. It "exists as a bulletin of an inner process; being but that process itself, *reporting itself* to us in such terms as we can physically apprehend." [4] Of course, the body is more than this, but our psychosomatic nature shows that this is one of its functions. We emerge from nature, but not only are nature and time necessary for a finite personal being to exist, they are also necessary for such a being to be known.

Hence nature is in a very real sense social. As Hocking points out,[5] it is in some sense everybody's nature, as energy is everybody's energy. There is an objectivity about nature, and yet it is a dynamic medium for social fellowship. "Nature *may be* interpreted in its relation to social consciousness, as the visible pledge and immediate evidence of our living contact." [6] Nature is the world of socially verifiable things. Habitually my judgments upon the facts of the natural order involve the idea of universality. Such facts belong to others as much as to my-

[2] W. E. Hocking, *The Meaning of God in Human Experience* (New Haven: Yale University Press, 1944, p. 265.

[3] M. Polanyi, op. cit. pp. 33 f.

[4] W. E. Hocking, op. cit. p. 263.

[5] W. E. Hocking, op. cit. p. 287.

[6] Ibid. p. 266.

self. The test of truth must be the validity of my proposition for others as well as for myself. Thus my experience of nature is tied up with my social consciousness, and implies a tacit knowledge of some all-embracing order in my world. We may quote Hocking again at this point:

> The only way in which I can know an object to be common is by catching it in the act of being common, that is, by knowing it as known by other mind. The social experience must have a prior and original recognizableness. And this recognition of other mind than my own is a simultaneous recognition of those aspects of experience which such mind needs for the maintenance of its intercourse with me, without loss of its own separateness of career.[7]

The otherness of nature is dependent upon social consensus. In particular, the otherness expressed in the scientific order expresses the consensus of the scientific community. Yet the ordering of nature as expressed in such consensus may indicate some all-embracing whole beneath the natural process.

One aspect of the function which nature serves as a differentiating medium lies in its shaping and molding of individuality. It is in the struggle with sense experience, the occupation with the physical and natural order, that individuality begins to appear and interest between personal beings is aroused. My own selfhood develops as I struggle with the natural order in which I am enmeshed and upon which I tacitly depend for my own physical existence. I am shaped as personal being in my commerce with the obstinate otherness of my natural environment.

The otherness and universality of nature further make something sharable between knowing minds. Here we and other personal beings have something that we can hold in common. In this natural order are laid the lines of communication and

[7] Ibid. p. 288, *n.* 1.

also the basis for such communication. The fact that our experience of nature is social makes it possible for us to share with other persons. We never know an empty mind nor would such a mind possess meaning for us. We desire to know a person who is in converse with his environment, who is in commerce with the same natural order as that which engages us, who has the same objects of thinking and willing as we have, who has developed his own unique personal qualities in active traffic with this natural order and with other persons in their somatic mode of existence.

Not only does this social environment of nature shape our individuality in this way, it also provides a field for our creative activity. Through our somatic unity with nature we are able to express our creative visions in the visible symbols of art as well as in the communicating sounds of poetry and literature. Through the development of his science, man learns to harness the forces of nature to his own ends and to make them into extensions of his own somatic activity. By his scientific method he probes ever more deeply into the secrets of the natural order, unveiling its invariants and learning its ordered processes. In so doing he has to do with an objective given. Though his scientific knowledge, like all knowledge, is personal knowledge and not without its subjective aspects, he may yet know himself and his fellow scientists to be probing ever more deeply into an independent natural reality. His models then become analogues, not to be identified with that reality, but pointing to it and offering valuable clues as to its structure. Likewise the artist, in seeking to express his creative vision in a natural medium, such as wood or stone, knows himself to be dealing with a resistant "given" which limits the expression he is seeking to make.

Nature offers a certain rigidity and resistance to creative vision and scientific investigation alike. It neither easily gives itself to artistic expression nor freely offers up its secrets to scientific observation and experimentation. Furthermore, it obstinately presents phenomena which compel us to change our models and theories as it presents new facts which our current position cannot embrace. Similarly, the visions of men may be wrecked upon "surd aspects" of nature as if some depth in nature would arbitrate on their truth. In his traffic with nature man has to develop personal character and individualizing traits.

But this very rigidity and resistance in the natural order may point to a personal presence behind nature. Its otherness rests back upon the Creator. It precedes us and evidently is not of our creation. It resists and opposes us, and its over-againstness takes on at times the form of a personal activity. It was no accident that primitive man in his animism ascribed a "soulish" activity to the natural order. Naturalism seeks to free nature from any subjective influence and make it impersonally objective. Yet it but skims over the empirically observable surface and misses the hidden depth. The obstinacy, independence, and resistance of the natural order are signs of some inexhaustible power which lies behind such an objective façade. Indeed, that otherness cries out for explanation.

W. E. Hocking declares that ". . . it is just in this character of ultimate opposition to me and my wishes, of high superiority to any doings or thinkings of mine, that Nature begins to assume for me the unthinkable aspect of Other Mind." [8] His panentheism would deny our own understanding of nature as both quasi-independent of and yet dependent on God, as not identifiable with the Creator and yet sustained by his creative will. Such emphasis on a God who is both transcendent and immanent does not prevent us from regarding nature as the realm through which divine personal disclosures may come to his creatures. The naturalist sees mind emerging from nature and reduces mind to a higher organization of physical energy. But the fact that mind emerges from nature, that, empirically, nature appears to create mind, might rather suggest that mind

[8] Ibid. p. 284.

is immanently active throughout the natural process.[9] The obstinacy and the creativity of nature would seem to reflect some aspects of what we meet in commerce with other personal beings. As other persons obstinately oppose me and by their resistance help to shape me, so I find myself limited and resisted within the natural process. And yet that limitation shapes my selfhood and the resistance develops my personal individuality. Can we not say that here, whether we recognize this or not, there is a personal presence of the Creator working through his created order to mold our finite personal being and challenge us to a personal response.

II. *Providence and the natural order*

We have not attempted to demonstrate the reality of God but rather have taken the standpoint of faith and commitment which brings with it its own psychological certitude and demands no logical demonstration. We have suggested, however, that viewed from such a position, the natural order in its relation to men does point to the personal presence of the Creator. The naturalist will have his own interpretation of the same data and reject our own reading of their significance. That should not surprise us, since all knowledge is personal knowledge and our reasoning is always determined by our prelogical commitment to some world-view which for us is self-evidential.

Yet this faith and commitment is evoked in us by a divine self-disclosure which comes to us through the media of nature and history, through the natural and social orders. Since our approach is through the Hebrew-Christian tradition, such self-disclosure reaches its climax at the personal level, so that the disclosures through nature and history are brought to a focus in the Incarnation.

[9] This is the argument of William Temple, *Nature, Man and God* (London: Macmillan and Co., Ltd., 1956), pp. 109–34.

In this theistic approach, we may see both the omnipresence of God throughout his created order in his creating and sustaining activity and also the special acts of disclosure which take place within this setting of general immanental activity. Such differentiation is in some sense related to the specific modes of the divine activity, on the one hand as Creator and Sustainer, and on the other as Judge and Redeemer. It places side by side the continuing, ontological aspect of the divine ground of the universe and the specific revelatory activity through what have been called "disclosure situations." Both alike manifest God's innermost being as absolute and loving freedom, but they must be differentiated as distinctive relations of God to his creation.

We cannot ignore either, for both are essential to the Christian understanding of God as Creator and Redeemer. They point to that essential mark of creaturehood as it is clearly expressed in human freedom with its unique quasi-independence and its potentiality for sinful rebellion. What figuratively God sustains with his left hand, he redeems with his right. Perhaps a pale analogy may be found in the activity of a good man whose goodness is manifested continuously in his habitual conduct, but whose supreme self-disclosure is seen in those extraordinary acts in which he breaks through the normal pattern of his conduct to perform the unexpected and unrequired gracious deed. This surely is what we mean when we speak of God's freedom in love. His relation to his creatures is not restricted to that habitual activity by which he continues his creative and sustaining intention. Rather than being bound by the invariant structures of nature which he has himself freely created, his love may move beyond and through such structures to create disclosure situations in which he deals redemptively with the personal beings to whom he has given a creaturely share in his own freedom.

Because science looks for the invariants in nature, regularities which can be made the basis for prediction, it deals with areas where the religious faith in providence is also concerned.

The causative and mathematicorational structure which science finds to be basic as the framework of the natural order is impersonal, but the man of faith affirms that a personal depth is operative within nature, and that this impersonal order has been abstracted from it. The days when Laplace could affirm that he had no need for the hypothesis of God have gone in the sense that the old scientific determinism has vanished. We have changed our models now and deal with probabilities not certainties. Scientific laws are no longer regarded as the regnant realities of the universe but as descriptions of the invariancies which the scientist abstracts from nature. Furthermore, even those invariancies would appear to be statistical. Though the scientist, in replacing his models, is actually probing deeper into the reality of nature, we must still not fall into the error of identifying his models with that reality. We have suggested that, at best, they are analogues, yet they would appear to be satisfactory analogues, for they do enable him to predict and control.

This means that there is truth in the picture which he presents to us, and that picture is one of a universe in which there is both order and randomness. There is uniformity, and yet there is also an element of contingency. This uniformity at the macroscopic level varies from complete reliability and deterministic movement, such as the regularity of the solar system, to situations where alternative behavior is possible. Yet this large-scale regularity of behavior to which the laws of classical physics apply has generally a statistical background. Here the regularity is statistical, representing the average behavior of a large number of microscopic entities. The gas laws, the constancy of stellar radiation, the tensile strength of such metals as steel, the constant freezing point of specific liquids, and the regular point of combustion of particular fuels—all these afford examples. Yet it might be argued that the microscopic background of such statistical laws is itself deterministic and not subject to randomness and contingency.

The only difficulty lies in the impossibility of measuring and correlating the diverse movements which our model postulates and which, in most cases anyway, are unobservable.

The quantum model raises new difficulties. For if the Copenhagen School be correct—and von Neumann seems to have demonstrated theoretically that is is—this model postulates an indeterminacy in nature itself. This is not merely due to difficulty of measurement, on the ground that the observing instruments and the entities observed are of the same order of magnitude, and thus disturb one another; it is inherent in nature itself. Here certain elements of the model or analogue are identified with nature on the ground that, at these points and only with such an assumption, are scientific prediction and also new and epoch-making discovery possible. W. G. Pollard reminds us that these contingencies at the quantum level are not evidence of gaps in knowledge which science may ultimately fill—David Bohm believes that they are,[10] but his opinion is a minority one and purely theoretical. Pollard writes: ". . . quantum mechanics has demonstrated over and over an entirely adequate predictive power in the sense that any aspect of natural systems which can be observed and

[10] David Bohm is arguing for a causative position which, he contends, will replace the present indeterminateness in quantum physics. See D. Bohm, *Causality and Chance in Modern Physics* (New York: Harper and Bros., 1961). His position has been criticized constructively in *Quanta and Reality*, ed. D. Edge (New York: Meridian Books, 1964) and in Heisenberg, Schrödinger, Born, and Auger, *On Modern Physics* (New York: Collier Books, 1962). Also consult *Turning Points in Physics*, ed. A. C. Crombie (New York: Harper and Bros., 1961). Von Neumann has shown that no conceivable change of parameters will enable us to avoid indeterminacy in quantum mechanics so long as this model is regnant. The great success of quantum theory, both in prediction and in creative advance with new insight precludes our changing from it to any other position. Bohm's position is purely theoretical, offers no practical advantage, and seems, at the moment, to afford no experimentally testable alternative.

measured can be dealt with unequivocally by quantum mechanics."[11] Now here, the quantum physicist deals with probabilities of a new kind. The classical laws of physics are statistical and offer probabilities, but the quantum laws offer probabilities of a different type and also of a much lower measure. What matters here is that causes cannot be assumed even as they may be theoretically in the statistical models of classical physics. If Schrödinger and Eccles be correct, it is at the level of these quantum laws that we may be touching the mysteries of life and mind!

To this element of indeterminacy at the quantum level, we must add the random element with which evolutionary biology has made us familiar—the random mutations of the genes and the operation of natural selection. We note that these mutations, too, arise at the quantum level, and, as we saw earlier, the probability of such gene changes is of the quantum order and not that of statistical macrophysics. The aspect of determinateness is seen in the continuing stability of the gene structures and in the process of metabolism, the biological fields, the colloidal suspensions, and the osmotic forces which such structures direct. Here, too, we have seen reason to postulate a directive orderliness amid the randomness, whether the former be associated with adaptive onto-mutations and "happy monsters" (an unproven hypothesis) or with a mysterious correlation of small independent mutations. If the latter position be adopted, "chance" would loom still larger. It would appear that the scientific observer must rest content with an order that is tied up with probability. "Chance" has become a permanent element in the scientific approach to nature.

It has been suggested that this contingent element, espe-

[11] W. G. Pollard, *Chance and Providence* (New York: Charles Scribner's Sons, 1958), p. 54.

cially at the quantum level, brings historical time into the process of nature and makes a place for providence.[12] Historical time has the quality of actuality. It actualizes possibilities. The alternatives of the present become the actualities of the past. At the human level, history is the story of man's freedom in commerce with his fellows and with nature. Thus we have, in human history, the contingencies arising out of nature and also out of human activity. From the standpoint of the historical positivist, history is full of chance. The great advances of the human story have arisen often out of what may be called the happy accidents of history. Groups and individuals and natural happenings come together, apparently by chance, into a fortunate collocation. Yet it is here that the man of faith finds the hand of God. So the superficially happy accident of a wind driving back the shallow waters of the "sea of reeds" when the Israelites are on its shores is in actuality for Moses the saving act of Yahweh. In this way the "chance" events of nature are actually manifestations of the divine presence. Such providential happenings bring to a focus for faith that personal depth of the universe which neither nature nor history discloses to a purely scientific observer. But it is the presence of the chance happening and contingent event which makes this faith in providence possible.

History has the further quality of dealing with the unique and unrepeatable. This has made us earlier suggest that we must understand nature in terms of history rather than history in terms of nature. General and closed laws cannot be discovered by the historical positivist. History at the best may offer open laws applicable in a very limited field.[13] It is con-

[12] See W. G. Pollard, op. cit. pp. 63–88. Insights of this book have been employed in the following discussion. It is a valuable contribution, although it has a little too much tendency to identify the scientific models completely with nature.

[13] Cf. E. C. Rust, *Towards a Theological Understanding of History* (New York: Oxford University Press, 1963), pp. 17–20.

cerned with the singular, with personal particulars, with individual decisions. In this it does not manifest the order and determinateness shown by nature. Yet we need to remember that, by the controlled conditionings of his experiments, the scientist in his laboratory excludes as far as possible the untoward and fortuitous. It is thus that he is able to discover his invariants. The field naturalist, on the other hand, is much more aware of the unusual and unrepeatable. There is enough determinateness and stability in nature to make causal explanation a necessary tool. But the field observer knows that there is more. And the quantum physicist is making us aware of an indeterminacy to which causal explantion does not as yet apply. Nature has in it the stuff of historical time. The scientist must take time seriously now, as thermodynamically time's arrow points inexorably forward. Evolution presents him with the unique and unrepeatable. By controlled laboratory conditions he may produce a living cell at some future date, but the "happy" collocation of happenings that first made life possible in history is in the remote and unrepeatable past. The difference at the human level is that man's freedom opens up new possibilities that indeterminancy, random mutations, and probability in nature cannot match. Human history is the process becoming self-conscious and beginning to control itself.

We cannot read off its meaning from the face of history,[14] and equally we cannot discern the directive depth of nature by the discipline of natural science. As we have continually affirmed, this waits on disclosure of personal depth. The category of providence is the religious man's way of expressing this dimension of divine personal presence.

Providence is indeed the sustaining continuation of that immanent divine creative presence and directing activity of the Spirit which we have already discussed in considering evolution. Here what the scientist estimates in terms of chance and randomness takes on a new complexion, even if we reject

[14] Ibid. pp. 1–16.

"onto-mutations." The unique and unrepeatable occur, and personal depth in the process is disclosed to the man of faith. The history of nature, like the history of man, takes on a directed meaning. Providential situations thus bring to a focus for faith an immanent and yet transcendent presence and activity which is present throughout nature and history, guiding and sustaining them. Thereby chance and probability, randomness and indeterminacy are woven into the fabric of history by the divine designer.

The views of nature offered by science and by providence are not inimical. They might be compared with the two ways of looking at man: body and mind. As man has personal depth which cannot be discerned by scientific methods, so the processes of nature and history have a divine personal depth which science and historical positivism do not grasp. By concentrating on the horizontal, as its way of knowing dictates, science ignores the depth which comes by an intuitive response to the wholeness of the process and of its individual aspects and which is brought to a focus in the disclosure situations peculiar to the religious consciousness. We have elsewhere suggested that this dimensional figure may offer us a useful analogy or model at this point.[15] In a three-dimensional space, such as that in which we live, a creature whose sensible capacities limit him to two of the three dimensions and who lives in what Abbott has called "Flatland"[16] will know the regularities, invariancies, and scientific probabilities in a two-dimensional form and explain them in that way. He will be oblivious to the dimensional depth in which there are forces operative, guiding his two-dimensional structures and observing the laws which apply to the latter. If that third dimension is opened up to him in some way, maybe even through

[15] Ibid., pp. 150 f. Cf. K. Heim, *God Transcendent,* trans. E. P. Dickie (London: Nisbet and Company, 1935), *passim;* H. H. Farmer, *The World and God* (London: Nisbet and Company, 1935), pp. 102 ff.

[16] E. A. Abbott, *Flatland* (New York: Dover Publications, Inc., 1952).

capacities for knowing which have been hitherto undeveloped, then a whole new way of understanding his world and a new attitude towards it becomes possible. The new attitude does not abrogate the old but embraces it. So the man of faith sees providential activity where the scientist qua scientist sees none.

Science by its method is concerned with the impersonal. In so doing it abstracts from the personal nature of reality with which providence is concerned. We may say that the personal takes on an impersonal form in science and that this impersonal form is derived and secondary. The personal form of reality becomes evident to faith as that is evoked in the primary disclosure of the Incarnation. The disclosure situations present in providential activity take their final coloring for the Christian from this initial and redemptive act. The divine disclosure is always mediated, though immediate, and it is personal, even when the medium of revelation is impersonal. Even history and society, despite their being patterned structures of personal beings in a multivariety of relationships, may also be treated impersonally and present an impersonal appearance. But the "It" aspect of reality is most apparent at the level of nature, and the "It" attitude has been easy to adopt at this level in the period of modern science. In describing this awakening to the personal dimension through divine disclosure, religious men frequently use the label "miraculous," and we need to discuss this because of its seeming implications for science and the claims of science.

III. *The category of miracle and divine self-disclosure*

In Biblical thought "miracle" is a religious category. The terms used to describe it in the Old Testament may be rendered respectively as "wonder" (*niphla'ah*) or "mighty work," "sign" (*oth*), and "portent" (*mopheth*). They manifested a mysterious depth in the universe and evoked an appropriate response in the recipient. They were disclosures of the presence of the living God in his world and were specially related to his gracious redemptive activity. What made them extraordinary was that they disclosed, often in unexpected ways, this saving presence. Thus what characterized miracle was its revelatory significance. Eichrodt defines the unique meaning of miracle in the Old Testament as that which points to God, as an outstretched finger, manifesting his power and his will.[17]

The Hebrew was not concerned with the natural setting of the miracle but with its meaning. He did not ask with modern man how or whether it could happen, but rather what it meant. Let us remember that our modern scientific understanding of nature must not be read back into Biblical thinking. For the Hebrew, nature was no independent entity governed by natural law as science so often regards it. The contrast was not between nature and supernature, but between God and his creation. And that creation was everywhere sustained by the activity of its Creator. The Hebrew mind paid little or no attention to the horizontal chain of secondary causes with which science is concerned. It saw rather the vertical dimension in which the whole creation waited upon God and drew its power and regularity from his gracious will. This meant that God was present, everywhere active in his created order. One distinctive note of miracle was that it was "more of the same thing." The living God who was dynamically present everywhere was here disclosing himself in an extraordinary way to fulfill his purpose.

Furthermore, the miracle was not necessarily accompanied by unusual or abnormal phenomena. Often a wonder is associated with normal natural processes, like rain and storm, hail and lightning. The miracle is often not so much in the natural process itself as in the time of its occurrence and the historical

[17] W. Eichrodt, *Theologie des Alten Testaments, Teil 2: Gott und Welt* (Berlin: Evangelische Verlagsanstalt, 1950), p. 84.

situation in which it takes place. Thus the Yahwist decribes the Exodus as occasioned by a wind driving back the shallow waters of the sea of reeds. But it was a divine disclosure because the fleeing Hebrews were there, ready to cross, and Moses was there to interpret the natural happening as the act of Yahweh in the deliverance of the people. Other cases could be cited which make it evident that it is not the abnormality of a natural event which makes it a miracle but its participation in a disclosure situation.

Again, there is a careful attempt to differentiate true from false miracles. Egyptian magicians and false prophets were alike able to produce extraordinary happenings,[18] and the final judgment on any miracle was that its claimed disclosure should be consistent with previous divine disclosures. An extraordinary happening is not of itself sufficient to indicate that the living God has acted in this particular event. Its revelatory aspect must cohere with what Israel already knew about God, and thus it was to be judged by the community of faith. On the other hand, the participant in the miracle was himself a part of the disclosure situation, which might evoke the commitment of faith in him or confirm his prior commitment. His interpretation of what had happened was in this sense personal, although the community of faith might come to share in it. If the miracle involved an unusual happening, it might cause shock and surprise to an unbeliever observing it, but it would not have revelatory significance unless it involved him too in a disclosure situation. Thus natural event is a miracle when it constitutes a disclosure situation, and one element in such a situation is the responsive faith of those who participate in it. It is certainly not offered to the credulous nor is it intended to gratify the curious and to satisfy those who desire the marvelous.

In the New Testament we find the same religious interpretation of miracle. The Greek words employed are parallel to

[18] Exod. 7:11, 22; 8:7, 18; Deut. 13:1 ff.

those used in Hebrew: "mighty works" (*dunameis*), "signs" (*semeia*). In the Synoptic Gospels, the "mighty works" of Jesus are set along side of his preaching as signs that the Kingdom of God has broken in with power in him, that the New Age has dawned.[19] The mighty acts were disclosures with Christological import. In and through them our Lord "confronted men with the challenge of the Kingdom and the claims of His Messiahship."[20] His miracles of healing pointed to his power to forgive sins, for man's psychosomatic unity suggested a close bond between the healing of men's bodies and the healing of their souls. "To open the eyes of the blind man is a sign of the disclosure of the divine truth to those who have the eyes to see."[21] We find the same emphasis in the Fourth Gospel. Here our Lord's "signs" are characterized by a power which differentiates them from all other "miracles." Such power is no detached force, but the power of the Father with whom he is in total communion.[22] The power of the Son is delegated from the Father, and his "signs" point to the uniqueness of his Person. In his acts the Kingdom of God has been manifested ultimately and decisively.

Yet such miracles were evident only to faith, and their performance was conditioned by faith. At times Jesus would and could perform no mighty acts because of men's unbelief.[23] Faith must be present in those who would receive the divine gift in our Lord's mighty works. Through this they too may participate in the power of God which is present in Jesus. Without the insight of faith, the miracles are causes of astonishment. For such men, our Lord could be a wonder worker with magical powers, but for the disciples the miracles are a

[19] See E. C. Rust, *Nature and Man in Biblical Thought* (London: Lutterworth Press, 1953), pp. 177 ff.

[20] Ibid. p. 179.

[21] Ibid. p. 178.

[22] Ibid. pp. 189 f.; See John 5:19.

[23] Mark 6:5, 6.

cause for thanksgiving that God's sovereign presence has been disclosed in him. It is true that, during the lifetime of Jesus, the disciples themselves lacked the full insight of the resurrection faith. Yet, blind as they were to the full significance of the mighty acts and waiting as they did for the insight born of the miracle of the Resurrection, they did have eyes to see the presence of the Kingdom in their Master. The disciples were distinguished by a spiritual receptivity to the divine disclosure in his Person. For others, he might be a mere extraordinary being, possessing some detached power substance, but for those on whose behalf he worked his mighty acts, the latter were signs that the gracious power of the Kingdom was present and active in him.

The Fourth Gospel would seem to suggest that the signs of Jesus not only are given to faith but may also evoke faith. Our Lord's works are in themselves a sufficient ground for faith, and men should believe at least for the very works' sake.[24] Yet there is no suggestion that signs of themselves evoke faith. The author of this Gospel is quite sure that faith is a divine gift. God may work through the signs to grant insight and to awaken faith, so that men see and respond to their divine significance. John records that, despite his many signs, men did not believe on Jesus (12:37), and that men followed him because they profited by his signs without grasping their import (6:26). A sign is not an independent event but a divine disclosure, and the insight and response of faith may be part of the divine activity in that disclosure. The power of a sign rests in its divine origin and in the faith it evokes, not in itself. We see this in the Johannine account of the opening of the eyes of the man who was born blind.[25] The fact that the man is born blind is spiritually a sign that the insight granted to the believer is something completely new. The healing points to Christ's power to release men from sin and open the blind eyes

[24] John 14:11.
[25] John 9.

of the spirit. The divine disclosure is patent only to those whose eyes have been opened by God's gracious activity.[26]

Thus the miracles of the New Testament carry with them, as do all divine disclosures, an aspect of hiddenness. The true meaning can only be spiritually discerned. God's presence is evident only to faith. He is active in his world, but even his miraculous disclosures are such only to those with spiritual receptivity. In such a disclosure faith itself may be awakened, yet not by the shock of an unusual natural event, rather because the event is so transparent to the divine activity that through it God awakens faith in the one to whom the miracle is directed. Thus the revelation will not be merely in the lifting up of the natural order into the divine activity, but also in the work of God in the heart of the human recipient. This much stands clear. A miracle is personal! It is given as a miracle, sign, disclosure only to those in whom faith has been awakened or is present. And faith is as much a miracle in the recipient as is the corresponding happening in nature. Both together constitute the miracle and the disclosure.

The religious category of miracle may now be defined more clearly. It is not fundamentally concerned with the normal or abnormal form of the natural happening. What matters is that this natural happening has been lifted up into a disclosure situation and has become a revelatory medium. Thus the first mark of a miracle is that it points to the divine presence in redemptive activity. Furthermore, such a divine disclosure gathers its veracity from its consistence with what God has already disclosed himself to be. Finally, this implies the condition of faith on the part of the recipient of the miracle, and, indeed, such faith is itself a miracle for it is a divine gift. As such it may even be a part of the miracle itself. Certainly a miracle reinforces and confirms faith by giving new insight, even when it is not a disclosure situation in which God evokes faith by opening blind eyes.

[26] Cf. E. C. Rust, *Nature and Man in Biblical Thought*, pp. 192 f.

We come now to the customary modern definition of "miracle" as a natural event which breaks the normal order of nature and is thus an intervention of divine power. This might be described as a nonreligious definition, involving the suspension of natural law. But then we must remember that what we call "natural law" is a property of our scientific models and is an abstraction from reality. Thus miracle is not a suspension of nature but of our model. We have seen already that Christianity is grounded in special revelation and thus with special intervention of God in his created order. But we have also stressed that he is present and active everywhere, creatively sustaining the whole creaturely process.

Natural law is our abstracted description of the regularities and invariants of the natural process. But this description has a statistical base, whether at the level of classical or of quantum physics. Biology, too, has the random element written into its constitution. Hence our consideration of providence above, insofar as nature is involved, as an historical understanding of nature. The scientist cannot *ipso facto* say that the unusual and unrepeatable will not occur. He believes that nature has a rational structure and, at the macro-level, that causal explanation is a useful tool. He expects regularity and uniformity in the process he observes, and this is the basis of his successful prediction. Yet probability and chance have increasingly to be taken into account, although they would seem to fall into regularity of pattern. It is difficult in a scientific age to believe that a special divine intervention means a break in this orderliness. Yet this difficulty is present because we have forgotten that the orderliness is associated with the model. The unique and unrepeatable is not absolutely ruled out by the scientific approach. A materialistic deification of the model has made the difficulty for us. The scientist will, of course, strive to bring the extraordinary event within the sphere of inquiry and explanation. He believes that science can justifiably lay claim to explain the natural order at his own selected levels of inquiry. If he now uses the categories of probability and chance this in no way invalidates his conviction. The probabilities of quantum physics have a mathematicorational base, and the mathematics of statistics provides an explanation at the levels of macrophysics and biology. Indeed, what is at present inexplicable may yet tomorrow become an area of scientific knowledge. Already many New Testament miracles may be explained scientifically since the frontiers of psychological science and extrasensory perception have been extended.

If we accept the semi-scientific and nonreligious definition of miracle, we fall into the trap of employing "miracle" to fill gaps in our scientific knowledge and of associating special divine intervention with the scientifically inexplicable. But science at present accepts probability and chance as parts of its exploratory machinery. As scientists enlarge their knowledge and extend their area of operation, many events labeled "miracles" on the basis of their extraordinary or inexplicable nature may cease to be miracles in this sense. Augustine wisely remarked that "a portent (miracle) . . . happens not contrary to nature, but contrary to what we know as nature." [27] If God be a God of order, it should not surprise us that he works through order or that what appears to us to be statistical order, arising from probability and randomness, should yet manifest order and directiveness in the eyes of faith. But here miracle ceases to be semi-scientific and becomes a religious category.

Hume's treatment of miracles is still significant here. It will be remembered that he defined a law of nature as that of which we have "a firm and unalterable experience." [28] Although he dismisses causation as not rationally demonstrable, he finds in experience a regularity of succession, and contends that "a miracle may be accurately defined, *a transgression of a*

[27] Augustine, *The City of God,* Book XXI, ch. 8 (Dod's translation).

[28] David Hume, "Of Miracles," Sec. X, *An Enquiry Concerning Human Understanding* in *The English Philosophers from Bacon to Mill,* ed. E. A. Burtt (New York: Random House, 1939), p. 656.

law of nature by a particular volition of the Deity, or by the interposition of some invisible agent." [29] Apparent exceptions may occur to such recurring sequences, but that is usually because of the limited experience of the individual concerned. Thus an Indian, who by his climate knows nothing of frozen water, would regard ice as such an exception, and would regard the sequence of frost and frozen water as incredible and at variance with his limited experience. Hume, therefore, argues that the evidence for a miracle must be exceedingly strong. The more it is evidently a break in the normal experience of regular sequence, the less credibility we shall give to it, for by the assurance of past experience and by the universal verdict of our fellows, we have a complete proof that miracles cannot occur in that area. Reports of such occurrences are so open to error and deception, that the true weight of evidence must lie against miracles occurring.

> The plain consequence is . . . "That no testimony is sufficient to establish a miracle, unless the testimony be of such a kind, that its falsehood would be more miraculous, than the fact, which it endeavors to establish; and even in that case there is a mutual destruction of arguments, and the superior only gives us an assurance suitable to that degree of force, which remains, after deducting the inferior." [30]

Thus in the report of a restoration to life, the measures of superstitious credulity and of trustworthiness in the bearer of the report have to be weighed against the actual happening of the fact itself, and the greater miracle of the two must be rejected.

Let us, at once, note that Hume's definition of miracle is completely deistic. The natural process goes on in invariable regularity, and God is allowed to operate only at certain

[29] Ibid. p. 657, footnote 21.
[30] Ibid. p. 657.

points. This is typical of the philosophic, religious, and scientific outlooks of the eighteenth century. If we believe in a God who is personally and immanently active throughout the process, so that the laws of nature are descriptions of the regularity of his sustaining activity, the issue of miracle is not such an impossible one, even on the definition we are now considering. God is not breaking into a process in which he is not already present and active.

Furthermore, we note that Hume's attack is much more upon reports of miracles occurring than on miracles themselves. He would introduce bias into historical judgment and prejudice a true estimate of historical evidence for the actuality of an event by unwarranted and prejudicial weighting. Historical claims should be dealt with on grounds which do not prejudice acceptance of a miracle before we start investigating its historical actuality. So often today this is exactly what does happen when the skeptical modern mind approaches the Gospel records. The naturalistic turn of mind, engendered by the success of modern science but by no means a necessary implication of modern science, has led too many to deny the Gospel records on what they are pleased to call "scientific grounds," before they have investigated the evidence. Now it is true that all historical knowledge is personal knowledge and that no historical investigation can be thoroughly "objective," since all of us approach history with absolute presuppositions. The Christian must also be prepared to accept all the critical apparatus that modern historical scholarship offers, so that he can determine as far as possible the *sitz im Leben* of the miracle stories themselves. By his faith commitment he will stand with the Gospel writers, but he will also endeavor to weigh fairly the historical evidence that is available. Yet he knows that his acceptance of the miracles will not be determined solely by the historical evidence, any more than will the denial of the miracles by the naturalist. The latter already feels that modern scientific empiricism has settled that issue, and the Christian knows that his faith in a risen and incarnate Lord has equally settled the general issue of miracle, however much the historical evidence may lead him to accept some of the miracles more than others. As Alan Richardson reminds us: "The view that physical science can solve the problem of the miracles can be justified only by the assumption that the only forces in the universe are those which physical science can measure and describe, but that is a philosophical and not a scientific assumption." [31]

At this point, let us return to the religious definition of miracle with which we began and leave the pseudo-scientific preoccupation of the second definition. It is clear from what has been said already that miracle is not always necessarily an interference with our models of the regular processes of nature, but it may be. In the latter case, modern science cannot, in the light of its contemporary method, rule it out. Generally chance and randomness average out in regularity and are thus concerned with the uniformity of nature. Yet even evolution would seem to speak of the historical and unrepeatable at the natural level. The emphasis on randomness and probability, though usually forming a basis for regularity, cannot offhand be said to rule out the unique. At the religious level, the Incarnation and the Resurrection of our Lord certainly present us with this kind of event. Within the Incarnation we have the miracles of Jesus himself. We have no right to dismiss the healing miracles as untrue. The fact that modern medicine is discovering much more about man's psychosomatic structure may mean that ultimately science will be able to "explain" them. But whether it does or not, they will still remain miracles in the religious sense. Furthermore, science cannot dogmatically affirm that the unusual and scientifically inexplicable event may not and has not occurred. This is not scientifically impossible. John Hick reminds us that "events

[31] A. Richardson, *Christian Apologetics* (New York: Harper and Bros., 1947), p. 174.

which have religious significance that evoked and mediated a vivid sense of the presence and activity of God may have occurred, even though their continuity with the general course of nature cannot be traced in our present very limited state of human knowledge."[32] We would add that such continuity may never be traced.

But a miracle is not constituted primarily by its normality or abnormality at the scientific level. It is not sufficient just to define a miracle as an extraordinary natural happening. It may be that, of course, as Christians affirm in the Resurrection and the Virgin Birth, but more is involved. We return to the religious definition of miracle. What constitutes a miracle is its participation in a disclosure situation. The normally impersonal appearance of nature takes on a personal structure for the participant in the miracle. That personal structure may be defined as a personal activity in which the word "God" describes the subject of the activity. Nature is responding to the participant in a personal way such that the personal and transcendent depth of the universe is disclosed to him in action. This may happen in physical healing or in some phenomenon of inanimate nature, like the burning bush or the wind driving back the waters of the "sea of reeds." It may, at the scientific level, be explicable in terms of accepted models, yet even then there is more than the empirical involved. In the case of the burning bush, St. Elmo's fire may be a scientific explanation, but time and place and the presence of Moses add a degree of "oddness," just as similarly the wind, Moses, and the escaping Israelites disclose an "odd" correlation. Scientific language is unable to express this oddness in which the participant experiences a personal presence. The significance of the event is that it evokes faith and discloses the living God personally active in grace and succor or in judgment and claim, in mercy or in reproof. A true miracle is differentiated

[32] John Hick, *Philosophy of Religion* (Englewood Cliffs, N.J.: Prentice-Hall, Inc., 1964), p. 39.

by its revelatory nature. God acts personally on behalf of the participant.

It has been pointed out that in the case of the Virgin Birth, the establishment of parthenogesis would not be sufficient to express the meaning. This is not a matter of physiology but "more" is involved. It is the activity of God, and the doctrine "is essentially a claim for mystery at Christ's birth as at Christ's death."[33] The Resurrection again is not a matter of establishing historically the reality of the Empty Tomb or of explaining by recourse to visions. More than the historical and the spatio-temporal are involved. As Ramsey reminds us: "The truth of the Resurrection is logically integrated with our full commitment in Christ."[34] This is the act of God for the believer, and when he confesses that "The third day he arose again from the dead" he is giving an odd structure to such a sentence. He is not merely dating an occurrence but affirming that in this way God has disclosed himself and worked the response of truth and commitment.

If we inquire how such claims to miraculous disclosure may be validated, we have to fall back upon the issues of consistency and coherence already elaborated in the third chapter of this work.

The true nature of a miraculous event then is known only to faith. The skeptic will still dismiss it and believe that one day a purely natural explanation will be available. To accept an event as miraculous is to believe in God. As we have seen in the Gospel accounts, the faith of the believer itself is an integral part of the miracle. Just as the opening of the eyes of the man born blind enabled him to see the physical world, so a part of any miracle and of the miraculous in all revelation is the gift of spiritual insight, the opening of the blind eyes of the spirit to see the glory of God in a disclosure situation. The

[33] I. T. Ramsey, *Religious Language* (London: S.C.M. Press, 1957), p. 132.

[34] Ibid. p. 131.

response of faith is the human response involving such cognitive insight, but it is difficult to think of faith in such a disclosure situation except as the work of God as well as the act of man. Like Thomas with the disclosure of the risen Lord, what can we too say but "My Lord and my God"?

IV. *The Incarnation and an unfinished universe*

Nature must be understood from the Christian standpoint only in terms of the final revelation in the Incarnation. In this full personal disclosure of the hidden ground of being all the processes of nature and human history are gathered up and transfigured with the divine glory. In becoming true man at every level of human life in its psychosomatic wholeness, our Lord gathered into his redemptive activity, not only humanity, but also nature. We may truly speak of his humanity as a representative and incorporating humanity. By his openness in love and self-giving he draws all men into his sacrificial activity and so acts for all men. Potentially all men are redeemed in him and may become real persons. His saving disclosure through his completely self-surrendered humanity becomes the focal point from which the creative forces of God flow through our broken and frail humanity. He becomes the reintegrating center for all men. As men are incorporated in him, they become a new creation and are integrated into the new humanity which is first manifested in his own person.

Not only, however, does the Incarnate Lord deal with a sinful humanity, but he permeates all nature with his presence. He crowns the whole creative process of evolution and gives it its true direction. This is a universe in the making, and the making of men is its object. It will never be completed until the aim of creation is fulfilled and the universe becomes a theater of God's glory with man accomplishing his true status as made in the divine image. Man's mishandling of his freedom has led to a mismanagement of his natural environment.

Man should have a covenant relation with nature as he

does with God. He is freely given by his Creator the capacity to replenish the earth, subdue it, and have dominion over all living things. When he breaks his covenant with God, he rejects also his obligation towards the natural order, animate and inanimate. He is a creature whose essential nature is bound up with his relationships—he is related to God, to his fellows, and to his natural environment. Let him reject his relation to his Creator and his other relationships go awry. He chooses his own glory instead of that of God, and builds his life around himself; he uses other persons and the natural order for his own ends. Not only does society fall apart because of man's rebellion, but also nature rebels against its mismanagement and fails to co-operate with man's plans.

The Old Testament writers repeatedly associate the perversion of nature with the sinful rebellion of man. The earth returns to wilderness, brings forth thorns and thistles, when man rejects the divine purpose.[35] The chaos out of which God called forth the ordered universe begins to take over once more. The animals do not live peaceably with man, but fear takes the place of trust. The ineffectiveness of man to control the animal creation is seen in "the wild animals, which have not entered into covenant with man, rove at will, and seek their prey in their own way because of man's impotence."[36] Their presence testifies to man's weakness. He leaves them free when he should have dominion over them. Hence Paul sees the whole creation groaning and travailing in pain together until now, waiting for the unveiling of the sons of God, of men living as God intended.[37]

The reference in Genesis 1:28 to man's subduing the earth is

[35] Gen. 3:18.

[36] E. C. Rust, *Nature and Man in Biblical Thought,* p. 57.

[37] Rom. 8:19. Bultmann and Cullmann agree in interpreting "creation" here as meaning created order. R. Bultmann, *Theology of the New Testament,* Vol. I, trans. K. Grobel (New York: Charles Scribner's Sons, 1951), pp. 230 f.; O. Cullmann, *Christ and Time,* trans. F. V. Filson (Philadelphia: The Westminster Press, 1951), p. 103. See also E. C. Rust, *Nature and Man in Biblical Thought,* p. 233.

a reminder that in a very real sense the created order is an unfinished one, waiting upon its true fulfillment in man's realization of his God-given destiny. The divine disclosure in the Incarnation bears with it the same implication. God became man, and, in becoming flesh, the Son redirected the created process and made it possible for sinful man to enter into his fuller heritage as a child of God. In co-operation with his Creator, rather than in rebellion against him, man could bring the process of nature and history to its destined culmination. Yet the Incarnation is a reminder that such is possible only by divine grace and not by man's self-centered efforts. That man still persists in the latter way is testified to by the success and the perversion of our scientific knowledge. Science is a testimony both to man's greatness and to his alienation. It reminds us that man was created to subdue the earth and to have dominion over all living things. Yet its misdirection, the tyrannical and imperialistic use of its achievements to destroy and oppress men, the direction of its technological developments for the enrichment of the few and not the good of all, the practical deployment of its powers in the interests of individual selfishness and corporate acquisitiveness, testify to the tragic perversion of man's nature, his estrangement from his Creator, and his consequent lack of co-operative unity with the forces of this natural environment. Science is at once man's glory and man's tragedy. Only when scientific accomplishments are understood in the light of the Incarnation can they be directed aright.

In the incarnate Christ, all the processes of nature are summed up and transfigured by union with God. The various levels of the evolutionary process minister to the creative emergence of man, and each of them is constituent of his psychosomatic wholeness. The chemistry and structure of the physical order, the organic patterning and genetic ordering of animate things, the instinctive behavior, the memory and the capacity to learn of psychic beings—all are built into the structure of man with his self-transcendent spirit. That man should mishandle his freedom and misdirect his spiritual gifts means that nature falls apart. But the Incarnation means a reintegration of man himself and the emergence of a new wholeness in the natural order.

This suggestion that nature is an unfinished order, waiting on man for its true destiny to be accomplished provides a tentative and partial answer to the element of randomness and suffering which science finds in its processes. The randomness and suffering are, of course, most evident in the Darwinian and Neo-Darwinian models of evolution, the kind of picture that shocked our Victorian forebears. Yet, as we have seen, the orderliness and invariancies which the scientist observes in nature have a statistical base. Probability and indeterminacy move down to the quantum level. Furthermore, the element of contingency and opposition would seem to hold throughout the universe, especially at the levels of animate nature. The realm of nature is evidently an aggregation of organized wholes, animate and inanimate, each manifesting its own regular ordering and laws but also interacting the one with the other. At the physical level the interaction is mechanical, and there is a manifest interchange of energy. As we move up the scale to living wholes or organisms, the interaction is more complex, and self-movement is involved. Yet evidently it is both the complexity and the contingency evidenced in the interaction of these wholes that makes development possible. We do not see universal harmony but organized wholes in vigorous interchange and often open conflict. Each inanimate structure is a concentration of energy whose field of influence extends over the area of other systems. Each living organism and group of like organisms proliferates abundantly, so that the very fecundity of its offspring encroaches upon the living space and existence of other groups of organisms. And here we are thinking of the whole spectrum of living things up to and including man himself.

Furthermore, living things find themselves not only in interaction and often conflict with one another but also in dynamic relationship with their physical environment. Yet, as we have already suggested, such warring systems with their attendant co-operation and conflict, pleasure and pain, satisfaction and suffering, are the inevitable concomitant of a process which is concerned with selves. At each level the systems of our world have their own characteristic nature and behavior. They act in accordance with their own being, and, as we move up the scale, they become more manifestly selves concerned to build up and maintain their own organized wholeness. Nor should this surprise us. For, if the Creator is concerned to create free personal beings who shall freely choose him out of love and not behave automatically, certain elements would seem to be inevitable. Austin Farrer reminds us that

> the purpose of a machine is to deliver the goods. What goods would a cosmic machine deliver, and to whom? Might the Creator have thought to glorify himself by constructing a cosmic gramophone, streamlined for the production of symphonic Alleluias? But that is not how, it seems, he thought to glorify himself; and he is wise.[38]

It is true that we cannot arrogantly stand in God's place and search his mind. Yet the Incarnation, insofar as it reveals free personal beings at the center of his purpose and that purpose as one of gracious claim, would appear to indicate certain requirements in the fulfillment of that purpose. First, such beings must live from their own inner nature, developing their organization against opposition and maintaining themselves against interference. Only so can they be true selves, with a measure of independence, and thus become bearers of the gift of freedom. Second, such beings will develop creatively only out of lower

[38] A. Farrer, *Love Almighty and Ills Unlimited* (Garden City, New York: Doubleday & Co., Inc., 1961), p. 55. I have found Farrer's treatment of this theme thought-provoking and original.

creatures in which progressively selfhood has been evolved and along with it a quasi-independence of other creatures and the physical order. Third, such lower beings will act according to their own limited principles of being, and, because they are unreflective, will tend to inflict damage on other organized wholes.[39]

Undoubtedly other ways than this creation of a physical universe were open to the Creator. Yet may we not see something more in our world? The struggle of warring systems, the way living things live on living things and struggle for existence, the survival of the fittest, nature red in tooth and claw, the fecundity and its accompanying waste—all these indicate a seemingly shadow side of creation. But it is out of such a process that there emerge the wonders of organization, the harmonies of nature, the co-operation of living things, the intricate ordering of atomic, molecular, and crystal structure, the sublimity of the far-flung universe, the aesthetic values of this creaturely world, the rich possibilities of man's reflective reason and creative spirit. Can we say that a beneficent Creator has not himself counted the cost in producing such riches, and that even in the divine the joy is the greater because he too shares the pain? This is the world which he has created and is guiding to its fulfillment through the co-operation and oftentimes the misdirectedness of his creatures, the latter being focalized in the freedom which he has planted in the heart of man.

But this unfinished aspect of the universe is the area in which such freedom may operate. Man by reflective thought and creative activity may subdue and direct the vast realm of interacting physical and biological structures. He may exercise his creative freedom in bringing harmony and order into the strife and tension. In this way, he may within the physical order manifest and fulfill his true nature as made in the image of God. W. E. Hocking points out that "a thing is properly

[39] Cf. Ibid. p. 56.

unfinished when *it* is finishable; when it has an identity that finishing will not change."[40] God has left an area within his created order where man himself may help to fashion and shape the structure of things and co-operate with the intention of his Creator. The structure of the universe is fixed, but the measure of contingency and the aggregation of interacting organized wholes, each governed by its own principle of being, leaves an area for such co-operation, while the over-all structure is declared good and finishable by its Creator. Perhaps it is more at the level of the spirit than of his physical environment that man's creative co-operation can have freest play. Here in forming societies and molding personal relationships he is called to reproduce in finite and visible form that living fellowship which God has manifested to him.

> I have some need to reproduce the relation to God in a visible relationship *within* God's world . . . in that need, whatever it is, I may find an inkling of God's own motive in creating just such a sphere of things as this visible Nature-field, in which spirits wander as shapes embedded.[41]

We help to mold and shape the character and personality of our fellows. We make friends as a result of our own love and concern. Resolution of will is as significant at the level of personal relationships as at the level of the physical.

The tragedy of man is that he refuses to co-operate with his Creator and so the universe, from being unfinished, becomes perverted. We must not fall into the error of associating the natural evil we have been describing with man's sin. Undoubtedly man's misuse of his freedom aggravates the tensions and interactions of the organized wholes at all levels of nature, but the terrible indictment on man is that he misdirects them and the whole process so that it is no longer directed for God's

[40] W. E. Hocking, op. cit. p. x.
[41] Ibid. p. 298.

glory. Rather it is only too often directed on the very destruction of the being who was made in God's image. Once more we return to the Incarnation. In Christ the whole universe and the whole of humanity are summed up in one human life, and the creative energies of man and his world are redirected once more. Here man is not only shown how he should live as God's partner, but is also lifted from estrangement back into divine fellowship and given the spiritual dynamic to fulfill his destiny.

v. *The sacramental universe and the cosmic Christ*

The picture that emerges is of the universe as an area in which God and man meet through the medium of a physical order in which man may fulfill his God-given destiny. That order is divinely created to safeguard man's freedom. If he is to respond in loving obedience to his Creator, that response must be one which he freely chooses. And so God will not force himself on his creature. He gives man quasi-independence, and part of the condition for this is the natural or physical order within which he places man. It provides the Creator with a screen through which he discloses himself while at the same time hiding himself. He provides man with no blinding vision of his glory but seeks to woo him, as he approaches him through the medium of the natural order and also the medium of society with its moral claims and its opportunities for love and sacrifice. So man learns to trust God by loving his fellows, by accepting his moral obligations, by trusting others who also mysteriously hide themselves within their psychosomatic structure. Periodically special divine disclosures deepen his comprehension of this God who hides and yet discloses himself through the world of nature and personal beings. At last, in one incarnate life, the full disclosure is given, and the true nature of God and his purpose are revealed to those who have the eyes to see.

Here man fully sees his true destiny. He is to be the child of God but the child of God in a loving and responsible relationship with his fellows and in harmony with his world. Already, in fragmentary ways, this destiny has been borne in upon him. To live at all he must subdue his environment and live to some degree responsibly in social groups. But his environment has tempted him to fix his eyes on the visible and to ignore the God behind. So his society splits asunder. Greed and selfishness take the place of love and service and responsible relationship. Nature becomes perverted. Instead of cooperating with his Maker to finish the unfinished aspects of nature which have made possible his own creative emergence as a free being, he perverts it and magnifies its tensions to his own destruction and undoing. His capacity to subdue nature is fully expressed in his science, and yet his science misses the vision of the whole, concentrates on the analysis of the parts, becomes prostituted so often to evil and ignoble practical ends.

Yet the Incarnation stands in the midst, while nature and history alike cry for the unveiling of men fulfilling their true destiny as brothers and disciples of the Son of God. The picture it presents to us is that of a universe which is created to be sacramental everywhere of God's presence, a world through which man may have fellowship with his Creator, as he cooperates with him in the fulfillment of his purpose. The universe exists to manifest God's glory.

As man emerged in the upward movement of creation, mind became individualized and selfhood became a reality. At the lower levels of the ant hill and the herd it would seem as if whatever psychic aspect of life there is belongs to the group rather than the individual. It may well be that extrasensory perception is a residual element from those early days of living things. But as individual embodied selfhood appeared and then reached its climax in man, communication became necessary through the individualizing media—bodily gestures and vocal sounds and ultimately, with man, language.

Men communicate with one another by symbols. The symbols convey meaning. Some, as H. H. Farmer points out, are extrinsic. They do not carry their meaning in themselves, but the meaning has to be learned. They are more of the nature of signs. A typical example would be our languages, where many different linguistic symbols may carry the same meaning.

Other symbols are intrinsic, carrying their meaning in themselves. Of these, perhaps our bodily acts provide the most obvious examples. Such symbols are expressive. The mind does not not have to learn them, for they are themselves so intimately bound up with that which they represent that a mind *en rapport* with spiritual and personal reality can immediately grasp their meaning. Such symbols point, like signs or extrinsic symbols, beyond themselves, but they participate in that to which they point.[42] They are organically related to that which they represent and awaken a response to such reality in the mind of the recipient. Thus, in the relationship of persons, the inflection of the voice, the physical appearance, the pattern of bodily activity so participate in the inner life of the person that they awaken a response in us. They point to something in the other akin to our own feelings, thoughts, and desires.

As we have already noted, our psychosomatic state means that we cannot thrust our thoughts and resolutions directly into the other's mind. We have to wait at his somatic frontier, respect his freedom and individuality, await his responsive acceptance. For this we use our signs and symbols, hoping that he will grasp the meaning they convey and make it a part of his own personal reflection and action.[43] Thus an intrinsic symbol, because it has not to be learned, provides a bridge between the other and me, disclosing to him new depths and dimensions of my innermost being and evoking new dimensions quite possibly in his own inner being. As Tillich points

[42] Cf. P. Tillich, *The Dynamics of Faith* (New York: Harper & Bros., 1957), p. 42.

[43] Cf. H. H. Farmer, *The World and God* (London: Nisbet & Co., Ltd., 1955), p. 71 f.

out, characteristics of the symbol are that it "not only opens up dimensions and elements of reality which otherwise would remain unapproachable, but also unlocks dimensions and elements of our soul which correspond to the dimensions and elements of reality." [44]

It is in this sense that we must understand the positioning of nature and other persons as divine media of revelation. They constitute a sacramental setting for our lives and become the means whereby God conveys his meanings to us. They become elements in a disclosure situation wherein God draws near to us. Berkeley [45] saw the universe in this way and likened it to the external and somatic appearance of persons by which we came to know them. We do not see persons, we see their physical characteristics, and through these we "see" them. Berkeley also compared the universe to divine language.

Such analogies must not be pressed too far or made exclusive. We cannot believe that the sole meaning of the processes of nature is to provide media of the divine disclosure while preserving human freedom and individuality. It is presumptuous to believe that this universe is solely for us. Undoubtedly it carries other meanings and is meaningful in itself quite apart from any functional purposes that it may serve—hence the elements of mystery and irrationality with which we have already concerned ourselves. Yet its sacramental aspect needs to be stressed, and in this sense the physical subserves the spiritual order and becomes a sign and seal of the presence of its Creator. H. H. Farmer remarks that "it is not in the least necessary to Christian faith to maintain that all creation should be a means to the end of human personality, but only that it should include all that is requisite to that end and nothing that should make its final achievement impossible." [46]

It is probably vague to speculate what might have happened

[44] Tillich, *Dynamics of Faith,* p. 42.

[45] G. Berkeley, *Alcphron,* Fourth Dialogue, S.5.

[46] H. H. Farmer, op. cit. pp. 73 f.

if man had not fallen. Yet we may see in the Incarnation and the life of the Church something of the divine intention for the natural order. Fallen man has so concentrated upon the physicality of this universe that he has failed to see it as a means of sharing in the life of God. Hence he finds himself in a material order in which he has to find times and places where he may be religious. His god has to be worshipped in specific shrines at regulated times, and the sacred has to be separated from the profane. Furthermore, he tends to identify his god with elements of nature or with the whole process. From idolatry and pantheism it is an easy stage to deny all such as superstition and finish in a completely secular and godless world. Yet, in some sense, secularization brings us nearer to God than does much of our religiosity, even our Christian religiosity, for we Christians have also divided the sacred from the profane and isolated our God to certain aspects of experience. Maybe, as Bonhoeffer suggested, we may find God nearer in a secularized world because we shall begin to look for him everywhere.

Now this is the meaning of the Incarnation. In becoming man, God has sanctified the whole of nature and humanity and drawn it up into his own life. In the Church, as the Body of Christ, men are drawn up into that life and required to serve God in transforming the life of the world. They are certainly not required to turn their back on the world. Indeed, the sacraments of the Church are anticipations of the transformation of the whole created order which God originally intended. Wordsworth, despite his pantheism, expresses something of this, when he writes:

> The earth, and every common sight,
> To me did seem
> Apparelled in celestial light.[47]

[47] "Ode on the Intimations of Immortality," *The Poetical Works of Wordsworth*, ed. T. Hutchinson, Rev. E. de Selincourt (London: Oxford University Press, 1961), p. 460.

Alexander Schmemann has contended that

> the only real fall of man is his non-eucharistic life in a non-eucharistic world. The fall is not that he preferred world to God, distorted the balance between the spiritual and the material, but that he made the world *material* whereas he was to have transformed it into "life in God," filled it with meaning and spirit.[48]

We would find fault with this somewhat one-sided understanding of the Fall, which we would interpret rather in terms of rebellion and a perversion of the natural order by human misuse and misdirection. Yet his description of the divine end for nature stands clear, and already, in the sacraments, we are bidden to see signs of this. For, in them, the material elements of bread and wine are taken up into the life of God and energized by the Spirit. They become symbols of the divine activity, media of divine disclosure, as they enter into the sacramental context. In this way they "foreshadow the transfiguration of the cosmos and herald the new heaven and the new earth."[49]

When to the Incarnation we link the pre-existence and Ascension of the Christ, we begin to grasp the whole universe as sacramental to the cosmic Christ. The cosmological setting within which the Fourth Evangelist set the incarnate Word takes on a deeper meaning. He who became man in the supreme divine disclosure is everywhere active behind his universe, bringing men into personal disclosure with himself. The pre-existence of the eternal Son, who could say in his earthly existence "Before Abraham was, I am,"[50] affirms that the whole plan of creation is vested in Him. He holds the secret to

[48] Schmemann, *For the Life of the World* (New York: National Student Christian Federation, 1963), p. 7.

[49] Neville Clark, *An Approach to the Theology of the Sacraments* (Chicago: Alec R. Allenson, Inc., 1956), p. 75.

[50] John 8:58.

the structure and meaning of this physical universe and the whole creaturely order.

The ascension of the Son of Man, who has ascended where he was before,[51] is the affirmation that his redemptive and reconciling ministry has been lifted up into the eternal order. When men lift him upon the Cross, the Cross becomes the ladder by which he is lifted up into heaven.[52] He who is the creative principle is also the cosmic redemptive principle, and so he is the light that lightens every man coming into the world.[53]

Whenever men grasp meaning, at whatever level, they are encountering the cosmic Christ. He is the revelatory as he is the sustaining principle, upholding all things.[54] In him all things hold together and the universe becomes a coherent and meaningful whole.[55] The Incarnation becomes the key to the universe.[56] And as the Spirit effected the creative plan of the Son within the physical order, so he still opens the blind eyes of men that through the world around them they may encounter the Christ who became incarnate and who has gloriously returned to his hiddenness in the triune mystery of God, leaving the Spirit as his alter ego.[57]

What then of science? Science is concerned to control and to predict. Its area is the natural order including man's somatic and psychological structure. As such it is applicable to all things which are subject to man. In this sense it is concerned with the physical universe, the biological order, and the psychological and sociological phenomena which go to make up the sacramental universe that we have been considering. We have no right to mark off areas of nature which science

[51] John 6:62.
[52] John 8:29, 12:32; Cf. Acts 1:9.
[53] John 1:9.
[54] Heb. 1:3.
[55] Col. 1:17.
[56] I Cor. 8:6.
[57] John 15:26, 16:14.

cannot penetrate or to set barriers of mystery in the natural order. We may expect that, at the biological level, science will in the course of time be able to produce living things. And, at the human level, the tremendous advances in neurological investigation and in our knowledge of the cerebral cortex should warn us against any presumptuous predictions as to what science will be able to say about the processes of mind. The developments of cybernetics should demonstrate the folly of such predictions. Now, in all such investigations, science is concerned with nature as an impersonal structure. Its avowed task is to investigate the processes of the creaturely realm with a view to understanding the general causal relationships which exist between its parts. In this way it can control nature, even bringing harmony into its contrarieties and directing its processes to humanly determined goals.

The method of science is that of putting nature to the question. In his experiments the scientist asks questions of nature and hopes by the answers he receives to gain greater control over the natural order and a larger power of prediction. In so doing he is understanding the structure which God has created and sustains. Thus he is endeavoring to rethink the thoughts of God. In the rational models which he devises to explain the laws he discovers and to enable him to predict further observations and even new discoveries, he is seeking to approach ever more closely to the structure of nature, the machinery which God uses to create finite limited psychosomatic personal beings and through which God discloses himself to them. It is significant that as we have seen, the scientist's great advances in knowledge, his revolutionary transformation of his basic models, occur not by observations, but by intuitive insights at the theoretical level which suggest new models and carry him on to fresh heights of discovery. His new models enable him to put the question to nature in new ways and to receive answers which stimulate him to further investigation. This intuitive aspect of science has been emphasized by Max Planck, who points out that "when the pioneer in science sends forth the grasping feelers of his thoughts, he must have a vivid intuitive imagination, for new ideas are not generated by deduction, but by an artistically creative imagination." [58] We note the emphasis on intuition and also that upon its aesthetic aspect. But, we have already pointed out that intuition is closely akin to the subjective side of revelation.[59] The alternation between patient observation and investigation and critical moments of intuitive insight makes up the history of scientific discovery, and the intuitive insights arise in situations much akin to those of personal disclosure.

I. T. Ramsey [60] points out certain elements in scientific insight which suggest its being within a disclosure situation. At the human level, we find a personal disclosure through aesthetic appraisal of a person's artistic creativity. True art expresses the personality of the artist. Now it is significant that aesthetic evaluation plays a large part in the development of models at the level of physical science—the carbon ring compounds, the balance and symmetry of mathematical formulae, to mention only two examples. Sir Lawrence Bragg has indicated this revelatory aspect of scientific knowledge.

> When one has sought long for the clue to a secret of nature, and is rewarded by grasping some part of the answer, it comes as a blinding flash of revelation: it comes as something new, more simple and at the same time more aesthetically satisfying than anything one could have created in one's own mind. This conviction is of something revealed, and not something imagined.[61]

[58] M. Planck, *A Scientific Autobiography* (London: Williams and Norgate, 1950) p. 109.

[59] See above chapter 3.

[60] I. T. Ramsey, *Religion and Science: Conflict and Synthesis* (London: S.P.C.K., 1965), pp. 13–24.

[61] L. Bragg, *Science and the Adventure of Living,* quoted in C. A. Coulson, *Science and Christian Belief* (Chapel Hill: The University of North Carolina Press, 1955), pp. 98 f.

Again, in personal disclosure we have moments of sudden insight when various understandings, often contradictory, of a person, jell and a new deeper understanding springs out to meet us. But science, too, has provided us with many models of reality, often of the same phenomena and sometimes seemingly contradictory. We think at once of the wave and particle pictures of atomic particles, or of the older atomic way of writing chemical reactions and the new models in which we are concerned with the electronic structure—

$2Na + Cl_2 = 2NaCl$ and $Na^{\circ} + {}_{x}\overset{xx}{\underset{xx}{Cl}}{}^{x}_{x} \rightarrow Na^{\circ}_{x}\overset{xx}{\underset{xx}{Cl}}{}^{x}_{x}$. It would seem as if once more we are penetrating into personal deeps.

But should this surprise us? Is not the whole universe sacramental of him who came in the Incarnation? Everywhere men are encountering Christ. What they glean of meaning in fragmentary ways is made coherent in him. We are striving to attain some coherence by a naturalistic process of reduction. Biology and psychology are reduced to the level of complex forms of physics and chemistry. But the full realities of life and personality are not satisfactorily dealt with in this way. Man does have an inner being which is more than a bundle of reflex actions. Human personality has an inward freedom and a sense of moral obligation which no causal scheme can finally explain. There is a beauty and harmony in the universe for which mere mechanical notions of material particles can never satisfactorily account. There is co-operation and directiveness in the process of living things to which random mutations in genes and natural selection do not hold the key. The universe points towards the incarnate Christ, in whom the principle of order and meaning has tabernacled in our midst. He is still disclosing himself to us in all his redemptive glory. Wherever men seek for meaning they are encountering him, and his immanent Spirit, present creatively and sustainingly throughout the created order, still opens our blind eyes that we may behold his glory, who holds all things together.

Subject Index

Name Index